ASAE Publication 8-85

Erosion and Soil Productivity

Proceedings of the
National Symposium on Erosion
and Soil Productivity

December 10-11, 1984
Hyatt Regency New Orleans
New Orleans, Louisiana

Published by
American Society of Agricultural Engineers
2950 Niles Road
St. Joseph, Michigan 49085-9659

Library of Congress Card Number (LCCN) 85-70630
International Standard Book Number (ISBN) 0-916150-69-0

NATIONAL SYMPOSIUM ON

EROSION AND SOIL PRODUCTIVITY

December 10-11, 1984
New Orleans, Louisiana

Sponsor:
American Society of Agricultural Engineers
2950 Niles Rd., St. Joseph, MI 49085-9659
phone (616) 429-0300, Eastern Time Zone

Cosponsors (with liaisons):

American Agricultural
Economics Association
(Clayton Ogg)

American Forestry
Association
(Neil Sampson)

American Society of
Agronomy
(Bobby A. Stewart)

American Society of Civil
Engineers
(Robert Rallison)

Canadian Society of
Agricultural Engineering
(James B. Arnold)

Farm and Industrial
Equipment Institute
(Dennis E. Lindemann)

Land Improvement
Contractors of America
(S. M. Wijkowski)

National Association of
Conservation Districts

Soil Conservation Society of
America
(Melville L. Palmer)

Soil Science Society of
America
(Bobby A. Stewart)

Tennessee Valley Authority
(John E. Culp)

U. S. Bureau of Reclamation
(Thomas H. Seldon)

USDA Agricultural Research
Service
(W. Ralph Nave)

USDA Cooperative State
Research Service
(Clarence F. Becker)

USDA Extension Service
(Fred N. Swader)

USDA Forest Service
(Farnum M. Burbank)

USDA Soil Conservation
Service
(Buell M. Ferguson)

Symposium Planning Committee:
Donald K. McCool, Symposium Chairman
Richard L. Bengtson, Local Arrangements Chairman
James M. Gregory, Finance Chairman
Calvin K. Mutchler, Proceedings Chairman
Clarence W. Richardson, Program Chairman
James M. Steichen, Publicity Chairman

FOREWORD

The detrimental effects of excessive erosion on soil productivity are well recognized by soil erosion researchers, soil conservationists and farmers. Early in the history of the U.S., high erosion rates caused abandonment of thousands of acres of cropland in the Southeast. In the 1930's drought and wind created the Dust Bowl and, in conjunction with the harsh economic conditions of the times, caused thousands of acres of cropland to be abandoned or converted to rangeland. At the same time, other areas experienced excessive rates of water erosion. Because the rate of technological advance was relatively flat, the effect of this erosion was readily apparent in reduced yields. With the improved technology of better crop varieties, inexpensive commercial fertilizer, and pesticides of the past 30 to 40 years, the deleterious effects of erosion are much less evident. Even rapidly eroding areas may show yield increases.

Most erosion researchers did not attempt to deal with the linkage between erosion, productivity, and technological change, assuming that erosion was detrimental and should be prevented or controlled at low levels. Economic analysis in conjunction with the 1980 appraisal of the Soil and Water Resources Conservation Act of 1977 (RCA) created concern with the validity of this assumption. This analysis indicated that, in general, erosion would have little or no impact on national crop production for the next 50 years, and that rapid technological progress might be expected to overshadow productivity losses to soil erosion. Many researchers and conservationists considered the analysis to be faulty, overly optimistic, or the time base to be too short. Realistic or not, the analysis revealed a major gap in knowledge about how erosion affects soil productivity at current technology levels, and generated considerable research aimed at investigating linkage between erosion and soil productivity. Most of the new field research was initiated no earlier than 1981 or 1982. By the autumn of 1984, a maximum of from three to four years of data were to be available for analysis, making late 1984 an ideal time for a symposium on erosion and soil productivity. Enough data would have been collected for analysis, to indicate trends, and for formulation of at least tentative relationships. It would be excellent timing for researchers and conservationists to gather, compare and disseminate results, and refine experiments and analyses. From this background was conceived the National Symposium on Erosion and Soil Productivity, with the purpose of assembling and disseminating current research results and information on erosion and soil productivity relationships.

The National Symposium on Erosion and Soil Productivity achieved the desired goals and purposes. Twenty-six speakers presented papers during the sessions and twenty-two presented information from their research during the evening poster session. Discussion was lively among the approximately 190 registrants. The presentations were well prepared and the analyses well done even though results of different researchers were sometimes conflicting. The Symposium brought out the need for more and longer-term research on the effects of erosion on soil productivity. Reports of field investigations documented the large variability of the soil productivity parameters, both in time and space. The large variability of field results in turn causes large variation in results of economic analysis of the costs of erosion. The discussions and comparisions of this state-of-the-art symposium will influence research for the following years.

Presentations of the opening and concluding invited speakers were essential to the Symposium. Neil Sampson's opening presentation provided valuable background as to the concern about the erosion-soil productivity linkage and set the tone for the meeting. Don Meyer's concluding remarks addressed the future of erosion-soil productivity research and its importance. In the next 100 years, world population may grow from four to six times its current four billion. Available cultivable land will change but little. Today, thousands are dying of starvation in drought-ridden parts of the world and this will be greatly intensified in the future if the slow but steady decline in soil productivity caused by wind and water erosion is not halted. We must consider the long-range world view as we apply the results from erosion-soil productivity research.

Donald K. McCool, Chairman
National Symposium on Erosion and Soil Productivity

Table of Contents

NATIONAL CONCERNS ABOUT EROSION AND PRODUCTIVITY

R. Neil Sampson
Fellow SCSA

Many people who had worked in agriculture, soil science, and soil conservation were gratified in the mid-1970's when the American public became aware of the fact that agricultural land and its productivity were an important national resource. Three prior decades of surplus crop supplies, low prices, and resulting farm policy frustrations had conditioned people to assume that America's farmers could feed the world no matter how many of their cropland acres were turned into subdivisions or raked by erosion's gullies. Those conditions had not translated into much public support for soil conservation -- or soil erosion research -- in the 1950's and 1960's.

But the situation changed dramatically in 1972, as the Russians entered the grain market in a big way, at a time when world stocks were down and U.S. crops were none too bountiful. Commodity surpluses disappeared, farm prices rose, and people began to wonder about the real depth of our farmland capacity. Could it be that we had begun to see the limits of growth in agriculture, and that future losses of farmland productivity would need to be more carefully monitored?

As these questions began to be debated, in the shadow of an energy crisis, the attention of farm policy leaders turned to production for what they hoped was a virtually unlimited world market. America's farmers were given the signal by USDA to dramatically increase farm output.

Their response was swift. Millions of acres that had previously been set aside were put back into crop production. Many millions more were plowed out of grass or trees and planted to crops for the first time in decades -- or, for that matter, for the the first time ever.

At the same time, a confluence of economic conditions and technology made it possible for many farmers to buy new tractors and tillage machines. These new tractors were larger, faster, more powerful and more stable than before. Farmers were grateful for their low labor requirements, speed, capability, and operating comfort.

But big, fast tractors don't handle big, wide machinery efficiently on little, patchy fields, so fencerows and windbreaks disappeared, contour terraces were obliterated, and the "odd areas" of grass, brush or trees that had previously been too steep or rough to cultivate were incorporated into the regular field operations. The new machines could go through these areas a lot easier than they could go around them.

The result was the extension of cultivation onto millions of acres that are highly susceptible to soil erosion. Increasing crop specialization -- also pushed by the new technologies -- led many farmers to reduce or eliminate

The author is: R. NEIL SAMPSON, Executive Vice President, American Forestry Association, Washington, D.C.

livestock, so row crops replaced pastures or hay crops in the rotation. Between 1967 and 1977, row crops increased 27 percent while total cropland dropped 6 percent and rotation hay and pasture dropped a whopping 40 percent! New markets for soybeans added millions of acres of a crop which, by its nature, provides little soil protection during critical periods of the year when rainfall is prevalent and erosion hazards high.

The net result of all these forces was a growing concern for the soil and its future productivity. Would erosion cause future yields to drop, or make farmers invest higher and higher costs to offset the topsoil declines being suffered? Would soil productivity, which is the capacity of a soil to contribute to crop yields under a fixed set of management conditions, decline because of soil erosion? If so, that would create an inflationary pressure on the price of food at the very base of the economic system -- a pressure that would not be easily avoided or overcome. Alarms on this issue had been sounded by soil conservationists as early as 1973, when the "fence row to fence row" planting opportunity first appeared, and by the late 1970's the public was concerned as well.

The Soil Conservation Service carried out an inventory based on a statistical sampling that gathered data which could be used in estimating the average annual soil loss that might be affecting America's productive soils. The result was the best and most extensive set of data ever compiled on the Nation's non-federal lands. This information documented what many experts feared: significant areas were suffering soil erosion at rates far above what soil scientists had established as the tolerance limits of the land. Some lands, comprising a small portion of the farmland resource, were experiencing very high rates of topsoil movement.

EROSION DATA NEEDS INTERPRETATION

Soil conservationists were well armed. They had the data, and they had the public's ear. The stage was set, it would seem, for major changes and improvements in the Nation's soil conservation programs. Just a few key questions remained, and here is where the whole analysis hit the shoals.

"So what?" people asked.

"What does a 10-ton per year erosion rate -- or 20 tons, or 100 tons -- mean to the soil?"

"How much erosion can a soil tolerate?"

"What is the effect of this erosion on soil productivity?"

"What will be the effect on food prices? Will they rise? How far, and how fast?"

"How will erosion affect the national well-being?" "How much should we spend to stop or slow it?"

Soil scientists and soil conservationists, hit with these questions, were forced to say they did not know the answers. We could not document the effects of different rates of soil erosion on productivity. We were convinced that it was harmful, but how harmful? We couldn't say with accuracy.

We were convinced that high rates of erosion were more damaging than low rates, but how much erosion could a soil tolerate? The evidence was mixed. Crop yields on many soils were the highest in history, in spite of erosion damage. And how high should erosion rates be before we could justify new programs -- or new costs -- to reduce it? In a nutshell, how much should farmers -- and society -- spend to control soil erosion?

2

We did not know. And that lack of knowledge was both an embarrassment and a challenge to the entire profession. It was also a serious deterrent to any attempt to improve public support for soil and water conservation efforts.

Today, as we enter 1985, neither farm commodities nor natural resources are perceived by the public to be in limited supply. We have a glut of wheat, plenty of corn and soybeans, no limits on petroleum supplies, and plenty of sawtimber to keep the forest products industry in business for the next few years. It is hard, today, to make a case for conservation on the basis that we might soon run out of resources or basic necessities.

Instead, we are short on dollars -- in both the public and private sectors. High federal deficits, high rates of real interest, growing numbers of farm bankruptcies, and steadily rising levels of farm debt are all signals. America -- and particularly America's farmer -- is critically short on capital. Under those conditions, saving dollars may become more important than saving topsoil. Soil conservation efforts -- both public and private -- must answer more stringent economic questions. It is no longer enough to argue for conservation programs because they are "good". The question is "how good," or "good for whom," or "how much conservation is enough?"

Because of these questions, conservationists, economists and policy makers turned to the scientific community in unison about 1980 and asked for new answers to the most basic questions underlying the whole soil conservation effort. The response has been impressive.

In only a few short years, research efforts to better link the data on soil erosion to its agronomic and economic effects on productivity have gone from virtually zero until today there are hundreds of such studies under way. This conference will, we hope, result in a better understanding of where that research effort has led. It should clarify what has been learned to date and outline areas where more work is still needed.

As one of the users of this essential research and its findings, let me congratulate both the sponsors and the participants in this important effort. I can assure you that anything you can tell us will be gratefully received. Even a few answers, or some indicated trends, or some new estimating methods, or some preliminary data that appears to support or reject some basic assumptions, will be gratefully received and intensively utilized.

But there are different audiences that need to know more about the relationships of erosion to productivity, and each audience will need different data and evidence. Therefore, you should not be surprised if the people who interpret and communicate the results of your research continue to come at you with requests for more information, or information in a different form. Let me suggest at least four different audiences for illustration.

RESEARCH INFORMATION FOR FARMERS

The first audience is farmers, and those who work directly with them. To the extent that soil erosion damages productivity, the people most directly affected will be farmers and farm families. It is they who will make the daily decisions that can encourage soil erosion or protect against it.

What crop should we plant?

Should we clean cultivate or no-till?

Is a cover crop needed?

Should crops be rotated?

3

These are basic questions that will be considered largely on the basis of the farmer's estimation of the economic outcome. Profit will be the determining factor as the farmer searches for a management combination that will maximize income, minimize cost, and result in the highest net return.

When profit considerations drive decisions, then we need to tell the farmer the economic implications of both soil erosion and soil conservation practices in order to have soil conservation fully considered in his actions.

How much will different rates of soil erosion hurt yields -- or drive up costs? How rapidly will those damages occur? Will the result be cumulative, and tend to grow steadily worse, or can it be easily offset by a future management or technology adjustment? Will different fields -- or different soils within a field or farm -- be affected differently?

Finally, can you give us new formulas or estimating tools the farmer can use to calculate the ultimate economic impact of his decisions, including the costs of erosion?

Without these facts, farmers and the technicians and advisors who work with them will have a difficult task in justifying any soil erosion control on economic grounds.

Granted, there are non-economic considerations that temper farm decisions. A farmer with a strong feeling of stewardship will trade off some profits to gain the satisfaction of knowing that he has done the "right thing" with his land. To many farmers, this soil stewardship ethic is one of the strongest driving forces in their lives, and researchers have found that stress among farmers (which is very high, incidentally) is worsened by worries about soil erosion and fears about the future of farming. These people don't ignore economics, they just use a different yardstick to balance profit with non-economic factors. Even conservation farmers, however, need to know clearly how soil erosion harms soil, for it will be these understandings that harden their resolve to carry out stewardship, even at a price.

There will not be a soil conservationist on every field, every year, to make an inspection of erosion conditions. But that farmer or farm manager will be there several times. How do we give them the skills and tools they will need to recognize and quantify what is happening to their soils?

We conservationists and writers have been guilty of showing pictures of huge gullies, or badly rilled Palouse hillsides, or corn rows with foot-deep gashes between every pair of rows, and calling it an example of serious soil erosion. A farmer may look at a field that shows none of these extreme signs, and decide that there is no erosion problem, even when the field is suffering fairly high erosion rates. How can we detect -- and teach them to detect -- the more subtle symptoms?

Can we help them realize that some fields are more vulnerable than others, because of soil differences or past erosion damage? Can we help them estimate the impacts on productivity that occur throughout the field? Our efforts to date have focused on the section of the hillside where sheet and rill erosion was occuring. What about the downslope areas that may suffer from ephemeral gullies? What about the footslopes where soil is deposited in the erosion process? What can we say about productivity impacts here?

Can we help them evaluate erosion and productivity impacts over time, so that they can see what effects today's actions may have in 5, 10 or 20 years?

None of these are easy questions, and they may be only a sample of the whole range that need to be answered. They indicate, however, the kinds of concerns that farmers and field technicians often express about soil erosion, productivity, and their need to know more.

4

INFORMATION FOR PUBLIC DECISION MAKERS

The second audience for information on erosion and productivity are public decision makers, at all levels of government, and the analysts who must supply information to these officials.

For these people, the soil-by-soil, field-by-field information developed for farmers will be of limited use, and when you get to the national level, it is virually worthless.

Policy analysts need to evaluate the macro-effects of soil erosion on productivity. These people need to know how the effects will relate to regional or even national situations. Are certain regions at greater risk than others, or suffering more significant losses, and are greater erosion control efforts therefore justified? This has been the entire thrust of the USDA targeting effort for the past few years, based on the 1977 NRI. But this process has had far less knowledge of the effects of soil erosion on productivity than the analysts trying to guide the process would have liked.

How can we calculate the true costs of soil erosion to society, so that we can balance erosion-control programs and investments with other opportunities to improve or protect agricultural productivity?

You may hear, before this conference ends, that current evidence indicates that the off-site damages of soil erosion inflict far greater costs on society than the on-site reductions in soil productivity. That may remain true, even when a full accounting of soil productivity impacts is routine, so the reduction of off-site damages may remain the strongest public policy argument in favor of soil conservation programs. But to the extent that erosion inflicts identifiable damage on soil productivity, and threatens to raise both public and private costs in the future, those impacts should be factored into the public policy equation.

INFORMATION FOR INDUSTRY

American industry discovered soil erosion in the late 1970's, along with the general public. Suddenly, as farmers became concerned, businessmen had to take notice as well. If farmers were not too sure that their soils were going to stay profitable for the long-term future, agricultural industry could not be too sure it could stay in business, either.

What are the implications of erosion and productivity as they relate to different crops or different types of agricultural technology? Soybean growers have been concerned about the links being made between erosion and soybeans, fearing that there would be a public backlash against their crop. Any controls on soybean growing would be a major concern to a significant industrial sector.

Certainly the manufacturers of tillage machinery felt a shock as farmers turned to conservation tillage. New products, new techniques, and a whole new agricultural technology have emerged, pushed by the twin need to cut costs and reduce soil losses. Business leaders need to know what other technological changes might be in store as we learn more about erosion and soil productivity. They may face either instant obsolescence of their products or see the opportunity to open up entirely new markets if they can understand soil processes better and correctly guess where farmer attitudes and farm technologies are likely to be headed.

American Agribusiness educates and influences farmers very significantly. If you don't believe me, take out any farm magazine and count the number of pages devoted to messages, including advertisements, from industry and compare them to the number of pages devoted to messages from Universities, Extension, SCS

5

and other public sources. Several years ago, most of the full-page color pictures associated with farm ads showed the field clean-tilled, usually up and down the slope.

Conservationists went to the companies, and pointed out that they were sending a subliminal message to farmers, suggesting that erosion-inducing cultivation was the modern way. One major equipment company, proud of its support for soil conservation, was somewhat taken aback to learn that 85 percent of its ad picture in the prior year showed poor conservation practices. They have made a significant change, as have many other companies. Today, because industry leaders have been made more aware of the soil erosion situation, conservation pictures are more prevalent. That is, in my opinion, a significant gain.

INFORMATION FOR THE PUBLIC

The last major audience that needs to understand the results of your research is the general public. A good public understanding is vital to the whole process of designing and implementing good soil conservation efforts. Without an informed public, there will be no political support for the basic research, education or conservation incentive programs that most of us believe to be in the public interest.

But making soil erosion and productivity information meaningful to the general public is a difficult task. The opportunities are few, and a painfully short time is available when the opportunity arises. Most often, we send our message through the media, where it is necessary to keep everything short, simple, and clear.

Unfortunately, few of the facts in this case lend themselves to short, simple explanations. These are complex relationships that demand a fairly careful, detailed response. Often, there simply is too little time for that. It is even more frustrating when the person giving the answer is trying to retain scientific credibility, and thus is compelled to explain both the complexity of the situation and the limits of current knowledge. Often, that kind of answer will get ignored by the media. It may simply be too long and complex for them to use.

Many of you have been asked questions like the following, then given a few seconds in which to frame the complete answer:

"Just how serious is the soil erosion problem?"

"Is it a crisis?"

"How long before our food supply will be affected?"

"Why should the average citizen be concerned with soil erosion?"

Many times I have felt trapped in a no-win situation with these questions. The reporter demands explanations that are not too technical, or complex, or vague. Professional collegues, on the other hand, criticize the final product as being too simplistic, or even misleading, because it generalized the situation in ways the existing data will not support.

The dilemma is that both critics are probably right, but there may simply be no way to bridge the knowledge and communications gap that exists between the research scientist and the lay person, to the satisfaction of all.

This dilemma does not indicate that scientists should direct their research differently, or accept untrue or unverified generalizations as accurate. I am trying to make the point, however, that facts and relationships can be scientifically known and still be virtually worthless without an effective communications effort. And since communications is both a sending and a receiving process, you need to know and understand your audience if you are to succeed.

A farmer, a Congresssional Committee, a County Executive, a company president and a TV reporter are vastly different audiences. Knowing those differences, and how to present your information to communicate with each, is vital. If you are depending on another communicator, such as myself, to take your research results and synthesize them for presentation to the public, I would ask for your tolerance and understanding of what may happen in those situations. Your data and findings may be placed in some far different -- and vastly simplified -- contexts. Hopefully, you will be willing to risk a bit of scientific purity for the improved public understanding we all seek.

THE NEED TO THINK WHOLE

As we go through all the necessary numbers and statistics that show the relevance of what we are learning about soil erosion and its impacts on the future productivity of the soil, let us resolve to do our best to avoid becoming some kind of chemical accountants.

Topsoil is a living entity, with structure, porosity and other characteristics that differentiate one soil from another. Properly functioning, topsoil teems with living organisms and life processes, working in complex cycles that contribute to the growth of higher plants.

When we study soil erosion, we are not simply adding up the pounds of dead dust that has been moved from one place to another -- we are studying a wound that has been inflicted on the living landscape. It is not enough to estimate how many pounds of dead chemicals it will take to replace the lost dust, we need to know how badly the soil has been injured.

We know that such soil wounds, like abrasions or cuts in plants and animals, can often be healed if proper conditions exist. We know that people can, by their actions, hasten the healing process of soils. But that should not be interpreted to mean that the original wound was of no consequence; some soil losses, like some wounds, can be highly injurious or even fatal. Deserts exist in some places in the world as a testament to that fact.

Let us remember that we are natural scientists, trying to understand one of the most important, most complex, and most marvelous of nature's elements -- the topsoil. Let us not only look for ways to understand what happens when erosion alters it, let us look for ways to understand its basic needs and functions more clearly. Instead of being content to reduce topsoil losses to levels that will minimize productivity loss, let us look for ways to regenerate topsoils, improve productivity, and strengthen the whole health of the earth's fragile skin.

Agriculture today has not changed in basic form for 10,000 years. It is still largely a matter of trying to plant a few seeds and harvest a many-fold increase. In the process between the planting and the harvest, we have, in just the last few decades, learned how to intervene in many constructive and helpful ways. It still holds true, however, that productivity (and profitability) will be enhanced as we get more of the "free" growing benefits provided by sun, wind, rain and soil. Those benefits will flow more readily from an undamaged, fully functioning topsoil than from a damaged one.

Perhaps, as we seek to quantify the relationships between soil health and productivity, we can learn more about the culture of good crops on good soils, rather than having to focus so much of our attention on ways to alleviate the unforeseen side effects of trying to force soils and crops to artificial and unsustainable levels.

7

Think about the current movement toward promoting human wellness rather than simply seeking cures for illness. Can we learn how to define soil wellness, and how to move toward it? If it is true that every soil, like every person, has a range of potential, and that humanity's needs will be more effectively and efficiently served by those soils that are working near the top of their range, can we learn how to communicate that idea in terms that are relevant to our audiences?

Finally, let us work to convince people that we must not succumb to the notion that we can "write off" some soils and simply let them wash or blow away. We all know of soils that don't produce all that much crop, so the nation's breadbasket would be affected little, if any, if they were sterile. The problem with letting them be wasted, however, whether by soil erosion on cropland, by wanton surface mining techniques, by overgrazing on rangelands, or by destruction of the forest, is that they never seem to stay in just one place. Instead, they become festering sores that pollute water and air, or sliding mountainsides that endanger lives and property, or creeping dunes that bury productive lands and snuff out human opportunities. We need to tell people what the costs will be if we allow those kinds of situations to occur.

I see, in the tremendous amount of work that has been done on soil erosion and productivity in the past five years, the promise that the day will soon be behind us when we have to answer "we don't know" to the critical "so what" questions about soil erosion. We are learning more each day, and that is encouraging. Yogi Berra was once quoted as saying that "it is amazing what you can see if you just look." I am impressed by the unprecedented amount of scientific talent that is "looking" at soil erosion these days. A goodly portion of that talent is here at this meeting. I am looking forward to your deliberations, and wish you the very best.

FIELD EVALUATION OF THE EFFECT OF SOIL EROSION ON CROP PRODUCTIVITY

D.L. Schertz   W.C. Moldenhauer   D.P. Franzmeier   H.R. Sinclair, Jr.
                Assoc. Member ASAE

Today, soil erosion remains a national problem after 50 years of major conservation efforts by federal, state, and local governments and many other institutions, organizations, and individuals. A shift from sod-based rotations to more intensive row crop farming beginning in the late 1940's has aggravated the erosion problem.

Loss of topsoil by erosion is believed to reduce soil productivity, but few data are available to quantify the reduction, especially data relevant to today's farming technology. In extreme cases, such as severe gullying or complete loss of topsoil, the effect of erosion on crop yields is obvious; however, with small annual reductions in topsoil the effect may not be recognized for several years.

The objective of this study was to determine the effect of past erosion on crop yields using slight, moderate, and severe erosion phases, for three Indiana soils. The study was conducted in the field under actual farming conditions by the U.S. Department of Agriculture (Agricultural Research Service and Soil Conservation Service) and Purdue University from 1981 through 1983.

Soil erosion can reduce crop yields in several ways. It reduces soil organic matter, fine clays, water retention capacity of soil, and plant rooting depth (Office of Technology Assessment, 1982). Other erosion-related factors affecting productivity include reduction of plant nutrients, degradation of soil structure, and nonuniform removal of soil within a field (USDA, 1981). Frye et al. (1982) and Leeper et al. (1974) concluded that the value of soil to crop growth was primarily related to soil properties that influence available water.

Uhland (1949) reported on several studies of the effects of erosion on crop yields. These studies were completed in the late 1930's and early 1940's in Missouri, Indiana, Iowa, Ohio, and New Jersey. The data showed a steady reduction in crop yields and organic matter as the depth of topsoil was reduced by erosion. Uhland reported a 47% reduction in corn yields on a field where erosion reduced the thickness of topsoil from 33 cm down to a range of 2.5 to 5.1 cm. He contended that only those who refuse to weigh the facts could believe that soil erosion did not reduce crop yields.

Several investigators have evaluated the effect of simulated erosion on crop yield through excavation of the topsoil to expose the subsoil and substratum. Latham (1940) reported 4-year average yields (1936-1939) of seed cotton of 1052, 340, and 91 kg/ha on the A, B, and C horizons, respectively, for a Cecil sandy loam near Moore, South Carolina. He also found that the addition of stable manure resulted in higher yields on each horizon. Engelstad and Shrader (1961), using an artifically exposed subsoil

The authors are: D.L. SCHERTZ, National Conservation Tillage Agronomist, USDA/SCS, Washington, D.C.; W.C. MOLDENHAUER, Soil Scientist, USDA/ARS, National Soil Erosion Laboratory, West Lafayette, IN; D.P. FRANZMEIER, Professor of Agronomy, Purdue University, West Lafayette, IN; and H.R. SINCLAIR, Jr., State Soil Scientist, USDA/SCS, Indianapolis, IN.

and an unaltered surface of a Marshall silt loam near Clarinda, Iowa, found that corn yields on the exposed subsoil could equal corn yields on the unaltered surface provided that sufficient nitrogen fertilizer was added. Where no nitrogen was added, the exposed subsoil yielded approximately 3136 kg/ha less than the corresponding unaltered surface. The study showed that in 1958 the exposed subsoil required 39 kg/ha more nitrogen than the unaltered surface soil to achieve the same level of corn yields and that in 1959 it required 58 kg/ha more. Batchelder and Jones (1972) concluded that corn yields on an artifically exposed, acid subsoil of a clayey, mixed, mesic, Typic Hapludult can equal those where topsoil was not removed, provided that sufficient lime and fertilizer are added and that the water supply is increased by addition of straw mulch and limited irrigation.

Estimates have been made on the general effects of erosion on crop yields, but these estimates are based on limited data. Shrader et al. (1963) graphed the difference in erosion effects on crop yields for renewable and nonrenewable soil profiles. Renewable soil, although damaged by erosion, could be restored to the full productivity of its original, noneroded state by adding fertilizer and using proper management techniques. Nonrenewable soil, however, could not be renewed to the full productivity of its original state because of unfavorable subsoil conditions, such as root restrictive layers. Fehrenbacher et al. (1978) published crop yield adjustments for erosion phases by slope groups in Illinois. They noted that erosion was especially detrimental to crop yields where exposed subsoil provided an unfavorable medium for root growth. Van Doren and Bartelli (1956) reported reductions in corn yields, for several silt loam soils in Illinois ranging from 69 to 220 kg/ha per 2.54-cm loss of topsoil. Hagen and Dyke (1980) estimated the average loss in the Corn Belt to be about 478 kg/ha per 2.54 cm of soil loss. Langdale and Shrader (1982) stated that in the Southeast, loss of a few centimeters of topsoil may affect crop yields significantly because of shallow soils underlain by acid subsoil that contains phytotoxic levels of exchangeable aluminum.

Technology advancement (fertilizer, seed varieties, planting equipment, etc.) has masked significant declines in productivity caused by soil erosion. Krauss and Allmaras (1982) reported wheat yields declined 725 kg/ha with an average epipedon loss of 13.4 cm over a period of 90 years in Whitman County, Washington when yield increases due to technology were not considered. Technology advances, however, increased wheat yields 1,446 kg/ha during the same period masking the yield reduction caused by erosion. They felt it will be more difficult in the future for technology to mask the effects of erosion on crop yields.

Frye et al. (1982) reported that an eroded Maury soil (Typic Paleudalf) had a 12% reduction in corn yield (4-year average) compared to its uneroded state. They also found that an eroded Crider soil (Typic Paleudalf) had a 21% reduction in corn yield (3-year average) compared to its uneroded state.

Several efforts are underway to determine the effect of erosion on crop yield through modeling. Crosson and Stout (1983) discussed the Yield - Soil Loss Simulator developed by the U.S. Department of Agriculture (USDA) for use in the 1980 Resource Conservation Assessment process, a model prepared by W.E. Larson and others at the University of Minnesota, a regression model used by Resources for the Future, and a recent effort by USDA Agricultural Research Service in development of EPIC (Erosion Productivity Impact Calculator). Until such models are validated with recent research data from erosion-productivity studies involving various soil and climatic conditions, accurate predictions on a national scale will be difficult.

METHODS AND PROCEDURES

Corwin, Miami, and Morley (fine-loamy, mixed, mesic, Typic Argiudoll;

fine-loamy, mixed, mesic, Typic Hapludalf; and fine, mixed, mesic, Typic Hapludalf, respectively) were the three soil series evaluated. The studies were conducted in Benton, Montgomery, and Whitley Counties, Indiana. In Benton County, three replications of slight, moderate, and severe erosion phases of the Corwin soil series were located in each of five separate fields. As a result, 15 sites were evaluated for slight, 15 for moderate, and 15 for the severely eroded phase. The same procedures were followed in Montgomery County for the Miami series and in Whitley County for the Morley series.

The management level of the landusers in each county varied. Each landuser was requested to keep all management practices, including production inputs, the same throughout the field where the erosion sites were located. Conventional tillage practices were used on all fields.

Erosion phases were determined in the field by Soil Conservation Service (SCS) soil scientists with assistance from the Agronomy Department, Purdue University, using SCS soil survey criteria (SCS, 1981). Thorough investigation of each site insured as much soil uniformity as possible over the site length. Each erosion site was located through the use of a compass and a measuring wheel device with location maps made for each field. The same sites were used each year. All field sites were in corn (Zea mays L.) in 1981 and in corn and soybeans (Glycine max L.) in 1982 and 1983. Several sites had to be omitted in 1983, however, as a result of the USDA Payment-In-Kind (PIK) Program. All corn sites were three rows wide and 6.1 m long. Corn yield was determined for each row, adjusted to 15.5% moisture, and averaged over the three rows to obtain the site yield. Corn yield for each erosion phase was determined by averaging the three replications in each field. Yields by county for each erosion phase were obtained by averaging across fields. (For more information on procedures, refer to D. L. Schertz, W. C. Moldenhauer, and D. P. Franzmeier. 1984. "A standarized sampling procedure to determine the effect of past soil erosion on corn productivity," presented at the 1984 Annual Meeting of the American Society of Agronomy, Soil Science Society of America, and Crop Science Society of America, Las Vegas, Nevada).

Soybean yield was based on three rows, 3 m long, in the middle of each 6.1 m site. For drilled beans, yield was based on an area 3 m long and 1.5 m wide in the middle of each site. The hand-cut soybean samples were tied in bundles, labeled, and hung on racks to dry. After threshing, yield was calculated for each site and adjusted to 13.0% moisture. Field averages by erosion phase and by county were made in the same manner as for corn.

Soil samples were taken in 1981, from each site to a depth of 15 cm, using a tube sampler to remove a soil core. Each soil core sample consisted of six subsamples per site. These soil samples were analyzed to determine percent organic matter, pH, phosphorus and potassium content, and soil particle size.

Soil moisture through the growing season was determined for selected sites in 1982 and 1983. For the moisture tests, a tube sampler extracted 15-cm segments of soil to a depth of 122 cm in Benton and Montgomery Counties and to a depth of 107 cm in Whitley County. The soil segments were immediately placed in cans, which were sealed with electrical tape to retain moisture and sent to the USDA National Soil Erosion Laboratory for analysis. The samples were weighed moist and then dried at 105°C for 24 hours and reweighed. Gravimetric moisture was determined by dividing the change in weight by the oven-dry weight. Multiplying gravimetric moisture percentages by their respective bulk density values provided volumetric moisture percentage. After harvest in 1982, soil pits were dug adjacent to the sites where growing season moisture was analyzed. The pits were on the down-slope side of the actual plot and three rows away from the edge of the plot in order to minimize any plot modification in the following year. Soil cores, 5.4 by 3.0 cm, were taken, using a hand-core sampler, from the Ap, Bt1, Bt2,

11

and C horizons. Loose bulk samples were also taken from each horizon. The soil cores were used to determine soil water retention at 0.010, 0.033, and 0.1 MPa; and the bulk samples were used to determine soil water retention at 0.2, 0.5, 1.0, and 1.5 MPa. These analyses were made in a ceramic pressure-plate apparatus. Bulk density for each horizon was determined from the soil cores. The soil water retention data were compared to the volumetric soil moisture percentage data collected through the growing season in order to evaluate plant stress.

An analysis of variance was used to test the significance of differences between yields, organic matter percentages, pH, phosphorus and potassium content, and particle size ranges for the three phases of erosion. Duncan's Multiple Range Test was used to test differences between means.

RESULTS AND DISCUSSION

As the erosion process takes place, the surface horizon is reduced in thickness. If the soil erodes faster than the surface horizon can be maintained, tillage will begin mixing the upper subsoil with the surface horizon. As this mixing takes place, several changes can occur, depending on the subsoil characteristics. Changes that may occur in the surface layer include increase in clay content, reduction in content of organic matter and plant nutrients, a change in the structure, and lower available-water-holding capacity of the soil. Any of the above changes can significantly affect crop yield.

Average values for contents of clay, organic matter, and phosphorus in the upper 15 cm of the soil in 1981 are in Table 1. In Miami and Morley soils, the clay content of the severely eroded phase was 43% and 53% greater, respectively, than that of the slightly eroded phase. The Corwin soil showed a trend toward an increase in clay content with erosion.

Table 1. Average values for content of clay, organic matter, and phosphorus in the upper 15 cm of three erosion phases of Corwin, Miami, and Morley soils, 1981.

Soil	Erosion Phase	Clay	Organic Matter	Phosphorus
		---------(%)---------		(kg/ha)
Corwin	Slight	20.8^{ab*}	3.03^a	69.0^a
	Moderate	19.6^a	2.51^b	68.1^a
	Severe	23.0^b	1.86^c	45.6^a
Miami	Slight	15.4^a	1.89^a	106.4^a
	Moderate	18.1^b	1.64^{ab}	96.5^a
	Severe	22.1^c	1.51^b	76.4^a
Morley	Slight	18.6^a	1.91^a	90.9^a
	Moderate	23.0^b	1.76^{ab}	74.3^{ab}
	Severe	28.4^c	1.60^b	56.4^b

* Numbers for a given soil not followed by the same letter are significantly different at the 5% level.

Organic matter content decreased significantly with an increase in erosion for each of the three soil series. The Corwin soil was highest in organic matter content of the three soils studied and had the greatest decrease in organic matter content as erosion phase increased. Uhland (1949) studied similar soils in Benton County and found dramatic reductions in organic matter content as topsoil depth decreased as a result of erosion. It

12

appears that soils high in organic matter content are likely to have greater percentage reductions in organic matter as erosion increases than soils inherently low in organic matter.

Phosphorus content in the upper 15 cm of the soil decreased by 34%, 28%, and 38% for the Corwin, Miami, and Morley soils, respectively, as soil erosion phase increased from slight to severe. Since phosphorus does not readily move in the soil profile, losses are likely to occur as soil particles rich in attached phosphorus are eroded from the soil surface.

Table 2 shows potential plant-available water determined from soil core information taken at selected sites in 1982. Plant-available water was assumed to be 100% of the water present between water potentials of -0.033 and -1.5 MPa in the A and B soil horizons where bulk densities were less than $1.7g/cm^3$, 25% of this water in the B horizons where bulk densities were $1.7g/cm^3$ or greater, and 15% of this water in all C horizons, most of which had bulk densities greater than 1.7 g/cm^3. These data indicate that past erosion may significantly reduce plant-available water. Soil depth to compacted, calcareous, glacial till was greater for the slightly eroded sites than for the severely eroded sites, and, as Table 2 indicates, potential plant-available water was less for the severely eroded sites than for the slightly eroded sites. Corn yields in 1981 and 1982 were generally highest where soil depth and potential plant-available water were greatest.

Table 2. Total potential plant-available water in the soil profile for Corwin Miami, and Morley soils.

Erosion Phase	Corwin	Miami	Morley
	--------------------(%)--------------------		
Slight	12.92	16.10	7.38
Moderate	9.77	11.47	6.21
Severe	6.63	4.76	3.62

Corn yields for each soil and erosion phase are shown in Table 3. Corn yields on slightly eroded sites were significantly greater than those on severely eroded sites in 1981 and 1982 for the Miami soil. Slightly eroded sites had significantly greater yields than severely eroded sites for both the Corwin and Morley soils in 1982. Although no significant differences in yield were found on the Corwin and Morley soils in 1981, the trend was toward lower yields on severely eroded sites. Moderately eroded sites showed a trend toward lower yields than slightly eroded sites and higher yields than severely eroded sites.

In 1983, yields did not differ significantly between erosion phases. This lack of difference in 1983 is likely due to the abnormally low rainfall (driest in 50 years) during the growing season and extremely low and variable corn yields ranging from 0 to about 8400 kg/ha. Analysis of the 123 corn sites harvested in 1983 showed 28% yielded less than 941, 67% yielded less than 3136, and only 11% had yields in excess of 6272 kg/ha. Although plant population at harvest was not recorded, visual observations in 1983 indicated more plants per row on slightly eroded sites than on severely eroded sites, even though each site in a specific field was planted at the same population. This difference in plant population at harvest may indicate some adverse soil condition, such as crusting or other structural change, on the severely eroded sites. Ears of corn harvested from the slightly eroded sites were stunted and not well filled; some stalks were barren. Many of the severely eroded sites had stunted ears as well, but they were better filled and had fewer barren stalks. The difference in kernel fill and number of barren stalks between the slight and severe erosion phases were likely due to the difference in plant population at

Table 3. Corn yield by erosion phase by year for Corwin, Miami, and Morley
          soils.
==
  Soil   Erosion Phase   1981   1982   1983

                                --------------------(kg/ha)------------------

Corwin   Slight   8214^a* (15)§ 8997^a (2)   2050^a (8)
              Moderate   7773^{ab} (15)   10382^a (2)   1729^a (8)
              Severe   7551^b (15)   7523^b (2)   1045^a (7)

Miami   Slight   9113^a (15)   11000^a (12)   4285^a (6)
              Moderate   8776^a (15)   10139^a (12)   4278^a (6)
              Severe   7216^b (15)   8488^b (12)   4294^a (6)

Morley   Slight   7356^a (15)   6547^a (6)   **
              Moderate   7232^a (15)   5420^{ab} (6) **
              Severe   6640^a (15)   4307^b (6)   **
==
* Numbers for a given yield for a specific soil and year not followed by the
   same letter are significantly different at the 5% level.
§ Numbers in parenthesis represent number of sites in corn.
** No sites in corn.

harvest. It is important to point out that the longer a study can be
conducted, the less influence an abnormal year will have on yield
differences.

The percent reduction in corn yield on severely eroded sites as compared to
slightly eroded sites is shown in Table 4. The most significant differences
occurred in 1982. In 1981 and 1982 the Miami soil showed the most consistent
decreasses in yield on severely eroded sites as compared to slightly eroded
sites.

Table 4. Reduction in corn yield between the slight and severe phases of
         erosion.
==
  Soil   1981   1982   1983

                             ------------------(%)----------------

Corwin   8*   16*   49
Miami   21*   23*   0
Morley   10   34*   **
==
*   Significantly different at the 5% level by soil by year.
** No sites in corn.

When the data from all three years were combined, no significant yield
differences were found using erosion phase as the only independent variable
in the regression analysis. However, when harvest year and soil difference
were added to erosion phase as independent variables, corn yields on
slightly and moderately eroded sites were significantly geeater than those
on severely eroded sites at the 5% level as shown in Table 5. This
regression gave an r^2 of 0.61.

Soybean yields for each soil and erosion phase are shown in Table 6.
Percent reduction in yield on severely eroded sites as compared to slightly
eroded sites is presented in Table 7. For Corwin and Morley soils, soybean
yields averaged 14% and 29% higher, respectively, on slightly eroded sites
than on severely eroded sites in 1982. For the Miami soil differences in
soybean yields between erosion phases were not statistically different in
1982; however, these data are based on only one field. In addition, this

Table 5. Calculated corn yield (1981-1983) across three soils by erosion phase using the regression equation with erosion phase, harvest year, and soil difference as independent variables.

Erosion Phase	Calculated Yield (kg/ha)
Slight	7587[a]*
Moderate	7207[a]
Severe	6384[b]

* Yields not followed by the same letter are significantly different at the 5% level.

field had severe weed infestations on the slightly eroded sites and very few weeds on the severely eroded sites. Soybean plants on the severely eroded sites were shorter in height than on the slightly eroded sites but had greater pod density. No significant differences in soybean yield occurred in 1983, although the trend was toward lower yields on the eroded sites. As was true for the corn yields for 1983, soybean yields were quite variable as a result of the drought. Soybean yields varied from 20 to 3619 kg/ha with 53% of the sites harvested yielding less than 1344 kg/ha, which is less than half the normal yield.

Table 6. Soybean yield by erosion phase by year for Corwin, Miami, and Morley soils.

Soil	Erosion Phase	1982 (kg/ha)		1983 (kg/ha)	
Corwin	Slight	3638[a]*	(13)[§]	**	
	Moderate	3206[bc]	(13)	**	
	Severe	3121[c]	(13)	**	
Miami	Slight	2914[a]	(3)	2793[a]	(6)
	Moderate	2939[a]	(3)	2472[a]	(6)
	Severe	3033[a]	(3)	2255[a]	(6)
Morley	Slight	2608[a]	(9)	1021[a]	(12)
	Moderate	2424[a]	(9)	1062[a]	(12)
	Severe	1857[b]	(9)	868[a]	(12)

* Numbers for a given yield for a specific soil and year not followed by the same letter are significantly different at the 5% level.
§ Numbers in parenthesis represent number of sites in soybeans.
** No sites in soybeans.

Table 7. Reduction in soybean yield between the slight and severe phases of erosion.

Soil	1982 (%)	1983 (%)
Corwin	14*	**
Miami	-4	19
Morley	29*	15

* Significantly different at the 5% level by soil by year.
** No sites in soybeans.

Since years 1982 and 1983 contain both corn and soybean yields, a corn-yield equivalent was also evaluated. All soybean yields were multiplied by a factor of three giving a corn-yield equivalent. The factor of three is based on average yields over the past five years for corn and soybeans in the three counties studied. This factor also agrees with that recommended by Fehrenbacher et al. (1978). Statistical differences between erosion phases for the calculated corn-yield equivalent (1981-1983) were the same as those presented in Table 5 although the individual yields were slightly different.

SUMMARY AND CONCLUSIONS

This study shows that past soil erosion can reduce corn and soybean yields significantly but that the amount of reduction varies by soil series and year. Levels of organic matter and phosphorus decrease and clay content generally increases in the upper 15 cm of the soil as erosion phase changes from slight to severe. In addition, the data indicate that erosion can reduce the amount of water potentially available to plants.

Additional studies, which are designed in a similar way, are needed on benchmark soils across the U.S. in order to determine the effect of erosion on crop productivity and to provide a basis for validating models such as EPIC. All studies must be similar in design criteria so they can be combined for broader interpretation. Length of the studies should be a minimum of three years, but preferably five years or longer because of variable weather conditions.

REFERENCES

1. Batchelder, A.R. and J.N. Jones, Jr. 1972. Soil management factors and growth of Zea mays L. on topsoil and exposed subsoil. Agron. J. 64(5):648-652.

2. Crosson, Pierre R. and Anthony T. Stout. 1983. Productivity Effects of Cropland Erosion in the United States. The Johns Hopkins University Press, Baltimore, Maryland. 103 p.

3. Engelstad, O.P. and W.D. Shrader. 1961. The effect of surface soil thickness on corn yields: II. As determined by an experiment using normal surface soil and artifically-exposed subsoil. Soil Sci. Soc. Am. Proc. 25(6):497-499.

4. Fehrenbacher, J.B., R.A. Pope, I.J. Jansen, J.D. Alexander, and B.W. Ray. 1978. Soil Productivity in Illinois. Cir. 1156, Coop. Ext. Serv., Univ. of Ill. Urbana-Champaign. 21 p.

5. Frye, W.W., S.A. Ebelhar, L.W. Murdock, and R.L. Blevins. 1982. Soil erosion effects on properties and productivity of two Kentucky soils. Soil Sci. Soc. Am. J. 46:1051-1055.

6. Hagen, L.L. and P.T. Dyke. 1980. Yield-soil loss relationship. Presented at the Workshop on Influence of Soil Erosion on Soil Productivity, Feb. 26-28, 1980, in Washington, D.C. Science and Education Administration-Agricultural Research. USDA, Washington, D.C.

7. Krauss, H.A. and R.R. Allmaras. 1982. Technology masks the effects of soil erosion on wheat yields: a case study in Whitman County, Washington. In Determinants of Soil Loss Tolerance. ASA publication No. 45, Chapter 7, Am. Soc. of Agron., 677 So. Segoe Rd., Madison, WI. p. 75-86.

8. Langdale, G.W. and W.D. Shrader. 1982. Soil erosion effects on soil productivity of cultivated cropland. In Determinants of Soil Loss Tolerance. ASA publication no. 45, Chapter 4, Am. Soc. of Agron., 677 So. Segoe Rd., Madison, WI. p. 41-51.

9. Latham, E.E. 1940. Relative productivity of the A horizon of Cecil sandy loam and the B and C horizons exposed by erosion. J. Am. Soc. Agron. 32:950-954.

10. Leeper, R.A., E.C.A. Range, and W.M. Walker. 1974. Effect of plant-available stored soil moisture on corn yields. I. Constant climatic conditions. Agron. J. 66(6):723-727.

11. Office of Technology Assessment. 1982. Impacts of Technology on U.S. Cropland and Rangeland Productivity. Congressional Board of the 97th Congress. Library of Congress Catalog Card No. 82-600596. Washington, D.C. 266 p.

12. Shrader, W.D., H.P. Johnson, and J.F. Timmons. 1963. Applying erosion control principles. J. Soil and Water Conserv. 18(5):195-199.

13. Soil Conservation Service. United States Department of Agriculture, 1981. Soil Survey Manual. Chapter 4, U.S. Department of Agriculture, Washington, D.C. 107 p.

14. Uhland, R.E. 1949. Crop yields lowered by erosion. USDA-SCS-TP-75., Soil Conservation Service, U.S. Department of Agriculture, Washington, D.C. 27 p.

15. United States Department of Agriculture. 1981. Soil erosion effects on soil productivity: A research perspective. J. Soil and Water Conserv. 36(2):82-90.

16. Van Doren, C.A. and L.J. Bartelli. 1956. A method of forecasting soil loss. Agr. Eng. 37:335-341.

CHANGES IN SOIL PRODUCTIVITY RELATED TO CHANGING TOPSOIL

DEPTHS ON TWO IDAHO PALOUSE SOILS

M. Bramble-Brodahl   M. A. Fosberg   D. J. Walker   A. L. Falen

Knowledge about the productivity losses from cropland erosion is important
for formulating conservation policy. Out of expediency, soil loss in excess
of a tolerance level has been used as a criterion for conservation action.
However, this simple measure ignores the possibility that excessive erosion
could cause more damage on some soils than others depending on the soil
characteristics and crops. This paper examines the impact of erosion on
winter wheat productivity on two soils in the Idaho Palouse. The cost of
erosion damage with these soils is examined with an erosion damage model.

The objectives in this study were to: (1) examine the response of winter
wheat yield to topsoil loss, (2) determine whether the yield-topsoil
relationship is dependent on the type of soil, (3) determine what soil
profile properties which are altered in topsoil loss appear to influence
yield, and (4) evaluate the economic and policy implications of our results.

Since erosion occurs slowly it is difficult to examine the response of the
crop-soil system to soil loss. We have evaluated the crop response to
differences in existing topsoil depth and the results are then extrapolated
to the yield response to topsoil loss. This approach assumes that the
relationship of yield to differences in existing topsoil depths is a
reasonable proxy for the yield-topsoil loss relationship. The approach
includes the "field history" of eroded soils. The changes in soil profile
properties as erosion occurs through time will be in part dependent on the
cropping and tillage history of the site.

The results presented are from data collected in 1982 and 1983 on two
mollisols from the Genesee, Idaho area. The soils were sampled in similar
landscape positions on south slopes with approximately 10 to 25% slopes.
The two soils differ in that one has an argillic subsoil (an increase in
clay and in soil structure) and the other soil has a subsoil which is
texturally similar to the surface horizons and is not as strongly
structured. The data were collected on fields where the 2 year crop
rotation was Stephens winter wheat with dry peas or lentils.

STUDY SETTING

The Idaho Palouse is located in northwestern Idaho. The landscape is
rolling loessal hills in which slopes up to 50 percent are farmed.

The soils of the area are predominantly mollisols formed in various

The authors are: MARY BRAMBLE-BRODAHL, Research Associate, MAYNARD A.
FOSBERG, Professor of Soil Science, DAVID J. WALKER, Associate Professor of
Agricultural Economics, ANITA L. FALEN, Research Associate, College of
Agriculture, Univ. of Idaho, Moscow, Idaho.

Published as Idaho Agricultural Experiment Station Journal Article No. 84732.

sequences of loess deposition (Krapf, 1978). The distribution of soils is dependent on microclimate and landscape position, coupled with the sequence of loess depositions in the profile.

The climate of the study area is characterized by mild year-round temperatures and predominantly winter precipitation. Winter temperatures at Moscow, Idaho average 0° C, with average lows of -4° C. Summer temperatures average 17° C, with average maximum temperatures of 28° C. Average annual precipitation is 58 cm, of which 35%, or about 20 cm, falls in the growing season (April to September).

Expected wheat yields on the soils studied are 3960 to 4620 kg/ha (USDA, 1981). In 1982 cooperators in the Genesee, Idaho area reported "usual" yields of 4620 to 5300 kg/ha. In this season Stephens wheat suffered winter-kill in landscape positions blown free of snow during the winter months (convex ridges in south to southwest aspects). Other than in these positions, there was little evidence of disease, and weed populations were moderate. In 1983, however, wheat yields were exceptional. Cooperators reported fields with yields of up to 8000 kg/ha. Over-winter survival and plant condition were good, presumably due to the mild temperatures and adequate moisture. The growing season was cool and precipitation was adequate and well timed. There was very little weediness due to the dense stands of wheat. Leaf rust was present in the lusher growing wheat.

MATERIALS AND METHODS

The soils in the study were sampled on south slopes (~10 to 25% slopes, 135° to 225° aspects) in ridge-shoulder and sideslope landscape positions. Erosion in these positions results in soil loss rather than deposition.

The two soils sampled were Naff (Fine-silty, mixed, mesic Ultic Argixe rolls) and Palouse (Fine-silty, mixed, mesic Pachic Ultic Haploxerolls) soil series. The modal uneroded Naff soils have a thick (18 to 50 cm), very dark brown silt loam mollic surface over brown silty clay loam (30 to 40% clay) argillic B horizons. The modal Palouse soils have very thick (36 to 76 cm), very dark brown mollic surfaces over brown cambic (non-argillic, 20-30% clay) B horizons.

We have focused our sampling to reflect the profile characteristics of these two soils. However, the range of horizonation and horizon characteristics encountered in our study area was somewhat different than those described in the modal soil profiles. Consequently, the data include soils which are technically transitional to, or actually in other related soil series. On Naff soils we included horizonation sequences of A-Bt, A-Bw-Bt, Bw-Bt, and Bt-Bt (without naming transitional horizons) and subsoil textures ranging from 35 to 45% clay. On Palouse soils we included horizonation sequences of A-Bw, Bw-Bw, with subsoil textures of 20 to 30% clay.

Sites were sampled on 5 cooperator farms. Though the same farms were used each year, different fields were sampled in 1982 and 1983. On each farm 10 to 15 sites were sampled within each soil. The sites were selected to cover the range of topsoil depths in the whole data set. With this sampling design, data from each farm constitute an estimate of the yield-topsoil depth relationship. Sites were selected on the basis of wheat vigor and absence of weeds.

At each site the soil profile was examined. Data were collected on thickness of the mollic epipedon (thickness of A, AB, and darker BA horizons) and on Naff soils, depth to the argillic (Bt) horizons. In the fall of 1982 and in the spring of 1983 at each site, a mix of the top

19

30 cm of soil was collected by bucket auger or soil probe (one sample equals 3 probe samples). Percent organic matter was determined from these soil samples by the modified Walkley-Black method.

Bulk density samples at 30 cm were collected by a core sampler. Two to three cores were collected on each site. Dry soil weights were taken on samples which were air dried, then oven-dried overnight at 105° C.

Wheat yield data at each site were collected from three, .9m x .9m, hand harvested plots. The subsamples were threshed, and an average of the 3 grain weights taken as yield data.

ANALYSIS

Relationships between yield, topsoil depth (thickness of the mollic epipedon and depth to argillic horizons), and soil profile properties were investigated using regression analyses. All analyses were run on SAS (SAS Institute Inc., 1982) statistical software. Least squares linear regressions were performed with Proc REG, and nonlinear regressions within Proc NLIN using the DUD algorithm.

Yield-topsoil depth relationships were examined by regressions relating yield to thickness of the mollic epipedon (MOLLDEP) on both soils, and on Naff sites, depth to the argillic horizons (DEPBT) as well. Two yield response forms were considered and are described in Eq. (1) and Eq. (2).

$$\text{Yield (kg/ha)} = LO + Ll(\text{topsoil depth in cm}) \tag{1}$$
$$\text{Yield (kg/ha)} = BO + Bl(1 - \exp(-B2(\text{topsoil depth in cm}))) \tag{2}$$

Equation 1 is a linear model which describes a uniform increase in yield as topsoil depth (MOLLDEP or DEPBT) increases. In this model LO, the Y intercept, is the yield at 0 cm topsoil depth, and Ll is the increase in yield per cm increase in topsoil depth.

Equation 2 is a nonlinear model in which the rate of change in yield as topsoil depth increases is not constant. In this model, the rate is greatest at shallower topsoil depths and then declines as topsoil depth increases. Yield appoaches a maximum yield level with increased topsoil depths. In Eq. 2 BO is the yield at 0 cm topsil depth (the Y intercept), Bl describes the difference between the yield at 0 cm topsoil depth and the maximum yield, and B2 defines the rate at which the maximum yield is approached as topsoil depth changes.

The choice of which model best described the yield-topsoil depth relationship within each soil and within each year was made on the following criterion. A priori, the nonlinear model is preferred based on agronomic theory because yield approaches an upper limit with increasing topsoil depth. In the analysis the nonlinear form was selected as the best description of the relationship when the R^2 value was equivalent to, or higher than the linear regression R^2, and the maximum yield predicted in the nonlinear model fell within or near the range of actual data. If the R^2 values were similar but the predicted maximum yield in the nonlinear model was well beyond the range of the data collected, the linear model was chosen to avoid extrapolating beyond the actual data.

Only linear regression models were considered in the relationships of yield to the soil profile characteristics of percent organic matter in a mix of the top 30 cm of soil (OM) and bulk density 30 cm (BD). The linear relationship was considered adequate for the description of the direction of change and the average change in the dependent variable related to a unit change in the independent variable.

Erosion damage cost estimates are based on an erosion damage model described by Walker (1982). The concept of erosion damage embodied in this model offers several desirable features: (1) the damage concept avoids confounding tillage yield penalty with erosion damage; (2) damage with erosive tillage systems can be measured relative to a static topsoil base or measured relative to a conservation practice which reduces but may not arrest erosion; and (3) the damage estimate correctly incorporates technology without confounding technology and erosion damage (Walker, 1983).

In this application the damage model estimates the cost of erosion from wheat production with conventional tillage. The cost of erosion damage is the present value of the lost future net income from reduced productivity due to erosion in the current year. The damage model requires information on: (1) the relationship between crop yield and soil properties affected by erosion; and (2) how the process of erosion changes those soil properties. In the application of the model in this paper, declining topsoil depth is used as a proxy for the deterioration of soil properties due to erosion. Because agronomic theory suggests a nonlinear yield-topsoil relationship, the nonlinear functional form was chosen for the erosion damage simulation.

RESULTS AND DISCUSSION

A summary of the means and range of values for YIELD, MOLLDEP, DEPBT, OM, and BD by soil and year are presented in Table 1.

Table 1. Means and Ranges of Data for Naff and Palouse Soils in 1982 and 1983.

	1982			1983		
	n	mean	min-max	n	mean	min-max
NAFF						
YIELD Kg/ha	32	4950	2856-7278	48	7930	4402-10367
MOLLDEP cm	32	27.1	0-61.0	48	28.2	0-66.0
DEPBT cm	32	45.0	10.2-81.3	48	39.4	0-114.3
OM %	32	2.33	.78-3.74	47	2.30	.82-3.80
BD g/cc	32	1.35	1.17-1.65	48	1.38	1.08-1.71
PALOUSE						
Yield kg/ha	27	5077	2354-7088	31	8405	6289-10054
MOLLDEP cm	27	43.4	0-88.9	31	38.6	0-111.8
OM %	27	2.26	.78-3.77	31	2.48	.85-4.10
BD g/cc	27	1.28	1.09-1.50	31	1.27	1.06-1.40

[a]YIELD=Yield of Stephens soft white winter wheat
MOLLDEP=thickness of the mollic epipedon
DEPBT=depth to the arsillic horizons
OM=percent organic matter in a mix of the top 30 cm of soil
BD=bulk density at 30 cm
n = number of samples

For Palouse soils in 1982, the YIELD-thickness of the mollic epipedon (MOLLDEP) relationship was linear (Table 2). The linear regression model with an R^2 of .43, described a 37.7 kg/ha increase in yield per cm

Table 2.   Linear and Nonlinear YIELD-Topsoil Depth Regressions for Naff and
            Palouse Sites in 1982 and 1983.

LINEAR REGRESSIONS(Yield=LO+L1(Tops)):

Soil	1982			1983		
	LO	L1	R^2	LO	L1	R^2
Naff MOLLDEP[a]	3982.0[b]	35.8	.18	6669	45.3	.30
DEPBT	2773	48.4	.50	6542	35.4	.49
Palo MOLLDEP	3439	37.7	.43	7530	23.4	.26

+++

NONLINEAR REGRESSIONS(YIELD=BO+B1(1-Exp(-B2(Tops)))):

Soil	1982				1983			
	BO	B1	B2	R^2	BO	B1	B2	R^2
Naff MOLLDEP	3633	2241	.041	.21	5874	2740	.076	.41
DEPBT	2358	8609	.008	.51	5832	4442	.020	.55
Palo MOLLDEP	3310	8900	.004	.44	6752	2757	.031	.32

[a]MOLLDEP=thickness of mollic epipedon in cm
DEPBT=depth to the argillic horizons in cm
YIELD=in kg/ha
[b]All coefficients are significantly different from zero at the .01
level except for L1 in the 1982 Naff-MOLLDEP regression which is
significant at the .05 level

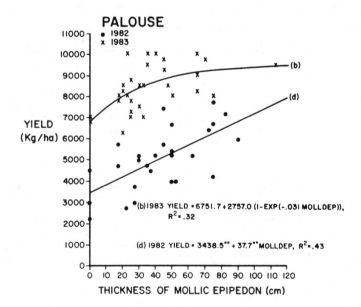

Figure 1. Palouse Data and Regressions for the Relationship of Yield and
          Thickness of the Mollic Epipedon in 1982 and 1983. (On linear
          regression '**' indicate the coefficients were significantly
          different from zero at the .01 level.)

22

increase in MOLLDEP from a yield of 3438 kg/ha at 0 cm MOLLDEP. While the
nonlinear model had a slightly higher R^2 of .44, the model described a
linear response over the range of data collected. The maximum yield
described by the fitted nonlinear model (B0+B1=12210 kg/ha) was well beyond
the data collected, and the rate of rise to the maximum was slow (B2=.004).
In this model, 90% of the maximum yield would occur around 500 cm MOLLDEP.
While there is considerable scatter in the data points, examination of the
plots in Fig. 1 for the 1982 data indicates the apparent linear trend in the
YIELD-MOLLDEP relationship.

In comparison, the 1983 YIELD-MOLLDEP relationship was weaker and more
nonlinear. The linear model had an R^2 value of .26 while the nonlinear
model improved the R^2 value to .32. A difference in yield of 2757 kg/ha
was described by the model between the minimum yield (at 0 cm MOLLDEP) of
6752 kg/ha and the maximum yield of 9509 kg/ha. The maximum yield was
within the range of the data collected, and this model predicts that 90% of
the maximum yield would be found around 33 cm MOLLDEP. Both the linear and
nonlinear regression results suggest a weaker YIELD-MOLLDEP relationship on
Palouse soils in 1983.

For Naff soils in 1982, the YIELD-MOLLDEP relationship was very weak (Fig.
2a). The linear model, though significant, had an R^2 value of .18. The
nonlinear model did improve the R^2 to .21 and the model defined was within
the range of data actually collected. Ninety percent of the maximum yield
is predicted to occur around 20 cm MOLLDEP. The R^2 values indicate a weak
correlation between yield and MOLLDEP on Naff soils in 1982.

In 1983, the R^2 for the linear model was .30. The R^2 for the nonlinear
model was .41. Ninety-percent of the maximum yield is predicted to occur at
15 cm MOLLDEP.

The subsequent results from YIELD-DEPBT regressions with Naff soil suggest
that MOLLDEP gives an incomplete description of what yield is responding to
in Naff soils. DEPBT is a better predictor of yields with Naff soils. In
1982 the YIELD-DEPBT relationship was best described by the linear model
with an R^2 of .50 (Fig. 2b). An increase in yield of 48.4 kg/ha was
associated with a cm increase in DEPBT from a yield of 2772 kg/ha at 0 cm
DEPBT. The nonlinear model exhibited the same problems encountered in the
1982 nonlinear Palouse model. The model over the range of existing data was
stongly linear, the predicted maximum yield (10967 kg/ha) was well beyond
the yields collected, and 90% of the maximum yield was predicted to occur
around 250 cm DEPBT. In 1983, the linear model had an R^2 of .49. The
nonlinear model improved the R^2 to .55, and the nonlinear YIELD-DEPBT
description was within the range of the data collected. A yield difference
of 4442 kg/ha was defined from a low yield of 5832 kg/ha at 0 cm DEPBT to a
maximum yield of 10274 kg/ha. B2, the rate of the approach to the maximum
yield as DEPBT increases, was .020. Ninety-percent of the maximum yield
occurrs around 70 cm DEPBT. The nonlinear model gives the best description
of the Naff YIELD-DEPBT relationship.

On Naff soils, DEPBT had a stronger relationship to yield than did MOLLDEP
in both years of data. If DEPBT did not contain some additional information
over MOLLDEP about soil factors which influence yield, the results of the
YIELD-MOLLDEP and YIELD-DEPBT analyses should have been more closely
related. However, there were obvious differences in functional form between
MOLDEP and DEPBT models, as well as differences in R^2 values. MOLLDEP is
a soil variable which qualitatively describes the portion of the rooting
environment with silt-loam textures and higher organic matter content.

In comparison to DEPBT it does not incorporate as much pertinent rooting
environment information in the context of winter wheat yield. DEPBT

23

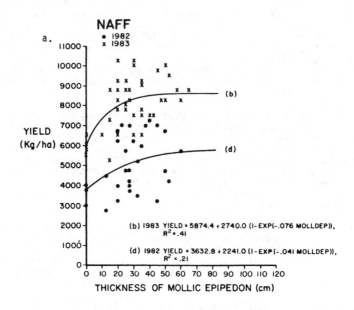

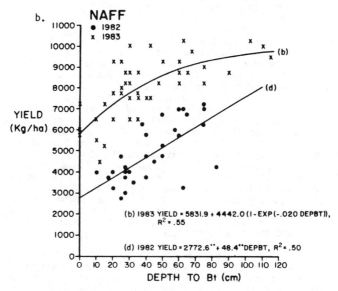

Figure 2. Naff Data and Regressions for the Relationship of Yield is the Thickness of the Mollic Epipedon (a) and Yield to the Depth of the Argillic (Bt) Horizons (b) in 1982 and 1983. ('**' on linear regressions indicate the coefficients were different from zero at the .01 level.)

24

qualitatively includes information about MOLLDEP (since the argillic horizons are below the mollic epipedons) as well as information about the location of textural and structural changes in the profile. The stronger relationship of DEPBT to YIELD in both years suggest that yield is influenced by soil factors related to the location of the argillic horizons in the profile as well as the soil factors related to MOLLDEP.

Taking DEPBT on Naff soils and MOLLDEP in Palouse soils as the best measures of topsoil depth for winter wheat yields, these two years of data do not definitively indicate the general form of the YIELD-topsoil depth relationships. However, some general and tentative statements can be made based on the comparative behavior of the relationships. Based on regression results the YIELD-topsoil depth relationship was consistently stronger on Naff soils over the two years. On Palouse sites, in addition to lower R^2's, there was a greater difference in R^2 values between 1982 and 1983. The yield-topsoil depth relationships were linear on both soils in 1982. If the shift to nonlinear response forms in both soils in 1983 was due to some environmental factor in that season altering the influence of topsoil depth on yield, the results suggest that this factor was effective at a shallower topsoil depth on Palouse soils than on Naff soils. The topsoil depth on Palouse soils at which maximum yield is approached is shallower, around 33 cm, than was the depth predicted on Naff soils, around 70 cm.

Additional insight into how yield responds to changes in topsoil depth was found in the relationship of yield to OM and BD on the two soils. As measured, these soil properties indicate the location in the profile of the transition from the surface horizons to subsoil horizons. Though they consequently have overlapping information, OM is a more direct measure of soil properties related to the mollic epipedon (i.e. fertility) while BD would reflect changes in textural and structural properties (which potentially influence plant-available water) of the profile.

Regressions of YIELD versus YEAR, OM, and BD were run within each soil to evaluate the effect of OM and BD on YIELD. The standardized coefficients for OM and BD suggested a difference in the influence of BD on yield between the two soils. OM had similar standardized coefficients on both Naff and Palouse soils (.37 and .44 respectively), while BD had a larger influence on the Naff soils (standardized coefficient = -.23) than on the Palouse sites (standardized coefficient = - .01) where it was not a significant part of the model. The R^2 for the Naff and Palouse models were .84 and .85 respectively.

The results of regression analysis of OM as a function of topsoil depth (MOLLDEP on Palouse soils and DEPBT on Naff soils, R^2=.42) indicated that the relationship of OM to topsoil depth was the same on both soils. Neither the intercept nor the topsoil depth coefficient were influenced by what soil the sites were on. For BD as a function of topsoil depth, there was a statistical difference between Naff and Palouse soils in the value of BD at 0 cm topsoil depth and in the decrease in BD per cm increase in topsoil depth (R^2=.52). In comparison to Palouse, BD on Naff sites had a higher value at 0 cm topsoil depth, and a more rapid rate of decrease as topsoil depth increased. The range of OM and BD value on the two soils are summarized in Table 1.

A difference in yield response to topsoil depth on the two soils appears to be related to the soil factors reflected in the BD measure. On both soils the BD measure reflects horizon changes as expressed in the physical soil properties of structure and texture. On Palouse soils changing topsoil depth appears to influence yield through a change in those soil properties reflected in the OM variable only. On Naff soils, though the YIELD-OM

25

relationship is influential, there is a component of yield response related to changes in BD.

The economic consequence of the different yield response to topsoil loss with these two soils was explored with an erosion damage model. The YIELD-topsoil functions for the economic analysis estimated from the data for Naff and Palouse soils respectively are:

$$Yield = 4105 + 5128 \ (1-EXP(-.016(DEPBT))) \qquad (3)$$
$$Yield = 5050 + 3473 \ (1-EXP(-.019(MOLLDEP))) \qquad (4)$$

Yield is in kg/ha. DEPBT and MOLLDEP are in cm.

The assumptions employed in the damage model analysis are: (1) annual soil loss of 23.3 Mg/ha for conventional tillage with winter wheat; (2) topsoil depth of 38 cm which is the average depth for the dominant landclass (IIIe) of the Palouse; (3) wheat price of $.13 per kg., (4) a 75-year time horizon over which damage from current erosion is estimated[1]; (5) a 4 percent real rate of discount; and (6) a proportional rate of technical progress of 1.7 percent annually, the rate occurring over the last 50 years in the Palouse.

The annual cost of erosion damage per hectare for the above conditions is $28.66 on Palouse soils and $40.28 on Naff soils. This cost is the present value of lost future income from reduced yields over a 75 year damage horizon due to erosion in the current year[2]. In this example, where the topsoil depth was assumed to be 38 cm for both soils, the cost of annual erosion is 40 percent greater on Naff soils because the slope of the yield-topsoil depth function is steeper for the Naff soil series.

CONCLUSION

On both soils, yield response to changes in topsoil depth was linear in 1982 and nonlinear in 1983. While the yield response on Naff soils was nonlinear in 1983, a change in yield was associated with a change in topsoil depth over most of the depths sampled. On Palouse soils in 1983, yield changed very little as topsoil depth increased beyond 30 cm (yield was close to the assymptotic upper limit). Finally, the soil profile factors influencing yield appear to differ between the two soils because of the type of subsoil. Yield is related to changes in both OM and BD on Naff soils, and is related only to changes in OM on Palouse sites.

These results indicate several things about how yield might respond to erosion. On Naff sites, regardless of how favorable the growing season is, the results suggest that yield will be affected by topsoil loss over much of

---

[1] In conceptualizing a measure of erosion damage, most farmers would have a finite time horizon over which they would be concerned about the consequences of current erosion. A time horizon of 75 years would incorporate 25 years of his own operation and 50 years of operation by his children and grandchildren. From an economist's standpoint, with a 4% real rate of discount, a 75 year time horizon (damage horizon) captures 95% of the present value of erosion damage into perpetuity.

[2] In estimating erosion damage cost with the damage model, the lost income is not necessarily constant in each year of the damage horizon. The income lost each year from current erosion can increase over the damage horizon if there is exogenous, land-complementary technical progress (Walker, 1983) and if erosion damage is measured relative to a conservation practice which does not completely arrest erosion.

the range of existing topsoil depths. On Palouse soils there was a greater difference in yield response between the two years. This greater difference may indicate that the yield-topsoil depth relationship is generally more variable on Palouse soils. Thus average response of yield to erosion with Palouse soil may depend on the prevalent growing season conditions.

The fact that yield is related only to OM on Palouse soils and is related to both OM and BD on Naff soils, suggests that it may be more difficult to repair the effects of topsoil loss on productivity for Naff soils. While it may be feasible to improve the soil factors related to OM, it will be more difficult to manipulate BD.

The differences in yield response to changes in topsoil depth on these two soils are reflected in the differences in the cost of erosion damage. These results highlight the importance of a more sophisticated criterion to judge the need for conservation action. With the recent interest in targeting conservation efforts to critical erosion areas, the cost of erosion damage could play an important role in the selection of target areas for conservation emphasis. The cost of erosion damage is a more comprehesive and relavent criterion than simple soil loss.

REFERENCES

1. Krapf, R. W. 1978. Characterization of loess deposits and paleosols of the Palouse formation in Idaho and Washington. PhD Dissertation. Univ. of Idaho. 134 pp.

2. SAS Institute Inc. 1982. SAS User's Guide: Statistics 1982 Edition, Cary, NC: SAS Institute Inc.. 584 pp.

3. United States Dept. of Agriculture. 1981. Soil Survey of Latah County Area, Idaho. Soil Conservation Service, U.S. Government Printing.

4. Walker, D. J. 1982. A damage function to evaluate erosion control economics. Amer. J. Ag. Econ., Vol 64(4):690-698.

5. _____. 1983. Targeting soil conservation with a net benefit function incorporating erosion damage and technology. Paper presented on October 28, 1983, at Iowa State University, Ames, Iowa.

0325a

SOIL EROSION–PRODUCTIVITY RESEARCH IN SOUTHERN ONTARIO

L.A. Battiston   R.A. McBride   M.H. Miller   M.J. Brklacich

Soil erosion presents a significant limitation to sustainable agricultural production in Ontario. Conservative, though cursory, estimates of erosion-induced row crop yield reductions indicate that the annual cost of sheet and rill erosion to the total agricultural production in the province which is directly attributable to yield losses alone is about $27 million (Cdn.), with an additional $40 million (Cdn.) stemming from nutrient and pesticide losses (Wall and Driver, 1982).

Existing rural land evaluation procedures are dependent on reliable estimates of crop yield if they are to meaningfully gauge the importance that specific land areas be delegated to particular agricultural uses. Long range planning for the optimum use of the agricultural land resource base is thus highly sensitive to changes in the potential productive capacity of soils caused by erosion or other soil degrading processes. This is of particular concern when issues such as the conversion of marginal and highly erodible land areas to agricultural use (Benbrook and Hidlebaugh, 1982) and the current trend toward abandonment of traditional farm management practices (i.e. substitution of crop rotation with intensive row crop monoculture (Miller, 1976)) are addressed in land evaluation assessments. As yet, however, the soil erosion-productivity relationship is poorly defined and understood (Williams, 1981) thus hampering long range planning activities of this kind.

Research prior to 1950 in the United States provided considerable evidence that the erosion of topsoil resulted in substantially lower crop yields, apparently due to the selective removal of the finer mineral soil fractions and organic matter in surface runoff and the concomitant loss of essential plant nutrients (Langdale and Shrader, 1981; Stallings, 1950). Corn yields in particular showed a significant and relatively constant decline with each centimetre of topsoil lost to past erosion in many individual plot experiments. Annual yield reductions, however, were reported to range from 37 to 173 kg/ha·cm of soil lost and varied with the soil type, the prevailing climatic conditions, and the farm management practices (Benbrook and Hidlebaugh, 1982; Stallings, 1950). Attainable yield levels have increased considerably since that time and the observed reductions in corn yield with topsoil loss have followed accordingly, ranging from 42 to 215 kg/ha·cm of soil lost in more recent studies (Benbrook and Hidlebaugh, 1982). It is now widely accepted among resource analysts that corn yield reduction rates of 75 to 100 kg/ha·cm of soil lost can be used with some confidence in land evaluation studies (N.A.L.S., 1981) even though there is evidence to suggest that a critical surface horizon thickness exists below which the relationship between topsoil depth and crop yield is non-linear (Larson, 1981). Aside from a limited number of plot experiments on artificially truncated (cut and fill) soils, however, no such body of information on the soil erosion-productivity relationship exists in Canada.

The authors are: L.A. BATTISTON, R.A. McBRIDE, Research Associates, and M.H. MILLER, Professor, Land Resource Sci. Dept.; and M.J. BRKLACICH, Research Associate, Land Evaluation Group, School of Rural Planning and Dev., Univ. of Guelph, Guelph, Ont., Canada.

It is now recognized that the causes of reduced crop productivity on eroded soils are more complex and more physically-based than was indicated from the results of these early studies. Indeed, the loss or reduced availability of plant nutrients may be of lesser importance over the long-term when compared to the difficulty of restoring the plant-available water-holding capacity and the surface soil structural properties of severely eroded soils (Williams, 1981) or replacing the physiological crop requirements provided by these soil qualities with existing technology (Larson, 1981). Despite increased understanding of the effects of undesirable properties of exposed subsoil on plant growth, available soil erosion-productivity models such as the RCA yield-soil loss simulator (Hagen and Dyke, 1980) and the numerical productivity index method of Pierce et al. (1983) remain unreliable (Williams, 1981; Benbrook and Hidlebaugh, 1982) or largely uncalibrated and untested. While the comprehensive, multi-component EPIC model (Williams et al., 1983) has been shown capable of realistically simulating soil loss and crop growth, the respective sensitivities of the crop yield and macronutrient cycling components to soil erosion remain unvalidated.

A recent two-year study (Battiston and Miller, 1982;1984) is the first investigation of its kind in Ontario to specifically address the objectives of determining the changes in physical and chemical soil properties caused by past soil erosion on a range of soils and of relating measured crop yields to changes in these soil properties. In so doing, this study has succeeded in quantifying yield changes attributable to soil erosion and in identifying the major causes of these yield changes. The objectives of this paper are to summarize the experimental procedures and major findings of this study and to report on a soil moisture-based crop modelling approach which has been applied in land evaluation studies to define a realistic soil erosion-productivity relationship for Ontario soil and climatic conditions.

EXPERIMENTAL AND ANALYTICAL PROCEDURES

Site Establishment and Experimental Design

Field trials were established during two consecutive growing seasons (1982-83) in grain corn (Zea mays L.) fields, henceforth referred to as 'sites', selected on several well-managed farms within a 300 km^2 study area in the Regional Municipality of Waterloo. Sites were chosen on texturally disparate soil series which were located on highly varied topography and which had evidence of a significant soil erosion problem. All mechanical farm operations were performed by the co-operating farmers. To ensure an unbiased evaluation of the erosion phase effect on crop yield both within and among the farm sites, only farmers using good management were selected. Other selection criteria also ensured, in so far as possible, that differences between sampling areas within a site could be attributed primarily to past erosion. Both false-colour infra-red and colour aerial photography was obtained of the entire study area in early May and in mid-July 1982 to assist in site selection and to assess the extent and severity of erosion.

During the first year of the study (1982), seven farm sites were selected and replicated sampling plots were set out on three landscape types: i) stable (effectively non-eroded; annual soil loss within accepted tolerance levels of 6.7 to 11.2 tonnes/ha·yr or less), ii) unstable (severely eroded with most or all of the humic A horizon removed and with exposed B or calcareous C horizons; annual soil loss greatly exceeds rate of soil formation), and iii) depositional (areas subject to topsoil deposition at the base of eroding slopes). Six plots were established on areas selected within each landscape type (each 4 m long x 4 rows wide) in two blocks of three adjoining plots.

Seven well-managed farm sites were similarly selected and sampling plots

established in 1983 based on the occurrence of four identifiable erosion
phases (C.S.S.C., 1978): i) non-eroded, ii) slightly eroded (up to 25% of the
humic A horizon removed), iii) moderately eroded (25-75% of the humic A
horizon removed; considerable mixing of underlying horizons in plow layer),
and iv) severely eroded (defined above).

Soil and Plant Analyses

The two outer rows of each plot were used exclusively to monitor crop response
by periodically determining plant height and leaf number as well as taking
whole plant (4 - 8 leaf stage) and leaf (50% silking stage) tissue samples for
essential nutrient analysis (N,P,K,Ca,Mg,Mn,Zn,Cu,B). The two inner rows were
harvested by hand after black layer formation to determine the total grain
yield (expressed as kg/ha at 15% moisture) for each erosion phase replicate.

Specific chemical and physical analyses were performed during both study years
to characterize the soil water and fertility regimes of each sampling plot and
to determine the magnitude of any erosion-induced change in these properties.
The mean depth and thickness of the major soil horizons were determined for
each plot. Soil samples taken of the surface 15 cm within the plot were
combined, mixed, and air-dried for the measurement of soil fertility levels
(P,K,Mg,Mn,Zn), particle size distribution, pH in both water and 0.01M $CaCl_2$,
and the percentages of organic matter and $CaCO_3$. The mean surface horizon dry
bulk density was determined from six undisturbed core samples (5 cm diameter x
3 cm long) taken randomly across each plot at a 5-8 cm depth. Subsurface bulk
soil samples were obtained from the major horizons in the centre of each plot
with a Dutch auger. These horizon samples were combined for each block
of three plots, mixed, air-dried, and analyzed for particle size distribution,
pH (water and 0.01M $CaCl_2$) and the percentages of organic matter and $CaCO_3$.
The dry bulk density of each major subsurface horizon occurring within the
surface 100 cm was measured from soil cores taken with a portable,
split-sleeve core sampling device. Intact soil cores (5 cm diameter x 6 cm
long) were extracted for each horizon and combined for each block of three
replicate plots to obtain a mean subsurface dry bulk density by horizon. The
laboratory procedures followed are those outlined by McKeague (1978).

Seasonal Soil Moisture Budget Calculations

Total pre-season plant-available soil moisture, as a volumetric percentage
(Θva), was estimated for each plot using the empirical water retention model
developed for Ontario soils in situ (McBride and Mackintosh, 1984a). This
regression-based model estimates the upper and lower limits of plant-available
water to a user specified depth or lithic contact based on soil texture, total
soil porosity, organic matter content, groundwater table depth, and the volume
of coarse fragments greater than 2 mm in diameter. The standard error of
estimate for negative pressure potentials ranging from -5 to -1500 kPa is 2.2%
moisture by weight or less.

For this study, it was assumed that the rooting depth was 100 cm and that all
plant-available soil moisture in this zone was subject to plant uptake.
Gravimetric soil moisture sampling indicated that the soils on all
experimental plots were fully recharged at the beginning of both growing
seasons and were presumed effectively at equilibrium with the groundwater
table (McBride and Mackintosh, 1984a). The position of the groundwater table
at planting (5 May to 24 May 1982, and 6 May to June 3 1983) was set in
accordance with the internal drainage class of the soils at each site
(Mackintosh and van de Hulst, 1978).

As no attempt was made to measure the quantity of soil water lost to deep
drainage or of precipitation lost to surface runoff (i.e. effective
precipitation), crop yield was related to a seasonal estimate of the soil
moisture deficit or surplus using only the estimated plant-available

30

moisture-holding capacity of the soil (Θva) and the total precipitation and potential crop evapotranspiration amounts from 10 May to 30 Sept. in a simple soil moisture budget. Cumulative precipitation and Class A pan evaporation measurements were obtained from the A.E.S. (Environment Canada) meteorological station nearest to the field sites. Potential evapotranspiration from a corn crop was estimated by applying the pan and crop coefficients reported by Doorenbos and Pruitt (1977) to the daily pan evaporation readings.

Grain Corn Productivity Estimates

An empirical yield vs. field water supply function (McBride and Mackintosh, 1984b) relates grain corn yield to a seasonal estimate of the soil moisture deficit or surplus with 5 cubic polynomial regression equations, each specific to a different heat unit zone (Brown, 1963) within the corn-growing region of Ontario. Verification of these functions has shown that they are best applied in estimating long-term mean yields obtained under relatively constant climatic conditions since yield response is not weighted for uneven precipitation distribution through the growing season. This is consistent with the requirement that a suitable soil erosion-productivity model simulate the influence of soil loss projected over extended periods on potential soil productivity (Williams, 1981). Since no long-term yield measurements have been reported on eroded soils in Ontario upon which to base a more rigorous verification of this procedure, the authors felt justified in applying this crop yield estimation technique to these two years of experimental results from the study of Battiston and Miller (1982; 1984).

As plant-available soil moisture (Θva) is one component of the seasonal soil water balance, the estimated grain corn yield responds to erosion-induced changes in Θva caused by the removal of the humic A horizon, an increase in the surface dry bulk density from the loss of organic matter and ensuing structural degradation, and the increased proportion of the potential root zone comprised of subsoil materials with low available water-holding properties (e.g. high clay content, high sand or coarse fragment content, or high dry bulk density) or bedrock.

During years with a seasonal soil moisture deficit, crop yield declines with Θva from the agroclimatic (photosynthetic) potential in response to increased severity and duration of plant water stress (Leeper et al., 1974; Stewart and Hagan, 1973). A decrease from the maximum attainable yield is also predicted with increasing Θva during growing seasons with a soil moisture surplus due to the occurrence of periodic intervals of low air permeability as excess gravitational water from precipitation is redistributed through the root zone. In instances where the water retention model predicts an equilibrium air-filled porosity (ϵ) of less than 10% in the surface 20 cm of soil due to a high groundwater table or erosion-induced structural deterioration, however, anticipated yields are further deflated 10% for each percentage that ϵ falls below this critical level in the upper root zone (Raghavan et al., 1979).

This model is entirely soil moisture-based and makes no adjustment to crop yield if soil fertility is below optimum levels. It's application thus isolates largely irreversible losses in long-term productivity arising from changes in the soil water regime.

The Extent of Erosion in the Study Area

Through a combination of air photo interpretation and ground truthing, the extent of moderately and severely eroded soils within the 300 km^2 study area was determined.

Experimental Results

The amount and distribution of precipitation were extreme and varied over the two field seasons that this study took place and, as such, provided an opportunity to examine the influence of annual weather patterns on the soil erosion-productivity relationship. Tables 1 and 2 summarize the corn yield response to the soil erosion phases and the major factors contributing to yield reductions.

Table 1. Summary of Grain Corn Yield Response to Erosion Phase

Erosion phase	Grain corn yield (15.5% moisture)	
	1982 (7 sites)	1983 (7 sites)
	(t/ha)	(t/ha)
Non-eroded	7.03	6.67
Depositional	6.91	----
Moderately eroded	----	5.59
Severely eroded	4.66	2.97

In 1982, precipitation during the growing period was 37% above normal. Corn yields on the non-eroded and depositional plots were not significantly different and were near the maximum attainable in this region (Table 1). Yields declined an average of 34% on severely eroded soils (Table 2) and this loss was clearly not compensated for by any yield increase in the depositional areas. Plant nitrogen deficiencies, arising from denitrification and deep leaching of nitrates and/or adverse erosion-induced changes in the soil water regime (low Θva or ε) were believed responsible for the yield reductions on the severely eroded sites in 1982 (Table 2). The second study year (1983) was much drier than normal giving rise to generally lower yields compared to the previous year. An average yield reduction of 47% over the six sites with both non- and severely eroded plots was observed and this was largely attributed to lower Θva values in the latter. From Table 1, the average yield reduction on moderately and severely eroded plots was about 30%.

Table 2. Summary of Grain Corn Yield Reductions on Severely Eroded Sites

Site	1982		1983	
	Yield reduction	Major cause(s)	Yield reduction	Major causes(s)
	(%)		(%)	
2	38	N, H_2O	52	H_2O
3	43	H_2O	38	H_2O
5	32	H_2O	35	H_2O
6	66	H_2O, N	59	H_2O
Average	45% (4 sites)		46% (4 sites)	
	34% (7 sites)		47% (6 sites)	

Table 3 contrasts the respective surface physical properties of soils belonging to different erosion/deposition phases on two sites in 1982. The soils of sites 3 and 6 had their highest Θva values in the depositional areas, decreasing markedly through the non-eroded and severely eroded phases. The depositional area of site 3 showed the greatest contrast to the upslope erosion phases with a humic surface horizon up to 84 cm deep and a concentration of organic matter and silt-sized mineral soil particles from entrainment in runoff water. The severely eroded surface soils on all sites had significantly lower organic matter contents than the corresponding non-eroded soils cultivated to a comparable depth, generally giving rise to an increase in dry bulk density. This, in conjunction with the exposure of subsoils with undesirable water retention properties, caused Θva to decrease from the non-eroded to the severely eroded phase soils. These erosion-induced changes in the physical properties of the root zone produced an appreciable within-site erosion phase effect on the magnitude of Θva as estimated by the water retention model.

Table 3. Surface Soil Physical Properties of Selected Sites (1982)

Site	Surface texture	Erosion phase	Organic matter	Dry bulk density	Estimated soil profile Θva
			(%)	(g/cm^3)	(cm H$_2$0)
3	fine sandy loam	Non-eroded	2.6	1.44	14.1
		Severely eroded	0.7	1.46	12.8
		Depositional	5.5	1.23	18.1
6	gravelly sandy loam	Non-eroded	3.7	1.37	7.4
		Severely eroded	2.2	1.68	5.1
		Depositional	4.3	1.38	11.1

Grain corn yields (kg/ha) from the non-eroded and severely eroded plots of several sites for both study years are plotted against the seasonal soil moisture deficit or surplus values in Fig. 1. Despite the range in Θva, Fig. 1 shows little variability in the grain corn yields among the sites on the non-eroded soils in 1982. The explanation for this is evident when the grain corn productivity model equation (McBride and Mackintosh, 1984b) for a 2700 to 3000 Corn Heat Unit accumulation is superimposed on the plotted yield data. The measured yield data lie near the apex of the productivity curve, which peaks at a deficit-surplus value of +13 cm of water. Clearly, the abnormally high precipitation amounts in 1982 coupled with the near normal evapotranspirational demand over the growing season produced a condition where soils with low Θva values did not subject the crop to prolonged periods of water stress and soils with high Θva values were not prone to chronically low soil air content levels. It is likely, however, that short intervals of poor surface soil aeration after major rainfall events limited crop yields in the minor surplus soil moisture range. All soil and plant nutrient (including micronutrient) levels were in the sufficient range on the non-eroded plots.

In contrast, the grain corn yields obtained on the severely eroded soils fall anywhere from 24% to 60% below those estimated by the empirical corn productivity function. The P and K soil analyses did not point to any major deficiencies in the availability of these nutrients with soil test ratings of medium to excessive for both. The leaf analysis did indicate, however, that either plant N or plant K concentrations were at deficient levels on the severely eroded plots of all sites.

The soil erosion-productivity relationship in 1983 is shown to be very different from that of the preceding year in Fig. 1 with grain corn yields decreasing markedly over the narrower range in Θva and as the seasonal soil moisture deficit approaches a lower extreme of -9.5 cm of water. This extreme yield response was caused by a very uneven temporal distribution of precipitation with prolonged dry periods in June and July in conjunction with an above normal evapotranspirational demand. The functional relationship is considerably less predictable under these extreme moisture deficit conditions with appreciable scatter existing about the yield estimation function. This is thought to be due in part to the wide divergence in planting dates among the sites as a result of wet soil conditions and poor workability in May. This led to a highly variable yield response depending on the correspondence of critical rainfall events to the more yield-determinate phenological stages (i.e. anthesis).

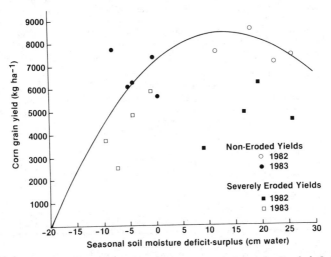

Fig. 1   Grain Corn Yields Measured on Non- and Severely Eroded Soils vs. Yields Estimated by the Field Water Supply Function

The recurrence of prolonged and severe plant water stress was visually apparent on all sites in the 1983 season and attested to the poor drought resistance of soils with Θva values of less than 16 cm (McBride and Mackintosh, 1984b). The suppression of certain erosion phase mean yields below estimated yield levels, however, further appeared to be related to plant nutrient status. Leaf analysis from all severely eroded phases in 1983 revealed N concentrations below those of the other erosion phases and in the low end of the sufficient range (i.e. 2.5% - 3.0%). This appears to have caused a general yield reduction being most pronounced on the site with the lowest measured yield which correspondingly had the lowest leaf N concentration at 2.50%. Leaching was the most probable mechanism of soil N loss as this was the most coarse textured and permeable soil on any of the 1983 sites.

Simple regression of measured grain corn yields from 1982 and 1983 against those estimated for all sites and erosion phases which did not exhibit yield-limiting nutrient deficiencies produces a correlation coefficient of 0.72 and a standard error of estimate of 890 kg/ha. With this level of predictive capability verified against annual yield data, a use for which this crop productivity model was never intended, there is a comparatively strong basis for its application in the assessment of long-term soil productivity changes with progressive erosion.

Table 4 provides an example of the possible application of this methodology to assess the magnitude of irreversible losses in potential soil productivity with erosion. By applying the productivity model to the soil information of a typical site from each study year and the 30-year climatic normals of the region, grain corn yield reductions of 9-10% would be anticipated over the long-term. This treatment considers only the largely irreversible, physical changes to the soil induced by past erosion and assumes optimum soil fertility through the addition of soil amendments.

Table 4. Estimation of the Loss of Potential Soil Productivity with Erosion
===

	Site 6 (1982) - gsl		Site 10 (1983) - loam	
	Non-eroded	Severely eroded	Non-eroded	Severely eroded
Estimated Θva (cm)	7.4	5.1	15.8	11.1
SMDS (cm)	-3.6	-5.9	+4.8	+0.1
Estimated grain corn yield (kg/ha)	6440	5815	8001	7266
Decline in potential productivity (%)	-9.7		-9.2	

===

Regional Extrapolation of Findings

Through the photo-interpretation of colour aerial photography and verification by ground truthing, it was established that approximately 18% of the agricultural cropland within the 300 km^2 study area was moderately to severely eroded. Application of the 30% yield reduction factor determined earlier would suggest that corn production within the study area has declined about 5.4% due to past erosion. At current price levels, this amounts to an average loss of farm revenue of about $44 (Cdn.) for each hectare of grain corn produced in the study area. Extrapolated to the entire Regional Municipality of Waterloo, where 24,300 ha. of grain corn were produced in 1981, this represents a total loss of production to the region valued at $1.07 million (Cdn.).

Huron County Case Study

In an attempt to assess the possible effects of continued soil erosion on the long-term prospects for grain corn production in Ontario, a procedure based on the concepts outlined above was applied to Huron County, an area where there has been a considerable increase in corn production in recent years. The six step procedure integrates established information on the susceptibility of different soil series to erosion with the soil erosion-productivity relationships described earlier.

Firstly, a total of 13 soil series were identified from the existing County soil survey which could physically support the production of grain corn and the total area of each presently cleared and available for agriculture was determined. Secondly, the Universal Soil Loss Equation (Wischmeier and Smith, 1978) was employed to estimate the soil loss for each series under 25 years of corn monoculture in the absence of conservation practices. Assuming that erosion is limited at the field level to 25% of the area of the affected field, these average soil loss values were converted into cm of soil lost from modal soil series profiles (Figure 2). Thirdly, with a stable groundwater table and a rooting depth presumed unaltered at 100 cm, the soil water retention model was used to estimate any change in Θva after 25 years of erosion for each series. The 30-year climatic normals of precipitation and potential evapotranspiration for this region were used to determine the respective soil moisture deficit or surplus values by series. Next, the appropriate crop productivity equation (2700-3000 Corn Heat Units) was employed to estimate the long-term mean grain corn yields of both modal and truncated soil series profiles (Table 5). Finally, the last two steps entailed the estimation of the impact of soil erosion on future prospects for food production for each soil series and for the County as a whole. Using land availability figures for Huron County and assuming all available agricultural land is used for grain corn production, the irreversible yield losses outlined in Table 5 and extended to all series considered amounted to 45,100 tonnes. This lost production potential amounts to a loss of 2.9% of the total production of grain corn in Huron County given current conditions. By applying this percentage loss to the actual grain corn production in the County in 1981, this represents an annual loss of about $1.3 million (Cdn.) after 25 years of corn monoculture.

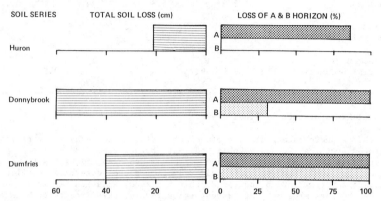

Fig. 2 Estimated Susceptibility of Selected Soil Series in Huron County to 25 Years of Erosion

Table 5. Estimated Effect of Soil Erosion on Grain Corn Yield

Soil series	Estimated grain corn yield[a]		Changes in yield	
	Modal profile	Truncated profile		
	(kg/ha)	(kg/ha)	(kg/ha)	(%)
Huron	5035	3106	-1929	-38
Donnybrook	5197	4263	-934	-18
Dumfries	4697	3327	-1370	-29

[a]assumes erosion is limited to 25% of the field area, and yields on the remainder of the field are unaffected by erosion

CONCLUSIONS

Soil erosion is responsible for significant changes in the fertility and physical suitability of Ontario soils as plant growth media. Grain corn yields were reduced an average of 30% on moderately to severely eroded soils from field trials conducted over a two-year period. Approximately 18% of the 300 km^2 study area belonged to these soil erosion phases suggesting an average reduction in crop yield of about 5% in this region of the province.

The pre-eminence of the availability of either water or essential plant nutrients (principally N) as erosion-induced soil limitations to crop growth was found to be very dependent on annual weather conditions. Yield losses attributable to nutrient deficiencies are potentially much greater than those arising from changes in soil physical properties. The loss of inherent soil fertility through the removal of organic matter and finer mineral fractions and the exposure of relatively infertile subsoils, however, has little influence on the long-term, potential productivity of soils since plant nutrition can be effectively managed with existing technology. Corrective soil amendments have been used successfully in the past to mask the effect of soil fertility depletion by erosion on crop yield although at the expense of escalating production costs.

The major physical properties affected by erosion influence the soil water regime of the root zone as revealed by the sensitivity of the plant-available moisture-holding capacity (Θva) to truncation of the solum horizons. The quantity of available water retained by the soils studied generally decreased with more advanced erosion on unstable landscapes. This was attributed to i) the deterioration of surface soil structure and the reduction of total soil porosity associated with the selective removal of organic matter, and ii) the extension of the potential root zone into subsoils with less favourable available moisture retention properties.

The soil moisture-based crop modelling procedure presented represents a means of estimating the effects of past or projected soil erosion on the long-term, potential productivity of Ontario soils for rain-fed crops. The procedure is particularly applicable in land evaluation assessments involving scenarios of long-term change in soil productivity.

REFERENCES

1. Battiston, L.A. and M.H. Miller. 1982. Soil erosion and corn yields in Ontario. A technical report prepared for the Grand River Conservation Authority and the Ontario Ministries of Natural Resources, Environment, and Agriculture and Food. 211 pp.

2. Battiston, L.A. and M.H. Miller. 1984. Soil erosion and soil productivity in Ontario. A technical report prepared for the Grand River Conservation Authority and the Ontario Ministries of Natural Resources, Environment, and Agriculture and Food. 52 pp.

3. Benbrook, C. and A. Hidlebaugh. 1982. The economic and environmental consequences of agricultural land conversion. National Agricultural Lands Study, Tech. Paper XIV. 142 pp.

4. Brown, D.M. 1963. A heat unit system for corn hybrid recommendations. Proc. 5th Natl. Conf. Agric. Meteorol., Lakeland, FL.

5. Canada Soil Survey Committee. 1978. The CanSIS manual for describing soils in the field. J. Dumanski (ed.). L.R.R.I., Agr. Canada, Ottawa, Ontario. 160 pp.

6. Doorenbos, J. and W.O. Pruitt. 1977. Guidelines for predicting crop water requirements. F.A.O. Irrigation and Drainage Paper No. 24, F.A.O., Rome. 144 pp.

7. Hagen, L.L. and P.T. Dyke. 1980. Merging resource data from disparate sources. Agr. Econ. Res. 32:45-49.

8. Langdale, G.W. and W.D. Shrader. 1981. Soil erosion effects on soil productivity of cultivated cropland. In Determinants of Soil Loss Tolerance. Am. Soc. Agron., Madison, Wisc.

9. Larson, W.E. 1981. Protecting the soil resource base. J. Soil and Water Conserv. 36:13-16.

10. Leeper, R.A., E.C.A. Runge and W.M. Walker. 1974. Effect of plant-available stored soil moisture on corn yield I. Constant climatic conditions. Agron. J. 66:723-727.

11. Mackintosh, E.E. and J. van de Hulst. 1978. Soil drainage classes and soil water table relations in medium and coarse textured soils in Southern Ontario. Can. J. Soil Sci. 58:287-301.

12. McBride, R.A. and E.E. Mackintosh. 1984a. Soil survey interpretations from water retention data I. Development and validation of a water retention model for Ontario soils. Soil Sci. Soc. Am. J., Vol. 48).

13. _____. 1984b. Soil survey interpretations from water retention data II. Assessment of soil capability ratings and crop performance indices (scheduled to appear in the Nov./Dec. issue of the Soil Sci. Soc. Am. J., Vol. 47).

14. McKeague, J.A. (ed.). 1978. Manual on sampling and methods of analysis. L.R.R.I., Agr. Canada, Ottawa, Ontario. 212 pp.

15. Miller, M.H. 1976. Soil erosion in Ontario. A report for the Ontario Soil Management Research Committee, Land Resource Science, University of Guelph, Guelph, Ontario.

16. National Agricultural Lands Study. 1981. Soil degradation: Effects on agricultural productivity. Interim report no. 4. Washington, D.C.

17. Pierce, F.J., W.E. Larson, R.H. Dowdy and W.A.P. Graham. 1983. Productivity of soils: Assessing long-term changes due to soil erosion. J. Soil and Water Conserv. 38:39-44.

18. Raghavan, G.S.V., E. McKyes, R. Baxter and G. Gendron. 1979. Traffic-soil-plant (maize) relations. J. of Terramechanics 16:181-189.

19. Stallings, J.H. 1950. Erosion of topsoil reduces productivity. S.C.S.-TP-98. U.S.D.A., Washington, D.C. 31 pp.

20. Stewart, J.I. and R.M. Hagan. 1973. Functions to predict effects of crop water deficits. J. Irrigation and Drainage Div., A.S.C.E. 99:421-439.

21. Wall, G.J. and G. Driver. 1982. Cropland soil erosion: Estimated cost to agriculture in Ontario. Ontario Institute of Pedology and Ontario Ministry of Agriculture and Food. 44 pp.

22. Williams, J.R. chairman. National Soil Erosion - Soil Productivity Research Planning Committee. 1981. Soil erosion effects on soil productivity: A research perspective. J. Soil and Water Conserv. 36: 82-90.

23. Williams, J.R., K.G. Renard and P.T. Dyke. 1983. EPIC: A new method for assessing erosion's effect on soil productivity. J. Soil and Water Conserv. 38:381-383.

24. Wischmeier, W.H. and D.D. Smith. 1978. Predicting rainfall erosion losses: A guide to conservation planning. Agr. Handbook No. 537. U.S.D.A., Washington, D.C.

FURROW IRRIGATION EROSION EFFECTS ON CROP PRODUCTION

D. L. Carter

Furrow erosion and sediment deposition redistributes topsoil within fields. Both of these processes are directly proportional to the energy of the furrow irrigation stream. This stream must be large enough at the application point to provide sufficient water for infiltration along the entire furrow length to meet the purposes of irrigation. Where slopes exceed about 0.7% on many silt loam soils, the flow velocity combined with the stream size at the upper ends of fields has sufficient energy to erode soil (Berg and Carter, 1980). As the furrow stream size decreases from infiltration along the furrow, the energy to erode and transport soil also decreases. At some point along the furrow the stream energy reaches a level where it no longer erodes soil. Then, further down slope, the energy reaches a level where the stream will no longer carry the accumulated sediment from upstream erosion. At that point sedimentation begins and continues downslope. The quantity of eroded soil actually leaving the field through the furrow depends upon the sediment load in the furrow stream at the entry point into the drain ditch at the lower end of the field and the duration of the flow at that point.

Furrow irrigation erosion and the resulting soil loss is generally greatest on the upper portion of fields (Berg and Carter, 1980; Carter and Berg, 1983; Mech and Smith, 1967) where the furrow stream size is largest and the energy to erode is greatest. Erosion is also often severe along portions of the furrow where the slope is greater than along other portions of the run length (Carter and Berg, 1983). Where furrow erosion occurs irrigation after irrigation, the topsoil is gradually eroded away. The impact of this topsoil loss on crop production is of concern. This paper reports results from a study to quantify crop yield losses resulting from furrow irrigation erosion.

SOILS OF THE STUDY AREA

The soils of the study area are Portneuf silt loam (Durixerollic Calciorthid) and similar silt loams, with a lime and silica cemented hardpan (caliche) that begins 0.3 to 0.45 m below the surface and varies in thickness from 0.2 to 0.45 m. The topsoil is pale brown (10YR 6/3) silt loam with a silt content ranging from 62 to 67%. The hardpan is white (10YR 8/2) silt loam, strongly cemented, with a silt content ranging from 65 to 75%, and a $CaCO_3$ content ranging from 25 to 35%. The soil below the hardpan is light gray (10YR 7/2) silt loam with a silt content generally greater than 70%, and this soil has little structure.

Areas where the hardpan soil or the soil below the hardpan has been brought to the surface by cultivation, or exposed by erosion and cultivation or land leveling, appear whitish in color in contrast to the pale brown topsoil. The upper ends of many fields in the study area are whitish because furrow irrigation erosion has reduced the topsoil depth sufficiently that plowing has fractured the white caliche layer and brought part of it to the surface.

The author is: D. L. Carter, Supervisory Soil Scientist and Research Leader, Agricultural Research Service, USDA, Snake River Conservation Research Center, Kimberly, Idaho.

Results of a survey we made of fields in the study area indicated that 70 to 75% of the fields exhibited whitish upper ends. The average portion of whitish soil on 14 farmer operated fields studied was 30%. Multiplying that value by the 70% of the fields with whitish areas gives a value of 21% of the area as eroded sufficiently that topsoil has been reduced from the original average of 0.38 m deep to a significantly shallower depth through which plows have fractured and brought portions of the caliche layer to the soil surface. We observed many fields where topsoil loss has exceeded 0.3 m immediately below the head ditch. The area has been irrigated for 78 years, and rough estimates of the yearly erosion loss can be made from the depth of soil eroded away from the upper ends of fields.

The soils of the study area represent more than a million hectares of irrigated land, and much more nonirrigated land in Idaho. Large areas of similar silt loam soils are present in Oregon and Washington and some other Western States. Not all of these similar soils have caliche layers.

STUDY METHODS

Two approaches were applied during the 1982, 1983, and 1984 growing season to evaluate the impact of furrow irrigation erosion on crop production. One approach involved 17 farmer operated fields. All of these fields had been furrow irrigated for 75 to 78 years except one which had been converted to sprinkler irrigation after approximately 65 years of furrow irrigation. Topsoil depth was measured using soil probes or augers along four transects parallel to the head ditch. These transects were located by measuring the distance that the whitish soil extended downslope from the head ditch where a transition zone was clearly evident between the whitish soil and normal topsoil. This transition zone represented where the plow depth was the same as the topsoil depth. The first transect was one half the distance between the head ditch and the transition zone. The second was at the transition zone, the third was about one-third the distance between the transition zone and the lower end of the field, and the fourth was approximately 30 m from the lower end of the field.

Crop yields were measured along these same transects for relating crop yield to topsoil depth. Over two seasons, data were obtained from six wheat (Triticum aestivum L.), seven dry bean (Phaseolus ssp.), two alfalfa (Medicago sativa L.), one sugarbeet (Beta vulgaris L.), and one Norgold Russet potato (Solanum tuberosum L.) fields.

The other approach involved field plots where the topsoil depth increased successively from 0.10 to 0.65 m. This plot area was formed by removing top soil from portions of the site and adding it to other portions. Six crops were grown on 24 successively deeper topsoil plots between the two extremes. The crops included wheat, dry beans, alfalfa, sugarbeets, barley (Hardeum vulgare L.) and sweet corn (Zea mays L.) The plots were fertilized with nitrogen, phosphorus and zinc to assure adequate levels of all plant nutrients. Some potassium treatments were applied to determine if potassium might be deficient where most of the topsoil was removed. Water was applied by furrow irrigation at a frequency sufficient to assure that water stress in the growing crops was not a growth limiting factor. These plots were cropped the 1983 and 1984 seasons. Plot areas were rotated so that the same crop was not grown on the same plots for two successive years except for alfalfa.

Crop yields were measured by harvesting specific lengths of rows for row crops and clipping specific areas for cereals and alfalfa. Sufficient replicates were harvested for statistical evaluation. These statistical evaluations included analyses of variance for potatoes where only one site was studied. Both linear and curvilinear regression analyses were applied to evaluate topsoil depth-yield relationships for other crops.

TOPSOIL DEPTH - CROP YIELD RELATIONSHIPS

Reducing topsoil depth from the original 0.38 m decreased yields of all crops studied. Wheat and sweet corn yields were decreased most and sugarbeet yields were decreased the least. Alfalfa and barley yields followed similar patterns with reduced topsoil depth, and the response of dry beans was cultivar dependent. Some bean cultivars were affected similar to sweet corn and wheat, while other cultivars were not significantly affected.

Relative yields of each crop at each topsoil depth were calculated based upon the maximum yield measured along a transect on farmers' fields or the maximum yielding plot in the plot study. Yields along other transects or on other plots were expressed as percent of these maximum yields. Linear regression analyses were made on the yield data for topsoil depth up to and including the original 0.38 m, and a separate analysis was made for topsoil depths greater than 0.38 m. The purpose of this type of analysis was to obtain an estimate of yield loss per unit of topsoil depth loss from erosion and the yield increase per unit of topsoil depth increase from deposition.

The percent maximum yield vs. topsoil depth relationship for wheat indicated that for each 0.01 m decrease in topsoil depth below the original 0.38 m, wheat yield was decreased 1.55% (Fig. 1). Increasing topsoil depth above original depth had no significant effect on wheat yield based upon this linear regression approach. The data in Fig. 1 include 1983 and 1984 plot yields and yields measured along transects in farmers' fields. Seasonal effects were evident on the research plots. Plotting the 1983 and 1984 data separately gave slightly different slopes. These lines are not shown, but the data points provide evidence of the slope differences.

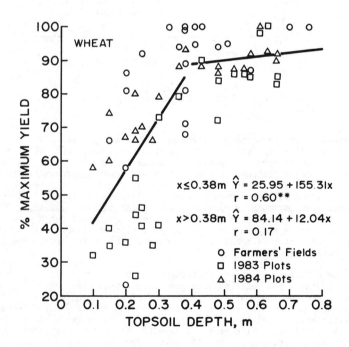

Fig. 1 The Effect of Topsoil Depth on Wheat Yield

The response of sweet corn yields to changes in topsoil depth was similar to that for wheat (Fig. 2). Sweet corn data were taken from the plot study only. Sweet corn yields were lower in 1984 than in 1983, and there was some evidence of seasonal effect, as was noted with wheat. As with wheat, increasing the topsoil depth above 0.38 m had no significant effect upon sweet corn yield.

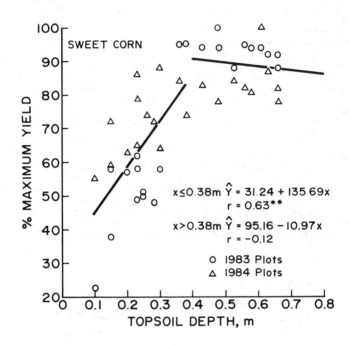

Fig. 2 The Effect of Topsoil Depth on Sweet Corn Yield

Many cultivars of dry beans are produced in the study area. We grew Royal Red kidney beans on the experimental plots in 1983, and they responded similarly to sweet corn and wheat to changes in topsoil depth. In contrast, the yield of red chili beans grown in 1984 was not significantly affected by topsoil depth. Results for the 1983 plot and farmer field data are shown in Fig. 3. Several different bean cultivars were grown on farmers' fields, and therefore, considerable variability is evident in the results. Dry bean yields were significantly increased by increasing topsoil depth above 0.38 m. The yield increase per unit increase in topsoil depth was less than the yield decrease per unit decrease in topsoil depth. Both relationships were statistically significant.

Barley and alfalfa yields were affected almost identically by changes in topsoil depth. The relationships for both crops are shown in Fig. 4. Because of the numerous data points for alfalfa resulting from three cuttings per season, the data points are not shown on the figure. The relatively low correlation coefficient for alfalfa indicates the wide variability in alfalfa yields at various topsoil depths. Even with this high variability, the relationship was significant at the 1% level for topsoil depths of 0.38 m and less.

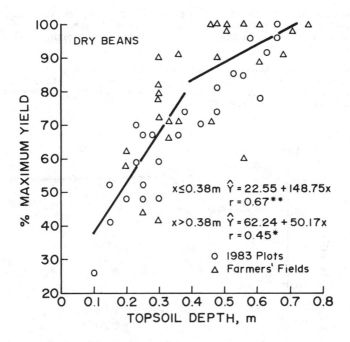

Fig. 3   The Effect of Topsoil Depth on Dry Bean Yield

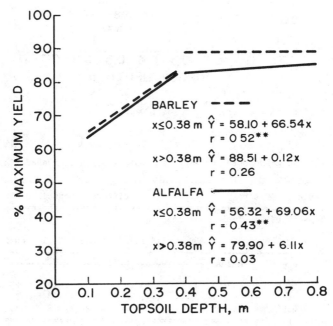

Fig. 4   The Effect of Topsoil Depth on Alfalfa and Barley Yields

43

The relationship for barley had less variability than for alfalfa. Neither of these crops were affected as severely by loss of topsoil as were wheat, sweet corn, and beans. Increasing topsoil depth did not significantly affect yield of these two crops.

High yields of sugarbeets were measured on all 1983 plots and on the one farmer field studied. The relationship between yield and topsoil depth was significant, but the effect of topsoil loss is less for sugarbeets than for the other crops studied (Fig. 5).

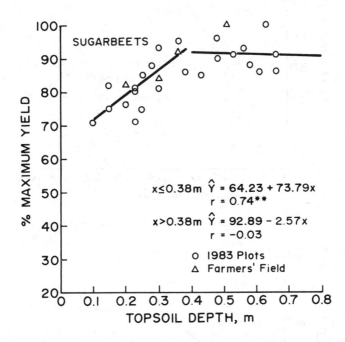

Fig. 5   The Effect of Topsoil Depth on Sugarbeet Yield

Potato yield and grade both decreased as topsoil depth decreased (Table 1).

Table 1. Potato yield and grade at different topsoil depth

Topsoil Depth	Yield	Baker >283g	113-283g	Total	No.2	Cull
m	Mg/ha	------------------- % -------------------				
Whitish	45	11	53	64	11	25
0.38	51*	25	47	72	8	20
0.56	62*	12	60	72	12	16

*LSD (0.05) = 3.59 Mg/ha

44

Only one farmer operated field was sampled, and the data were evaluated by analyses of variance. Yield along three transects are shown. Total yield continued to increase up to a topsoil depth of 0.56 m indicating that topsoil depth increases from sediment deposition benefitted potato yields. The percent No. 1 grade was greater where the topsoil was 0.38 m deep or deeper than on the whitish soil area.

Curvilinear regression analyses were completed for all of the crops except potatoes for the 1983 and 1984 data. Significant relationships were obtained for all crops when using the equation $y = a + b \ln x$, where y is yield and x is topsoil depth. Yields for all depths were included in the same analyses instead of separating yields for depths of 0.38 m and less and those greater than 0.38 m. The equations and R^2 values are presented (Table 2) but the relationships are not illustrated. All relationships were statistically significant. These relationships tended to indicate a greater yield increase with increasing topsoil depth than was actually the case. The scatter of data points was greater along the upper portions of the curves. Therefore, we concluded that the linear relationships give a better representation of the true effects of topsoil depth increases on crop yield. Additional curvilinear regression analyses will be made using different equations and additional data from the next season. Ultimately, a curvilinear relationship over the entire topsoil depth range would be most usable for making predictions.

Table 2. Curvilinear regression equations and correlation coefficients relating crop yield to topsoil depth for 1982 and 1983 data. All relationships were significant at the 0.001 probability level.

Crop	Equation	R^2
Wheat	$\hat{Y} = -57.17 + 37.23 \ln X$	.518
Sweet Corn	$\hat{Y} = -65.66 + 39.26 \ln X$	.799
Dry Beans	$\hat{Y} = -46.98 + 33.68 \ln X$	.685
Barley	$\hat{Y} = -\ 2.90 + 23.59 \ln X$	.765
Alfalfa	$\hat{Y} = \ \ 7.94 + 19.28 \ln X$	.389
Sugarbeets	$\hat{Y} = \ 45.25 + 11.68 \ln X$	.529

DISCUSSION

Results of our investigations clearly show that topsoil loss from furrow irrigation erosion decreases crop yields in the study area. Today, significantly lower yields of most crops are being harvested on at least 20% of the farmed area. There is also evidence that yields of some crops may be greater where deposition of soil eroded from upslope portions of the furrow has increased topsoil depth. However, yield increases per unit of topsoil depth increase are small where they occur, whereas yield decreases per unit of topsoil depth decrease are larger and are additive to rather high percentages in yield reduction as erosion removes more topsoil year after year.

The factors causing the yield decreases where topsoil depth is decreased and where subsoils have been brought to the surface have not been identified. Our plot studies and farmer management have appeared to have ruled out both

45

plant nutrient deficiencies and water deficits by assuring adequate levels of both for growing crops. At present, we do not know how to restore production on these areas where it has been reduced. Perhaps returning topsoil from deposition areas to eroded areas will restore yield potential, but this needs to be verified. Even if this approach restored yield potential, the cost may be prohibitive. Furthermore, there are many fields in the study area where much of the eroded soil has been carried off the field into drainage streams. This lost topsoil cannot be returned.

The fields in the study area have been furrow irrigated only 75 to 78 years, and erosion has seriously reduced yield on more than 20% of the area. Farmers in the area are confronted with a serious problem in the future. It is difficult to predict how rapidly the yield reduced area will expand, but it is important that every practice available be applied to limit additional erosion.

Results of these investigations apply to over a million hectares of irrigated land in Idaho, and likely apply to large areas of similar soils in several other western states. Additional research is needed to determine if similar relationships between yield and topsoil depth exist on soils without caliche layers. We are planning research of this kind for future growing seasons. Also needed is research on possible methods to restore productivity of eroded areas. We are investigating the feasibility of using earth-moving equipment to move topsoil from deposition areas to eroded areas to determine if such a practice will restore the productivity of the eroded areas.

The economic impact of furrow irrigation erosion is serious. More than 20% of the land in our study area has a yield reduction from about 10% to as much as 70%. If we assume an average yield reduction of 40% over the eroded area, we find that the productivity of the entire area has been reduced nearly 10% by the erosion that has occurred over the past 75 to 80 years, compared to the potential production had there been no erosion. A 10% decrease in gross income without any decrease in expenses can have a serious impact on farmers' operations. Furthermore, until we find a method to restore that productivity, and without erosion control, the reduced income not only occurs every year, but it becomes greater as erosion reduces yield on more land and further decreases yield on already eroded areas. These estimates are conservative, because there are areas where the topsoil depth has been reduced by erosion, but not yet sufficiently to expose the white caliche layer. These areas also have reduced yields, and were not included in our surveys.

All available erosion control technology for furrow irrigated land should be applied to reduce further erosion and topsoil loss. This is important from the economic standpoint of present operators and to maintain productivity of the land for future generations.

SUMMARY

Furrow erosion and sediment deposition redistributes topsoil within irrigated fields. Where slopes exceed about 0.7% on many silt loam soils, the upper ends of fields have been severely eroded. Studies conducted on Portneuf silt loam and similar soils with a white, caliche and silica cemented layer originally beginning at a depth of about 0.38 m, showed that erosion has been sufficient to expose the white, caliche layer on 70 to 75% of the fields over about 78 irrigation seasons. The area now visually exhibiting whitish color as a result of erosion and plowing to expose or bring to the surface, white, caliche, represents more than 21% of the farmed area.

Yields of all crops grown in the study area are severely reduced on those portions of the fields that are whitish in color as a result of erosion.

Significant linear relationships between crop yield and topsoil depth were developed for wheat, barley, sweet corn, dry beans, alfalfa, and sugar beets, and a significant yield reduction was measured for potatoes. Wheat, dry beans, and sweet corn yields were reduced most, alfalfa and barley yields were reduced somewhat less, and sugar beet yields were least affected by topsoil loss from erosion.

Results showed that furrow irrigation erosion has significantly reduced crop yields on more than 20% of the cultivated land in the study area. These results indicate that crop production has been reduced about 10% by erosion that has occurred over the past 75 to 80 years, compared to the potential production had there been no erosion. A 10% decrease in gross income without any decrease in expenses can have a serious economic impact on farmers' operations.

REFERENCES

1. Berg, R.D. and D.L. Carter. 1980. Furrow erosion and sediment losses on irrigated cropland. J. Soil and Water Cons. 35:267-270.

2. Carter, D.L. and R.D. Berg. 1983. A buried pipe system for controlling erosion and sediment loss on irrigated land. Soil Sci. Soc. Am. J. 47: 749-752.

3. Mech, J.S. and D.D. Smith. 1967. Water erosion under irrigation. In: Robert M. Hagen, Howard R. Haise and Talcott W. Edminster (Eds.). Irrigation of Agricultural Lands. Agronomy 11:950-963, Am. Soc. Agron., Madison, Wisc.

SOIL EROSION EFFECTS ON CROP PRODUCTIVITY AND

SOIL PROPERTIES IN ALABAMA

T.A. McDaniel   B.F. Hajek

Soil erosion can result in reduced soil productivity and crop yields. Yield reductions of 34 to 40% were observed on eroded soils relative to slightly eroded soils for Zea mays (corn), Gossypium hirsutum L. (cotton), and Avena sativa (oats) in the 1940's on Piedmont soils (Adams, 1940). A 22% reduction was seen on legumes. Similar observations were made by Frye et al. (1982) on silty Kentucky soils, by Langdale et al. (1979) on Georgia Piedmont clayey soils, and by Buntly and Bell (1976) on Tennessee silt loam soils. Erosion levels are not defined in terms of productivity loss, however as yields have increased over the years with the application of new technology, the relative yield reduction due to erosion remained near constant (Langdale et al. 1979).

Soil productivity is closely governed by available water capacity, rooting depth, available nutrient storage capacity, and soil physical conditions. Degradation of these properties by erosion lessens productivity (Pierce et al., 1983). Surface soil thickness has much influence on these properties as well as on productivity. It has been correlated with yield in numerous studies (Robinette et al., 1982; Langdale et al., 1979; Thomas and Cassell, 1979; Phillips and Kamprath, 1973). There are indications that as surface soil erodes and subsoils are mixed into the Ap horizon by tillage, the clay content of the surface soil increases (Frye et al., 1982). Mixing may also impart undesirable characteristics of the subsoil to the surface (Phillips and Kamprath, 1973).

When surface thickness is lessened plant available water may be decreased due to the lower volume of surface soil (Buntley and Bell, 1976). Puckett (1983) reported decreases in available water when clay increased beyond a certain point on Coastal Plain soils of Alabama. Frye et al. (1982) made similar observations. When surface soils are mixed with subsoils that have low pH, high soluble Al, low levels of available nutrients, and high bulk densities root growth is often restricted (Pierce et al., 1983; Moore, 1981; National Soil Erosion-Soil Productivity Research Planing Committee, 1981; Phillips and Kamprath, 1973). Murdock et al. (1980) indicated that the lowered availability of nutrients on eroded silty soils in Kentucky is likely caused by the removal of finer soil particles and organic matter. Nitrogen losses with erosion are common because most soil N is found in organic matter (Langdale and Shrader, 1982). Phosphorus, however seems to be most affected by erosion in the southeast (National Soil Erosion-Soil Productivity Research Planning Committee, 1981). The transportation of P from an area, attached to soil particles, is responsible for part of the loss, but the majority is due to fixation caused by erosion exposing subsoil material (Murdock et al., 1980; Thomas and Cassel, 1979). Frye et al. (1979) pointed out that the increase in clay content and loss of organic matter also encouraged development of physical conditions unfavorable for plant growth.

The authors are: T.A. McDaniel, Graduate Research Assistant and B.F. Hajek, Professor, Auburn University, Auburn University, Alabama.

Because of the random nature of erosion, it is often difficult to obtain data from randomized statistical field plot designs (Langdale and Shrader, 1982). Langdale et al. (1979) found that the complex nature of erosion caused, "considerable variability," in studies using standard statistical design.

Surface thickness and clay content are the primary indicators of erosion on the soils of the Southeastern United States (Langdale et al., 1979). These characteristics combined with nutrient availability greatly influence productivity.

The purpose of this research was to conduct an extensive on-farm study to determine the effects of erosion on yields of major crops and on selected soil morphological, physical, and chemical properties.

MATERIALS AND METHODS

Farmer's fields in Alabama's Lower Coastal Plain, Black Belt Prairies, and Tennessee Valley regions were selected for this study. Crops included corn and soybeans in the Coastal Plain in 1981, 1982, and 1983, soybeans in the Black Belt Prairies in 1982, and 1983, and soybeans and cotton in the Tennessee Valley in 1982 and 1983. Figure 1 shows the distribution of counties where fields were located. Observations were made on 50 fields in 1981, 90 in 1982, and 94 in 1983. All fields were in map units of soil series known to be major agricultural soils in that region. The soils and their classification are shown in Table 1. Each field was under uniform management and planted to a single crop and variety. Each had various levels of erosion. In most cases plots were located on simple uniform slopes of three to eight percent. The specific past practice or agent responsible for water erosion varied from field to field.

Figure 1. Alabama Counties in Which Field Plots Were Located.

Table 1. Classification of Soils.
==

Soil Series	Family or higher taxonomic class
	Coastal Plain
Bama	Fine-loamy, siliceous, thermic Typic Paleudults
Dothan	Fine-loamy, siliceous, thermic Plinthic Paleudults
Lucedale	Fine-loamy, siliceous, thermic Rhodic Paleudults
Malbis	Fine-loamy, siliceous, thermic Plinthic Paleudults
Orangeburg	Fine-loamy, siliceous, thermic Typic Paleudults
Red Bay	Fine-loamy, siliceous, thermic Rhodic Paleudults
	Black Belt Prairies
Demopolis	Loamy-skeletal, carbonatic, thermic, shallow Typic Udorthents
Oktibbeha	Very-fine, montmorillonitic, thermic Vertic Hapludalfs
Sumter	Fine-silty, carbonatic, thermic Rendollic Eutrochrepts
Vaiden	Very-fine, montmorillonitic, thermic Vertic Hapludalfs
	Tennessee Valley
Decatur	Clayey, Kaolinitic, thermic Rhodic Paleudults
Dewey	Clayey, Kaolinitic, thermic Typic Paleudults

==

Two plots were set up within each field. One was set up on an area showing
only slight signs of erosion (Level 1), the other on an area where moderate
erosion had occurred (Level 2). In some plots, erosion levels did not fit
the specific definitions for slight and moderate erosion as given by the
Soil Survey Staff (1951). Severely eroded areas and depositional positions
were avoided. Generally, plots were located such that those with a greater
surface soil thickness were upslope from those of lesser thickness. Each
plot was made up of three replicates located approximately 15 m apart.

Soil data, which included surface soil thickness, color (Munsell), texture,
and slope, were collected from each replicate. Estimates of the amount of
material from the B horizon mixed into surface soil was based on soil color
and texture. Surface and subsoil samples were taken from each plot for
determining P, K, Mg, Ca, organic matter, pH, particle size distribution, and
Fe_2O_3.

Yields were obtained for each replication from row segments adjacent to each
boring where soil samples and measurements were taken. Soybean yields were
determined by clipping three 1.5 m row segments, bagging the entire plant,
and later combining with a plot combine. Yields were reported at 13%
moisture.

Corn yields were determined on an 8.8 m row segment. The ears on the
segment were counted with the ear nearest but inside the zero end of the
tape and the ones nearest the 2.5 m, 4.5 m, and 6.5 m marks being harvested.
Yield was calculated from the average weight of grain per ear and ear count.
Moisture was converted to 15.5%.

Cotton yields were determined by hand harvesting three 1.5 m row segments
per replication. Open bolls were counted as picked, mature unopen bolls
were also counted. The average weight per boll and boll count were used to
determine seed cotton yields.

Yield data were analyzed using an analysis of variance of a completely
randomized design. Each field was analyzed as an individual test due to
variation in soils, rainfall patterns, and cultural practices between fields

Yields

Averages For All Fields: Average yields and percent yield reduction for all years, soils, crops, and regions are given in Table 2. In general, differences in soybean and cotton yields between years reflect seasonal rainfall differences (Table 3). Severe drought stress caused cotton yields to be reduced by more than one-half in 1983 (relative to 1982 yields). The effect of moisture stress on soybeans and corn was not as severe as for cotton.

Table 2. Average Yields and Percent Yield Reduction on Eroded Areas for All Fields, Soils, Crops and Years.

Soil Region	Crop	Year	Erosion Level		Yield Reduction[a]
			Slight	Moderate	
			------kg/ha------		%
Coastal Plain	Corn	1981	4829	3638	26
		1982	5833	4328	26
		1983	5708	4641	19
	Soybean	1981	2621	1680	34
		1982	2285	1680	26
		1983	1680	1478	12
Black Belt Prairie	Soybean	1982	1949	1546	23
		1983	1478	1411	5
Tennessee Valley	Soybean	1982	2486	1747	30
		1983	1411	1075	24
	Cotton	1982	3207	2654	17
		1983	1258	996	21

[a]Relative to yields on slightly eroded sites.

Table 3. April-October Rainfall in 1981, 1982, and 1983.

	Coastal Plain				Prairies			Tennessee Valley		
Month	1981	1982	1983	30 yr. Avg.	1982	1983	30 yr. Avg.	1982	1983	30 yr Avg.
	----------(mm)----------									
April	44	160	229	124	185	223	128	186	214	120
May	120	100	90	113	64	126	149	85	258	107
June	92	111	202	131	102	176	99	92	161	74
July	103	212	96	172	137	58	129	137	14	104
August	129	114	163	129	98	60	108	137	38	80
September	62	76	105	124	59	101	98	29	50	85
October	58	42	74	66	34	46	72	52	44	65
Totals										
Apr.-Oct.	608	815	959	859	679	790	783	718	779	635
June-Sept.	386	513	566	556	396	395	434	395	263	343
June-Aug.	324	437	461	432	337	294	336	366	213	258

The percent yield reduction on corn and soybean on moderately eroded soils was lowest in 1983. The lowest reduction was 5% for soybean yields in the Black Belt Prairie. The highest yield reduction on moderately eroded soils, relative to slightly eroded, was 34% for soybean in the Coastal Plain in 1981. The average percent yield reduction for the period 1981-1983 on moderately eroded soils was 24% for corn and soybeans in the Coastal Plain. For the two-year period (1982-83), the soybean yield reduction on moderately eroded soils was 14% in the Black Belt Prairie and 27% in the Tennessee Valley. Cotton yields for the same period were reduced by 19% on moderately eroded sites in the Tennessee Valley.

Averages for Fields with Lower Yields on Eroded Sites: Yields were not always higher on soils with slight erosion (Table 4). In 1981, 30 soybean and 20 corn fields were harvested. Of these, 20 soybean and 14 corn fields had lower yields on moderately eroded soils. In 1982, 50 soybean fields were harvested. Thirty six (72%) had lower yield on moderately eroded sites. Of the 12 cotton fields and 28 corn fields harvested in 1982, all cotton fields and 19 corn fields had reduced yields on moderately eroded soils. In 1983, 30 of the 51 soybean fields (59%), 23 of the 28 corn fields (82%) and 11 of the 15 cotton fields (73%) had lower yields on moderately eroded soils.

Table 4. Total Fields Harvested, Total Fields Where Yield was Lower on Moderately Eroded Sites (Level 2), and Fields where Yield was Significantly Lower at =0.30 and 0.10.

Region	Soybeans Total fields	Lower on Level 2[a] Total	.30	.10	Corn Total fields	Lower on Level 2[a] Total	.30	.10	Cotton Total fields	Lower on Level 2[a] Total	.30	.10
							1981					
Coastal Plain	30	20	15	13	20	14	13	9	--	--	--	--
Black Belt Prairies	--	--	--	--	--	--	--	--	--	--	--	--
Tennessee Valley	--	--	--	--	--	--	--	--	--	--	--	--
							1982					
Coastal Plain	29	20	14	9	28	19	13	13	--	--	--	--
Black Belt Prairies	10	7	5	1	--	--	--	--	--	--	--	--
Tennessee Valley	11	9	8	6	--	--	--	--	12	12	8	6
							1983					
Coastal Plain	29	17	15	13	28	23	18	12	--	--	--	--
Black Belt Prairies	12	7	3	1	--	--	--	--	--	--	--	--
Tennessee Valley	10	6	5	5	--	--	--	--	15	11	8	6

[a]Significantly lower yield on moderately eroded soils at given levels.

Overall, reduced yields were observed 69% of the time on moderately eroded soils in the Coastal Plain, 64% on Black Belt Prairie moderately eroded soils and 79% on moderately eroded soils of the Tennessee Valley.

Variability of yields between fields was high since fertility, tillage, and weed control practices differed between operators. Time of planting and varietal differences caused some fields to suffer less moisture stress at critical periods. These variables and others cannot be controlled on farmer-field research of this type.

In order to determine what soil properties were affected by erosion to the point that yields were reduced, only those fields in the Coastal Plain and Tennessee Valley that showed relative yield reduction on moderately eroded soils at confidence levels of 90% were used for analyses. In the Black Belt Prairie only two fields showed reduced yields at this level, consequently all fields with reduced yields were considered. Table 5 shows the average yields for these fields and Table 6 gives the average percent yield reduction on moderately eroded sites, relative to slightly eroded, for all soils, crops and years.

Coastal Plain: The average yields of soybeans on slightly eroded soils were highest on Dothan map units (Table 5). Relative soybean yield reduction on moderately eroded sites were also greatest on this soil (Table 6). Corn yields were highest on soils in the Rhodic subgroup (Red Bay and Lucedale), however, the percent yield reduction in these soils was usually the lowest. This was the case for both corn and soybean crops.

The average yield reductions for soybeans on moderately eroded soils relative to slightly eroded were 29% in 1981, 26% in 1982 and 38% in 1983. Corn yield reductions averaged 22% in 1981, 21% in 1982 and 25% in 1983.

Table 5. Crop Yields on Slightly (1) and Moderately (2) Eroded Areas of Major Soils Cropped in the Coastal Plain, Black Belt Prairies and Tennessee Valley Region of Alabama.

Soil Series	Soybean 1981		1982		1983		Corn 1981		1982		1983		Cotton[a] 1982		1983	
	1	2	1	2	1	2	1	2	1	2	1	2	1	2	1	2
							---(kg/ha)---									
Coastal Plain																
Dothan	2789	1837	2661	1788	2285	1142	4704	3432	5096	4124	5559	3700	----	----	----	----
Malbis	2218	1714	2386	1680	1949	1646	6272	6021	5268	3700	5833	3293	----	----	----	----
Orangeburg	2576	1949	2701	2016	2195	1333	4140	3308	4319	3503	4484	3700	----	----	----	----
Bama	2979	1814	1546	1743	1859	1232	----	----	4704	3669	5206	4014	----	----	----	----
Red Bay & Lucedale	2184	1764	2397	1994	----	----	6648	5645	5708	4453	6554	6037	----	----	----	----
Weighted Mean[b]	2550	1811	2463	1815	2119	1304	4801	3763	4848	3848	5505	4145	----	----	----	----
Black Belt Prairies[c]																
Demopolis	----	----	650	448	1344	941	----	----	----	----	----	----	----	----	----	----
Sumter	----	----	1915	1445	650	560	----	----	----	----	----	----	----	----	----	----
Oktibbeha	----	----	2621	2218	1109	1042	----	----	----	----	----	----	----	----	----	----
Vaiden	----	----	2352	1848	2150	2083	----	----	----	----	----	----	----	----	----	----
Weighted Mean	----	----	1638	1269	1095	970	----	----	----	----	----	----	----	----	----	----
Tennessee Valley																
Decatur	----	----	1764	1075	1646	1277	----	----	----	----	----	----	3340	2583	1388	883
Dewey	----	----	2715	1667	1210	370	----	----	----	----	----	----	3461	2878	1482	920
Weighted Mean	----	----	2292	1404	1501	975	----	----	----	----	----	----	3380	2681	1431	900

[a]Seed Cotton

[b]Weighed means were calculated because number of fields were not equal for each soil.

[c]Summary of all fields in the Black Belt Prairie that showed reduced yields on eroded sites.

Table 6. Percent Yield Reductions on Moderately Eroded Soils Relative to Slightly Eroded.

	Soybean 1981	1982	1983	Corn 1981	1982	1983	Cotton 1982	1983
				---%---				
Coastal Plain								
Dothan	34	33	50	27	19	33	--	--
Malbis	23	30	16	4	30	44	--	--
Orangeburg	24	25	39	20	19	17	--	--
Bama	39	20	34	--	22	23	--	--
Rhodic[a]	19	17	--	15	22	8	--	--
Mean[b]	29	26	38	22	21	25	--	--
Black Belt Prairies[c]								
Demopolis	--	31	30	--	--	--	--	--
Sumter	--	25	14	--	--	--	--	--
Oktibbeha	--	15	6	--	--	--	--	--
Vaiden	--	21	3	--	--	--	--	--
Mean[b]	--	23	11	--	--	--	--	--
Tennessee Valley								
Decatur	--	39	22	--	--	--	23	36
Dewey	--	39	69	--	--	--	17	38
Mean[b]	--	39	43	--	--	--	21	37

[a]Rhodic Paleudults, Red Bay and Lucedale series.

[b]Weighted mean was used because number of fields were not equal for each soil.

[c]Summary of all fields with reduced yields on moderately eroded soils.

Black Belt Prairies: Yields on both erosion levels were low on the alkaline (calcareous) Sumter and Demopolis soils. Rainfall in both years was below normal during much of the growing season, especially in 1983 (Table 3). Yield reductions in 1983 on moderately eroded sites relative to slightly eroded were highest on Demopolis soils (30%) and lowest on Vaiden soils (3%). The average yield reductions on moderately eroded sites were 23% in 1982 and 11% in 1983 (Table 6).

Tennessee Valley: This region of Alabama experienced above normal rainfall during the 1982 growing season (Table 3). Crops did not have any extended periods of moisture stress during this year. However, 1983 was extremely dry during the growing season (Table 3) and yields were substantially lower (Table 5). The soybean yield reduction on moderately eroded sites of both the Dewey and Decatur soils were the same in 1982 (39%). However, in 1983 yield was reduced 22% on moderately eroded Decatur and 69% on moderately eroded Dewey sites. Cotton yields were well above average on both levels of erosion in 1982. Yield reduction on moderately eroded sites was 21%. In 1983, the cotton yield reduction was 37% on moderately eroded soils.

There was a definite trend for the relative yield reduction on moderately eroded soils to increase as soybean yields increased in all regions and as corn yields increased in the Coastal Plain (Tables 5 and 6). Cotton in the Tennessee Valley showed an opposite trend.

Soil Properties

Single and multiple factor regression analyses, mean values and standard deviations were determined from both erosion levels for yields and the following soil properties; surface soil thickness, surface and subsoil clay content, Fe_2O_3, organic matter, P, K, Mg, Ca, and pH. These analyses indicated that surface thickness, surface and subsoil clay, Fe_2O_3, organic matter, and surface P were most frequently related to yield differences within fields. All of these soil properties have been related to erosion effects (Langdale et al., 1979; Frye et al.; 1982; National Soil Erosion-Soil Productivity Research Planning Committee, 1981). Averages of these properties changed very little for each soil by using data from all fields, from fields that showed yield reductions at all confidence levels, or at alpha levels of 0.10. However, SD's and CV's were significantly less for soil properties at both erosion levels when only fields that showed yield differences at greater than the 90% confidence level were considered. Since variation around means was the lowest, only data from these fields were used to establish means, limits and ranges for soil properties of slight and moderate erosion levels of Coastal Plain and Tennessee Valley soils. All fields that had lower yields on eroded sites in the Black Belt Prairie were used.

The typical value for surface thickness, surface soil clay, subsoil clay, Fe_2O_3 and P was set as the mean. Limits and ranges were set at plus-minus one SD around the mean.

The mean value and standard deviation of each characteristic are shown in Table 7 for Coastal Plain soils, Table 8 for Black Belt Prairie soils, and Table 9 for Tennessee Valley soils. There are different means and limits for soil properties from each region due to large inherent differences between these soils (Table 1).

Coastal Plain: Characteristics of slight and moderate erosion, on Coastal Plain soils, are summarized in Table 7. The average surface thickness of slightly eroded soils was greater than moderately eroded for all soil series. The ranges of slight and moderate overlapped only on the Red Bay and Lucedale soils. The average thickness for slight erosion was 23 cm and was 13 cm for moderate.

Table 7. Mean Values and Standard Deviation of Soil Characteristics on Slightly (1) and Moderately Eroded Soils where Yields were Significantly Lower on Eroded Areas at = 0.10 on Coastal Plain Soils.

Soil Series		Surface Soil Thickness		Clay Surface		Subsoil		Fe_2O_3 Surface		Subsoil		Organic Matter Surface		Subsoil		Phosphorus Surface	
		1	2	1	2	1	2	1	2	1	2	1	2	1	2	1	2
		(cm)						(%)								(kg/ha)	
								Coastal Plain									
Dothan	Mean	25	14	8	15	21	30	1.27	1.75	2.46	3.37	1.19	1.01	0.58	0.41	59	17
	SD	2	2	3	4	7	5	0.26	0.55	0.60	0.85	0.36	0.23	0.14	0.09	29	12
Malbis	Mean	20	11	10	16	22	28	1.28	2.05	2.73	3.21	0.53	0.55	0.71	0.55	57	29
	SD	2	4	3	7	6	5	0.21	0.79	1.10	1.03	0.13	0.23	0.39	0.28	24	19
Orangeburg	Mean	22	14	11	16	24	29	1.67	2.06	3.16	3.44	1.30	1.16	0.64	0.49	57	34
	SD	4	4	4	6	6	5	0.60	0.63	1.30	1.06	0.68	0.42	0.27	0.16	27	18
Rama	Mean	21	13	12	16	24	24	1.76	2.01	2.95	3.14	2.01	1.32	0.55	0.47	46	20
	SD	3	2	4	4	4	5	0.35	0.34	0.56	0.62	0.10	0.14	0.19	0.13	16	10
Red Bay & Lucedale	Mean	20	13	14	19	28	32	2.39	2.94	2.96	4.27	2.29	1.29	0.77	0.58	71	32
	SD	4	4	5	5	4	7	0.41	0.90	1.16	1.64	1.39	0.31	0.19	0.12	35	10
Weighted	Mean	23	13	10	16	23	29	1.55	2.02	2.90	3.30	1.35	1.06	0.63	0.47	56	25
	SD	3	3	4	5	6	5	0.38	0.61	0.91	0.91	0.49	0.84	0.22	0.14	27	15

Table 8. Mean Value and Standard Deviation of Soil Characteristics on Slightly (1) and Moderately (2) Eroded Soils where Yields were Lower on Moderately Eroded Areas on Black Belt Prairies Soils.

Soil Series		Surface Soil Thickness		Clay Surface		Subsoil		Organic Matter Surface		Subsoil		Phosphorus Surface	
		1	2	1	2	1	2	1	2	1	2	1	2
		(cm)				(%)						(kg/ha)	
				Black Belt Prairies (Central)									
Demopolis	Mean	16	12	24	23	31	31	--	--	--	--	25	60
	SD	2	3	3	4	12	4	--	--	--	--	13	60
Sumter	Mean	19	13	28	29	38	40	--	--	--	--	30	31
	SD	4	3	7	7	4	5	--	--	--	--	22	25
Weighted	Mean	18	13	26	26	35	36	--	--	--	--	25	41
	SD	3	3	5	5	7	5	--	--	--	--	19	66
Oktibbeha	Mean	17	14	37	49	57	59	3.17	3.20	1.85	1.75	54	43
	SD	1	3	8	9	7	14	0.37	0.37	1.17	1.68	44	27
Vaiden	Mean	13	11	36	40	41	50	--	--	--	--	20	13
	SD	2	2	12	11	5	6	--	--	--	--	11	9
Weighted	Mean	15	13	27	45	49	55	3.17	3.20	1.85	1.75	37	28
	SD	2	3	10	6	6	10	0.37	0.32	1.17	1.68	28	18

Table 9. Mean value and Standard Deviation of Soil Characteristics on Slightly (1) and Moderately (2) Eroded Soils where Yields were Significantly Lower on Moderately Eroded Areas at = 0.10 on Tennessee Valley Soils.

Soil Series		Surface Soil Thickness		Clay Surface		Subsoil		Fe_2O_3 Surface		Subsoil		Organic Matter Surface		Subsoil		Phosphorus Surface	
		1	2	1	2	1	2	1	2	1	2	1	2	1	2	1	2
		(cm)						(%)								(kg/ha)	
								Tennessee Valley									
Decatur	Mean	18	11	26	35	34	44	2.81	3.85	3.85	4.28	1.14	1.07	0.53	0.47	52	31
	SD	2	2	6	6	6	8	1.12	1.41	1.60	1.49	0.37	0.32	0.08	0.10	21	17
Dewey	Mean	18	10	22	31	35	46	2.74	2.83	3.02	4.10	1.34	1.10	0.69	0.62	49	35
	SD	4	3	7	6	8	10	1.13	0.96	0.85	1.85	0.32	0.38	0.55	0.16	32	49
Weighted	Mean	18	11	25	34	35	45	2.79	3.54	3.59	4.22	1.20	1.08	0.58	0.52	50	34
	SD	3	3	6	6	6	8	1.12	1.28	1.36	1.60	0.35	0.35	0.23	0.12	25	19

The surface and subsoil clay contents were higher on moderately eroded sites on all soils. Average surface soil clay values were 10% on slight and 16% on moderate. Average subsoil clay was 23% and 29% on slight and moderate, respectively.The overlap between the ranges at one SD of clay values on slight and moderate was 3% in the surface and 4% in the subsoil. It should be noted that lower surface soil clay values generally correspond to lower subsoil clay and that higher surface soil values correspond to higher subsoil values. The ratio of surface soil to subsoil clay on slightly eroded soils is expected to be less than 0.45 to 0.55.

The Fe_2O_3 content of the surface soil and subsoil was higher on moderately eroded than on slightly eroded sites (Table 7). The average Fe_2O_3 content in the surface soil on slight was 1.55% and 2.02% on moderately eroded areas. Subsoil Fe_2O_3 on slight averaged 2.90%, while moderately eroded areas averaged 3.30%. As expected for these highly weathered soils there was a trend for Fe_2O_3 to increase as clay increased on slight (correlation coefficient 0.94) and moderate erosion (correlation coefficient 0.99).

Surface soil organic matter was generally higher on slightly eroded soils. The averages were 1.35%, on slight and 1.06% on moderate. Subsoil organic matter was higher on less eroded sites in all soils, with averages of 0.63% on slight and 0.47% on moderate.

Surface soil P averaged 56 kg/ha on slightly eroded and 25 kg/ha on moderately eroded soils. The average on slight was near the high side of the medium soil test rating while that of moderately eroded was in the low rating range (Cope et al., 1980).

Black Belt Prairies: Characteristics of soils on both erosion classes of Black Belt Prairie soils are summarized in Table 8. The soils were in alkaline (calcareous) and acid groups. Data from all fields where yields were lower (significant or nonsignificant) were used in these calculations since only 2 fields were significant at the 0.10 alpha level. The soils here appeared to be more eroded than those in other regions. This was most evident on the alkaline soils where the only major difference between erosion was surface thickness. The average thickness on slightly eroded sites was 18 cm while the average on moderately eroded sites was 13 cm. Clay contents were essentially the same. Average available P values were higher on moderately eroded areas.

The difference between erosion levels was more evident on the acid Black Belt Prairie soils. There was a small overlap (one centimeter) in the range of surface thickness, but there was a clean break, at one SD, between surface clay content of slightly and moderately eroded sites. As in Coastal Plain soils, P levels in surface soils were higher on slightly eroded sites. Respective average values for each soil characteristic for slight and moderate erosion were; surface soil thickness 15 cm and 13 cm, surface soil clay 27% and 45%, subsoil clay 49% and 55%, surface soil organic matter 3.17% and 3.20%, subsoil organic matter 1.85% and 1.75%, and P 37 kg/ha and 28 kg/ha.

Tennessee Valley: Characteristics of Decatur and Dewey soils in the Tennessee Valley region are shown in Table 9. From field observations, the soils of the Tennessee Valley appeared to be more uniformly eroded than in other regions in Alabama. Larger areas of each erosion level were found in these fields than were found in the Coastal Plain or Black Belt Prairies.

Differences between erosion levels were evident in both surface soil thickness and clay content. There was some overlapping of clay percentages but the general difference on each erosion level was clearly expressed. The average surface thickness on slightly eroded sites was 18 cm and 11 cm on moderately eroded sites.

Surface soil and subsoil clay were higher on moderately eroded soils. There was a 3% overlap in the average ranges in the surface soil and a 4% overlap in the subsoil at one SD. Average surface soil clay values on slight and moderate erosion were 25% and 34%, respectively. Average clay content in the subsoil was 35% on slightly eroded sites and 45% on moderately eroded sites. Surface soil to subsoil clay ratios are not as clearly defined on these soils as in the Coastal Plain. Ratios less than 0.65 to 0.75 are generally expected on slightly eroded Dewey and Decatur soils.

Surface soil Fe_2O_3 averaged 2.79% on slightly eroded and 3.54% on moderately eroded sites. The average subsoil Fe_2O_3 was 3.59% on slight and 4.22% on moderately eroded sites. Both organic matter and P were higher on slightly eroded soils. The average P on slightly eroded soils was in the high soil test range, and in the medium range on moderately eroded soils.

SUMMARY

Yields were reduced on moderately eroded sites in 65% of the fields studied. The aveage yield reduction was 22%. Erosion sites were selected within fields using concepts given in the Soil Survey Manual and later revisions (Soil Survey Staff, 1951). The slight and moderate erosion limits given here are based on, or supported by data from fields where yields were significantly reduced on moderately eroded sites. The erosion levels defined by these limits should probably be designated as levels 1 and 2 instead of slight and moderate. This would reduce uncertainty as to definitions of classes of eroded soils and better relate the classes to soil productivity. The range of values of a soil characteristic in each erosion level was different for different soils, but the trends were similar. Surface soil thickness decreased, clay and Fe_2O_3 increased, organic matter decreased and surface soil P was generally lower on areas where yields were likely to be reduced.

Although yields were not lower on all soils they were lower in most instances when the decrease in surface soil thickness and increase in surface soil clay percentages progressed beyond a limit. By better understanding yield-limiting soil parameters, better and more economical approaches may be taken to control erosion and to increase the productivity of eroded soils.

REFERENCES

1. Adams, William E. 1949. Loss of topsoil reduces crop yields. J. Soil and Water Cons. 4(3):130.

2. Buntley, G.J., and F.F. Bell. 1976. Yield estimates for major crops grown on soils of west Tennessee. Bul. No. 561. Tenn. Agri. Exp. Sta., Knoxville.

3. Cope, J.T., C.E. Evans, and H.C. Williams. 1981. Soil test fertilizer recommendations for Alabama Cir. No. 251. Ala. Agric. Exp. Sta., Auburn.

4. Frye, M.W., S.A. Ebelhar, L.W. Murdock, and R.L. Blevins. 1982. Soil erosion effects on properties and productivity of two Kentucky soils. Soil Sci. Soc. Am. J. 46:1051-1055.

5. Langdale, G.W., J.E. Box, R.A. Leonard, A.P. Barnett, and W.G. Fleming. 1979. Corn yield reduction on eroded Southern Piedmont Soils. J. Soil and Water Cons. 34(5):226-228.

6. Langdale, G.W. and W.D. Shrader. 1982. Soil erosion effects on soil productivity of cultivated cropland. pp. 41-51. In: B.L. Schmidt, R.R. Allmaras, J.V. Manning, and R.I. Papendick (eds.) Determinants of Soil Loss Tolerance. Soil Sci. Socl. Am. Spec. Publ. No. 45. Madison, WI.

7. Moore, B.L. 1981. Chemical factors affecting root growth in six Coastal Plain soil profiles. M.S. Thesis. Auburn Univ., AL.

8. Murdock, L.W., W.W. Frye, and R.L. Blevins. 1980. Economic and production effects of soil erosion. Southeastern Soil Erosion Control and Water Quality Workshop. Nashville, TN. pp. 31-35.

9. National Soil Erosion-Soil Productivity Research Planning Committee, Science and Education Administration- Agricultural Research. 1981. Soil erosion effects on soil productivity: A research perspective. J. Soil and Water Cons. 36(2):82-90.

10. Phillips, J.A., and E.J. Kamprath. 1973. Soil fertility problems associated with land forming in the Coastal Plain. J. Soil and Water Cons. 28(2):69-73.

11. Pierce, F.J., W.E. Larson, R.H. Dowdy, and W.A.P. Graham. 1983. Productivity of soils: Assessing long-term changes due to erosion. J. Soil and Water Cons. 38(1):39-44.

12. Puckett, W.E. 1983. Hydraulic and related physical properties of Coastal Plain Soils. M.S. Thesis. Auburn Univ., AL.

13. Robinette, C.E., J.E. Foss, and F.P. Miller. 1982. Soil land-scape and corn yield relationships in Maryland. M.S. Thesis. Univ. MD, College Park.

14. Soil Survey Staff. 1951. Soil Survey Manual. Agri. Handbook 18, U.S. Govt. Printing Office, Washington, D.C.

15. Thomas, D.J., and D.K. Cassel. 1979. Land-forming Atlantic Coastal Plains soils: Crop yield relationships to soil physical and chemical properties. J. Soil and Water Cons. 34(1):20-24.

TOPSOIL DEPTH AND MANAGEMENT EFFECTS ON

CROP PRODUCTIVITY IN NORTHCENTRAL IOWA

Stanley J. Henning   Jabir A. Khalaf

Continuing loss of topsoil is a major concern for row crop production in
Iowa. The removal of topsoil on many glacial till soils by erosion processes
or construction activities exposes dense clay or clay loam subsoils that may
be infertile and poorly suited for growing crops. Topsoil removal frequently
removes a large portion of plant-available nutrients, including
micronutrients. In addition to its effects on soil fertility, topsoils
removal alters soil physical properties and soil-water relationships. Some
soil physical properties that may be affected are surface texture and soil
water storage. Changes in these properties will affect the effective root
zone in the soil. If the new surface material is less permeable than the
original, infiltration will be slowed and runoff decreased.

The lower productivity of subsoils as compared to surface soils has been
widely recognized. To avoid productivity losses, topsoil should be preserved.
Otherwise, an extensive fertility program and other management practices are
essential to restore productivity. Fertilizer has frequently been used to
reclaim eroded or desurfaced soils. Subsoils are also known to be
unproductive because of extremely poor physical conditions, acidity or toxic
concentrations of aluminium or iron. Preparing a seedbed in exposed subsoil
is difficult. Germination and emergence are often poor because a clay
subsoil becomes extremely hard on drying. The crust that forms inhibits crop
seedling emergence.

The problem of topsoil can be studied by removing and replacing topsoil
to specified depths to determine its effect on crop productivity. Areas
suitable for this research are created where topsoil is removed, stored and
replaced in order to "borrow" subsoil for highway and other construction
projects. Crop production is often unsatisfactory on borrow areas unless
topsoil is replaced. By replacing varying thicknesses of topsoil, borrow
areas provide sites where the effects of topsoil depth can be related to crop
response to loss of topsoil caused by erosion.

MATERIALS AND METHODS

In 1977, the Agronomy Department at Iowa State University and the Iowa
Department of Transportation initiated research to determine how much topsoil
should be replaced at borrow areas. Research plots were constructed in the
fall of 1978 in Hamilton County near Webster City, Iowa (SE¼, NE¼, Sec 11,
T88N, R26W). Nicollet loam (Aquic Hapludoll) was the dominant soil with
inclusions of Clarion loam (Typic Hapludoll). Topsoil was removed from an
area of approximately three hectares and stockpiled until construction
activities were completed. Subsoil was removed as need to construct and
elevate a roadbed adjacent to the site. The exposed subsoil was a calcareous,
unweathered, and unoxidized Late Wisconsin glacial till of Cary age
(deposited approximately 14,000 years ago). Soils at this site had formed
under prairie grasses.

The authors are: STANLEY J. HENNING, Assistant Professor of Agronomy, Iowa
State University, Ames, Iowa 50011, and JABIR A. KHALAF, Lecturer, University
of Baghdad, Baghdad, Iraq.

The layout of the plots is shown in Fig. 1. From left to right, there are three replications of topsoil treatments. The depths of topsoil are 0, 15, and 30 cm. From front to rear, there are four ranges of plots with each range separated by an alleyway. A tile drain was installed in the center of each alleyway as well as at the front and rear of the plots.

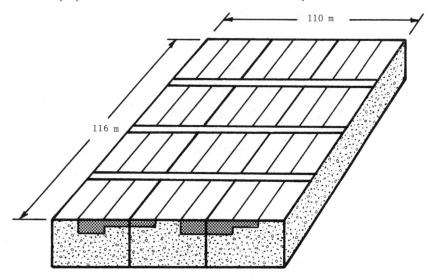

Fig. 1 Block Diagram of Research Area

Each replication in each range is designated as a main plot and assigned an alfalfa treatment. Six main plots had an alfalfa treatment of no previous growth and six main plots had two years growth of alfalfa before initiation of row crop production. Row crop production consists of corn and soybeans grown in alternate years on each plot. Each year, corn and soybeans are grown on three main plots of each alfalfa treatment.

A final treatment was included in 1982 that consisted of seed-applied fungicide. Two levels were used; 0 and 2.08 g of Apron (CIBA-GEIGY) per kg of soybean seed. This treatment was not applied to corn.

The corn and soybean planting and fertilization record is given in Table 1. All plots were chisel plowed and disked in the fall. Preemergence herbicides consisted of Lasso and Bladex applied at label rates to corn and Lasso and Amiben applied at label rates to soybeans.

Weather data was obtained from the record of the National Oceanic and Atmospheric Administration reporting station located 4.8 km northeast of the research site.

Soil samples were obtained in the spring of 1981 at selected depths to determine soil test values for pH, P, and K (Table 2). In the fall of 1982, 6.65 cm diameter soil cores were obtained to measure soil bulk density and soil test values for pH and P by the Bray No. 1 and sodium bicarbonate extraction methods. (Table 3).

Leaf samples were obtained from soybeans in 1981 and 1982 when the first blossoms appeared. The most recently matured trifoliate leaf was collected

60

Table 1. Corn and Soybean Management Record

Year	Hybrid or cultivar	Planting rate	Planting date	N	P	K	Zn
				----	(kg/ha)	----	
	Corn:						
1979	Pioneer 3541	51,600 seed/ha	May 13	230	60	100	5.6
1980	Pioneer 3541	51,600 seed/ha	April 30	180	30	50	-
1981	O's Gold 1106	51,600 seed/ha	June 3	180	30	50	-
1982	O's Gold 6880	51,600 seed/ha	June 12	180	30	50	-
	Soybean:						
1979	NK,S1492	67.2 kg/ha	May 13	39	49	93	5.6
1980	NK,S1492	67.2 kg/ha	April 30	-	30	50	-
1981	Corsoy	67.2 kg/ha	June 3	-	30	50	-
1982	Corsoy 79	67.2 kg/ha	June 12	-	30	50	-

*Fertilizer applied

Table 2. Soil Test Values Measured in 1981[a]

Topsoil depth	Sample depth	pH	Available P	Available K
--------- (cm) -----------			------- (kg/ha) -------	
0	0-15	7.7	2.8	380
	15-30	7.6	2.5	286
	30-45	7.6	2.4	292
	45-60	7.6	2.4	313
15	0-15	6.7	98.2	498
	15-30	6.8	48.4	403
	30-45	7.4	10.3	340
	45-60	7.4	2.3	336
30	0-15	6.7	117.4	621
	15-30	6.5	58.2	489
	30-45	7.1	22.9	426
	45-60	7.3	2.4	344

[a]Determined by the Soil Testing Laboratory, Iowa State University

Table 3. Soil Bulk Density and Soil Test Values Measured in 1982

Topsoil depth	Sample depth	Bulk density	pH	Available P	
				Bray No. 1	Sodium bicarbonate
--------- (cm) -----------				-------- (kg/ha) --------	
0	0-15	1.53	7.6	3.8	30.4
	15-30	1.91	7.6	1.0	20.4
	30-60	1.91	7.6	1.4	8.9
	60-90	1.88	7.5	1.3	12.6
15	0-15	1.11	6.7	15.3	137.9
	15-30	1.64	6.5	6.5	43.1
	30-60	1.94	7.4	0.2	22.2
	60-90	1.91	7.5	0.9	9.5
30	0-15	0.98	6.3	16.6	133.3
	15-30	1.40	5.7	11.7	84.0
	30-60	1.75	6.8	5.2	43.2
	60-90	1.89	7.8	3.0	33.3

from 12 plants, dried, ground, and analyzed for P content by the Soil
Testing Laboratory, Iowa State University. Counts of soybean plant density

at harvest were obtained by counting all the soybean plants bearing pods in 6.1 m of row. Corn yields and soybean yields were obtained from a sample area consisting of two adjacent rows, each 6.1 m long. The rows were 0.76 m apart. Corn yields were adjusted to a standard moisture content of 15.5%.

RESULTS AND DISCUSSION

Corn and soybean yield responses to treatments at the borrow area are presented in Tables 4 and 5, respectively. These yields can be compared to the Hamilton County reported corn and soybean yields which are presented in Table 6. Corn yields are comparable between the borrow area and county in 1979 and 1981 but in 1980 and 1982, the borrow area yielded much less. Weather conditions in 1980 and 1982 were stressful. The county yields were reduced but those at the borrow area were reduced even more. Soybean yields at the borrow area were comparable to reported county yields throughout the four-year period.

Analysis of variance of corn yield response to treatments (Table 7) shows that yield increases from topsoil were significant only in 1979 and 1981. The yield increase results from the replacement of the first 15-cm increment of topsoil. Alfalfa treatment did not affect corn yields in either 1981 or 1982. In addition, there was no corn yield response due to interactions between the treatments.

The analysis of variance for the soybean yield response to treatments shows that significant yield increases result from topsoil replacement.

Table 4. Corn Yield Response to Topsoil Depth and Alfalfa Treatments

Topsoil depth	Year			
	1979	1980	1981	1982
cm	---------------- (kg/ha) ---------------			
	No alfalfa			
0	4733	4720	6806	5205
15	8554	5020	7471	4956
30	7831	4620	8561	5030
	Alfalfa			
0	-	-	7135	4412
15	-	-	7895	4324
30	-	-	8420	5851

Table 5. Soybean Yield Response to Topsoil Depth and Alfalfa Treatments

Topsoil depth	Year			
	1979	1980	1981	1982
---- cm -----	---------------- (kg/ha) ---------------			
	No alfalfa			
0	1270	1020	514	985
15	2602	2130	1470	1916
30	2732	1950	1893	2040
	Alfalfa			
0	-	-	1706	1221
15	-	-	2414	2224
30	-	-	2884	2436

In 1979 and 1980, the yield increase resulted from the replacement of the first 15-cm increment of topsoil. During the last two years, there was an additional yield response when the topsoil depth was increased from 15 to

Table 6. Hamilton County Reported Corn and Soybean Yields[1]

==
Year	Corn	Soybean
	--------- (kg/ha) ---------	
1979	8818	2735
1980	7859	2728
1981	8994	2957
1982	8053	2560
==

[1] Iowa Agricultural Statistics, Iowa Crop and Livestock Reporting Service

Table 7. Analysis of Variance of Row Crop Yields to Topsoil Depth, Alfalfa
and Fungicide Treatments.

===
Source of variation	Degrees of freedom	1979	1980	1981	1982
		Corn			
Topsoil depth	2	**	NS	**	NS
0 vs 15 & 30 cm	1	**	NS	**	NS
15 cm vs 30 cm	1	NS	NS	NS	NS
Alfalfa	1	-	-	NS	NS
		Soybean			
Topsoil depth	2	**	**	**	**
0 vs 15 & 30 cm	1	**	**	**	**
15 cm vs 30 cm	1	NS	NS	**	*
Alfalfa	1	-	-	*	*
Fungicide	1	-	-	-	NS
===

**,*, and NS Significant at 1 and 5% levels and not significant, respectively
===

30 cm. Previous alfalfa growth significantly increased soybean yields in the
years that this treatment could be tested.

The effects of previous alfala growth on corn and soybeans is opposite from
what is expected. Alfalfa is expected to increase corn yields because of its
nitrogen contribution. However, an examination of the nitrogen fertilization
rates (Table 1) indicates that more than an adequate amount of nitrogen is
available for the corn yields achieved at the borrow area. Consequently, the
contribution of nitrogen from alfalfa was not important to increase corn
yields.

Soybean yields are not expected to be increased by previous alfalfa growth
because the soybean plant fixes nitrogen too. Nevertheless, alfalfa did
affect soybean yields and this effect was related to improvement in the
health of the soybean crop. An indication of crop health is obtained by
measuring plant density at harvest. Where alfalfa had been grown, there
were significantly more plants producing pods at harvest (Tables 8 and 9).
Replacement of topsoil also resulted in greater plant density at harvest.
There was, however, no interaction of treatment effects on plants surviving.
In 1982, a fungicide treatment also was included and it significantly
increased soybean survival at harvest too. However, the fungicide treatment
had no effect on soybean yields (Table 9).

Analysis of the most recently matured soybean leaves at beginning bloom
provides information concerning the mechanism responsible for the response
to alfalfa growth (Table 10). Phosphorus content of soybean leaves is least
where soybeans are grown without topsoil or with topsoil but with previous
alfalfa growth. The phosphorus content of the recently matured leaves
reflects the level of plant available phosphorus in the soil where the

soybean roots are actively growing. The level of available phosphorus in the
subsoil is very low but that in the topsoil is very high (Tables 2 and 3).
Consequently, the low leaf phosphorus content suggests that the soybean roots
are actively growing in the subsoil beneath the topsoil if alfalfa had been
grown in 1979 and 1980. It is likely that the root channels of alfalfa
plants would provide the means for growth of soybean roots into the subsoil.
Where there is no alfalfa growth on topsoil, the soybean roots do not have an
easy entry into the subsoil.

Table 8.   Soybean Plant Density at Harvest
===

Topsoil depth	No fungicide		Fungicide	
	1981	1982	1981	1982
cm	---------------- Plants/m --------------------			
	No alfalfa			
0	8.5	16.0	-	17.9
15	13.7	20.4	-	25.1
30	14.8	21.3	-	23.8
	Alfalfa			
0	18.4	21.0	-	21.9
15	24.4	24.7	-	27.2
30	27.8	24.7	-	25.9

===

Table 9.   Analysis of Variance of Soybean Harvest Plant Density Response to
           Topsoil Depth, Alfalfa, and Fungicide Treatments.
===

Source of variation	Degrees of freedom	Year	
		1981	1982
Topsoil	2	**	**
0 vs 15 & 30 cm	1	**	**
15 vs 30 cm	1	NS	NS
Alfalfa	1	*	*
Fungicide	1	-	**

===

**,* and NS Significant at 1 and 5% levels and not significant, respectively.

Table 10.   Leaf Phosphorus Content at Beginning Bloom.
===

Topsoil	Year	
	1981	1982
	Phosphorus content	
cm	------- % --------	
	No alfalfa	
0	0.36	0.45
15	0.42	0.51
30	0.42	0.50
	Alfalfa	
0	0.36	0.41
15	0.37	0.43
30	0.38	0.45

===

CONCLUSIONS

Corn yields are increased by the replacement of topsoil over glacial till
subsoil. The response is limited to only the first 15-cm increment and
further increases are not noted. This response is likely to be explained by
the topsoil providing a seedbed superior to that in subsoil. In years of
drought and heat stress, corn yields are depressed more on the shallow soil
at the borrow area than from the undisturbed soils in the county. Data

concerning the availability of water from the different depths of soil would be useful to explain corn yields responses where weather stress is encountered.

Topsoil replacement over glacial till subsoil provides a superior seedbed for soybeans as well. However, yields continue to increase when more topsoil is replaced. This may indicate that additional increments of topsoil can provide more water to the soybean crop to help it withstand weather related stress. The increased incidence of soybean diseases on subsoil and shallow topsoil is a major result from this study. To grow soybeans with moderate success requires treatment of the soil with alfalfa and treatment of the soybeans with fungicides.

This research provides conclusions concerning problems encountered in relating topsoil losses from erosion to reduced crop productivity. First, topsoil provides a superior seedbed. Reduced plant density from inferior seedbeds may result in decreased yields. Secondly, weather related yield reductions on shallow topsoil will become more severe as the stress is increased. Finally, the occurrence of diseases observed in soybeans may become more severe so that crop yields are catastrophically reduced.

An encouraging result of this research is the restoration of crop productivity potential by using cultural practices such as growing legumes on severely desurfaced soils. Secondly, certain technologies such as the development of improved fungicides may overcome the real hazard of increased disease incidence.

SUMMARY

Research was initiated in 1978 to evaluate the changes in productivity resulting from the removal of topsoil in Northcentral Iowa. Topsoil was removed and replaced over subsoil at 0, 15, and 30-cm depths. Selected management practices such as the growth of alfalfa and the use of fungicide on soybeans were included to determine if they would lessen the loss of productivity where topsoil thickness was diminished. Corn and soybean production were initiated (1) immediately and (2) after two years of alfalfa growth following restoration of topsoil. Corn yields were increased by the replacement of topsoil but there was no significant difference between 15 or 30-cm depths. Soybean yields increased as topsoil thickness increased. Alfalfa growth before initiation of row crop production did not increase corn yields but did increase soybean yields. Previous alfalfa growth increased the survival of soybean plants as did the fungicide treatment.

EFFECT OF TOPSOIL THICKNESS AND HORIZONATION OF A VIRGIN

COASTAL PLAIN SOIL ON SOYBEAN YIELDS

D. E. Pettry   C. W. Wood, Jr.   J. M. Soileau

A recent national study reported that despite decades of soil and water
research in the U. S. the relationship between soil erosion/topsoil
thickness and productivity is not well understood (SEA, 1981). It is clear
that applied research directed at quantifying the relationships between soil
erosion/topsoil thickness and crop yields is severely lacking for
Southeastern Coastal Plain soils. Much of the applied research of this
nature was done several decades ago (Millar, 1923; Latham, 1940; Adams,
1949; Uhland, 1949) before today's high level of agricultural technology had
evolved. It is often difficult to extrapolate from these results. More
recent research indicates subsoil acidity and aluminum toxicity limit
rooting depth and proliferation (Adams, 1981).

The objectives of this study were to evaluate the effects of topsoil
thickness on soybean yields and to quantify the effects of fertilization and
other management factors on restoring productivity of eroded soils.

METHODS AND MATERIALS

Study Site

The study area was located in Pontotoc County, Mississippi in Major Land
Resource Area 133B (Interior Flatwoods region of the Southern Coastal
Plain). The area has a humid, temperate climate with hot summers and mild
winters with 223 freeze-free days and 1200 mm of annual precipitation. The
site has an elevation of 128 m above mean sea level. Soil temperatures are
in the thermic regime (15-22°C).

The site was located in a Falkner silt loam with a slope of 1%. The Falkner
series is a member of the fine-silty, siliceous, thermic family of Aquic
Paleudalfs. These soils are somewhat poorly drained and have brown silt
loam A horizons with sub-jacent yellowish-brown silt loam Bt horizons.

The study site had not been cultivated previously according to historical
data. Aerial photographs show the site to be heavily wooded in 1937. The
site was recently converted from forest to pasture, and several trees and
large stumps remained. The site represents an undisturbed soil area that
had not had previous management factors imposed upon it that could affect
productivity.

The authors are: D. E. PETTRY, Professor Soil Science, C. W. WOOD, Jr.,
Research Assistant, Mississippi State University, and J. M. SOILEAU,
Research Soil Sci., Tenn. Valley Authority, Muscle Shoals, AL.,
respectively.

Soils

Soil morphology at the study site was characterized in detail from an excavated pit and auger holes prior to plot construction. Representative soil samples from major horizons were collected for laboratory characterization. Samples were air-dried and sieved to remove coarse fragments (>2 mm). Particle size distribution was determined by the hydrometer method (Day, 1965) and sieving. Clay and silt fractions were separated by sieving and centrifugal sedimentation. They were analyzed via X-ray diffraction with a Norelco Geiger counter spectrometer using Cu $K\alpha$ radiation and a Ni filter.

Exchangeable cations were extracted with $1\underline{N}$ neutral NH_4OAc and determined by atomic absorption spectrophotometry. Extractible acidity was determined by the barium chloride-triethanolamine method (Peech, 1965). Organic matter was determined by digestion in chromic acid (Allison, 1935). Exchangeable aluminum was determined by the methods of Yuan (1959). Soil pH was measured in water and in $1\underline{N}$ KCl using a 1:1 soil-to-liquid ratio.

Soil bulk density was determined by the undisturbed core method (Blake, 1965).

Plot Construction

A Latin square plot design was employed with four treatments and four replications of each treatment. The plots were 10.6 m long and 7.6 m wide to accomodate 6 rows planted at 0.96 m between rows, and with 3 m between plots. The plots were constructed in the spring of 1982 with a tractor and pan scraper by cutting and filling the A and/or Bt1 horizons. Parabolic-shaped waterways (2 m wide and 0.3 m deep) were constructed adajacent to each plot to facilitate surface drainage. The plots were levelled by hand, chisel plowed to a depth of 34 cm, disced and tilled with a power tiller. The treatments were as follow:

        Treatment 1 (T1) - 22.5 cm topsoil (A horizon)
        Treatment 2 (T2) - 15 cm topsoil (A horizon)
        Treatment 3 (T3) - 7.5 cm topsoil (A horizon)
        Treatment 4 (T4) - 0   topsoil (Bt1 horizon)

Plot Preparation and Planting

1982 Season: Based on soil analyses, lime was applied at the rate of 8,980 kg/ha and incorporated by power tiller. Plant macronutrients (0-24-24) were applied at a rate of 392 kg/ha. Fritted micronutrients consisting of 4% zinc, 4% manganese, 8% iron, 1.6% boron, and 4% copper were applied at a a rate of 280 kg/ha. Treflan (Trade name of ELANCO Company), a pre-emergence herbicide was applied for grass control. The fertilizer and herbicide were incorporated with a tiller. Centennial variety soybeans were planted May 31, 1982. The seeds were inoculated with peat-based rhizobium and treated with molybdenum. Plots were cultivated twice with a tiller during the growing season. Soybeans were harvested November 9 and threshed in a stationary rasp type thresher.

1983 Season: Based on soil tests, lime was applied at rates of 1,120 to 4,000 kg/ha and incorporated to a depth of 15 cm with a tiller. Plant macronutrients (0-20-20) were applied at a rate of 392 kg/ha and incorporated. Treflan was applied for grass control. Centennial variety soybeans were planted June 2. The seeds were inoculated with peat-based rhizobium and treated with molybdenum prior to planting. Plants were cultivated twice during the growing season and harvested November 11.

Plant leaf samples were collected at first bloom in August, 1983 from each subplot (upper fully developed trifoliate leaves) for tissue analyses. The leaves were dried at 70°C, ground in a Wiley mill and ashed at 495°C for 4 hours. The ash was taken up in 2 N HCl, diluted and cations were determined by atomic absorption spectroscopy. Phosphorus was determined by the phosphovanadomolybdic method.

RESULTS AND DISCUSSION

Soil Properties

The A horizon was dark grayish brown (10YR 4/2) with a silt loam texture and an average thickness of 15 cm. Silt contents ranged from 68 to 76% in the surface horizons and clay contents ranged from 10 to 17%. A thin, lighter colored grayish brown (10YR 5/2) silt loam E horizon indicated lack of previous cultivation. The underlying Bt1 horizon was light yellowish-brown (10YR 6/3) silt loam extending to 37.5 cm depth (Table 1).

Table 1. Morphological Description of Representative Pedon of Research Plot Area.

Horizon	Depth cm	Description
A	0-15	Dark grayish brown (10YR 4/2) silt loam; weak fine granular structure; very friable; many fine roots; extremely acid; gradual wavy boundary.
E	15-20	Grayish brown (10YR 5/2) silt loam with common medium distinct yellowish red (5YR 5/8) mottles; weak fine granular and weak fine subangular blocky structure; friable when disturbed; slightly firm in place; very strongly acid; clear wavy boundary.
Bt1	20-37.5	Light yellowish brown (10YR 6/3) silt loam with few fine faint pale brown (10YR 6/3) mottles and few fine distinct strong brown (7.5YR 5/6) mottles; weak fine subangular blocky structure; slightly firm; many fine roots; patchy clay skins on ped faces; extremely acid; gradual wavy boundary
Bt2	37.5-57.5	Light yellowish brown (10YR 6/4) silt loam with many coarse faint light brownish gray (10YR 6/2) mottles and common medium distinct reddish yellow (7.5YR 6/0) mottles; weak fine subangular blocky structure; slightly firm; patchy clay skins on ped faces; extremely acid; gradual wavy boundary.
Btg1	57.5-82.5	Gray (10YR 6/1) silt loam with many coarse distinct yellowish brown (10YR 5/6) and few fine distinct yellowish red (5YR 5/6) mottles; weak fine subangular blocky structure; slightly firm; few fine round black concretions; patchy clay skins on ped faces; few fine roots; extremely acid; gradual wavy boundary.

2Btg2	82.5-120	Gray (10YR 6/1) silt loam with fine distinct yellowish brown (10YR 5/6) mottles; weak fine subangular blocky structure; slightly firm; clay skins on ped faces; very strongly acid; gradual wavy boundary.
2Btg3	120-162.5	Gray (10YR 6/1) silty clay loam with many fine distinct yellowish brown mottles; moderately fine subangular blocky structure; slightly firm; clay skins on ped faces; very strongly acid; gradual wavy boundary.

The soil was extremely acid throughout the solum before liming (Table 2). Organic matter contents ranged from 2 to 3% and diminished rapidly below the epipedon to levels less than 1%. High levels of exchangeable Al occurred throughout the sola and comprised 20 to 50% of the cation exchange capacity before liming. Exchangeable Ca and Mg increased abruptly below the lithologic discontinuity. Base saturation increased to levels greater than 35% at depths of 125 cm or greater below the top of the argillic horizon. Cation exchange capacities also increased below the discontinuity reflecting increased montmorillonitic clay. Sand and silt fractions were dominantly siliceous.

Research Plots

Bulk density data obtained before and after plot construction show no compaction, but rather an increase in pore space due to cultivation (Table 3). The Bt1 horizon had higher bulk density levels than the A horizon before and after construction. Slight variations occurred after two cropping years but no substantial compaction was noted (Table 4).

Table 3. Mean Bulk Density Values Before and After Plot Construction and Planting, 1982

Before Construction		After Construction	
Horizon	Bulk Density	Treatment	Bulk Density
	(mg/m^3)		(mg/m^3)
A	1.37	T1 (22.5 cm A horizon)	1.19
Bt1	1.59	T2 (15 cm A horizon)	1.19
		T3 (7.5 cm A horizon)	1.33
		T4 (Bt1 horizon)	1.34

Table 4. Mean Bulk Density of Plots After Two Cropping Years.

Treatment	Bulk Density After 1 Crop Year	Bulk Density After 2 Crop Years
	(mg/m^3)	(mg/m^3)
T1 (22.5 cm A horizon)	1.22	1.24
T2 (15 cm A horizon)	1.27	1.36
T3 (7.5 cm A horizon)	1.40	1.36
T4 (Bt1 horizon)	1.33	1.40

A high degree of uniformity existed in the particle size distribution of the plots upper horizon after two crop years (Table 5). Very little variation occurred in the silt fraction, and slightly higher differences were noted in the sand and clay fractions.

69

Table 2. Soil Chemical Characteristics of Typifying Pedon of Research Plots Before Plot Construction.

Horizon	Depth	pH	Organic Matter	Exchangeable Cations					Al[a]	Total[b]	Base Saturation
				Ca	Mg	K	Na	H			
	(cm)		(%)	------------------------(cmol (p+)/kg)-------------------							(%)
A	0-15	4.3	2.8	3.05	0.67	0.21	0.17	9.49	2.8	13.59	30.2
E	15-20	4.6	1.6	2.12	0.52	0.20	0.16	9.10	3.6	12.10	24.8
Bt1	20-37.5	4.1	0.4	0.71	0.54	0.06	0.09	11.94	8.7	13.34	10.5
Bt2	37.5-57.5	4.1	0.6	0.65	0.47	0.07	0.09	12.41	9.7	13.69	9.3
Btg1	57.5-82.5	4.5	0.1	0.94	0.36	0.16	0.17	13.22	10.3	14.85	10.9
2Btg2	82.5-120	4.7	0.1	1.71	0.48	0.17	0.27	15.31	11.8	17.94	14.7
2Btg3	120-162.5	5.0	-	6.34	1.50	0.18	0.69	15.81	12.2	24.52	35.5

aNot included in the summation of exchangeable cations.
bSummation of exchangeable cations

Table 5. Mean Particle Size Distributions of the Surface Horizons of Plots.
===
                                                                  Textural
Treatment   Sand   Silt   Clay   Class
                           -------------(%)-------------

T1 (22.5 cm A horizon)   14.5   75.0   10.3   silt loam
T2 (15 cm A horizon)   13.5   75.3   11.1   silt loam
T3 (7.5 cm A horizon)   12.4   74.9   12.4   silt loam
T4 (Bt1 horizon)   11.8   75.0   13.1   silt loam
===

Soil pH, exchangeable Ca, Mg and K levels were considerably higher after two
cropping years reflecting the lime and fertilizer applications (Table 6).
Exchangeable Al and acidity were much lower due to liming with trace levels
of aluminum remaining on the exchange complex. Organic matter content of
the Bt1 horizon plot had increased 0.5% in two years from incorporation of
crop residue and winter vegetation.

Plant Growth and Yields

Germination and plant emergence were two to six days later in the T4
treatments (Bt1 horizon). Plant heights throughout the growing season were
consistently greater in treatment T1 (22.5 cm A horizon) and T2 (15 cm A
horizon). Treatments T3 (7.5 cm A horizon) and T4 (Bt1 horizon) attained
3/4 the height of plants in T1 plots. Plants in treatment T4 (Bt1 horizon)
were not as green as plants in other treatments for the first four weeks of
the growing season. No appreciable differences were noted in root
nodulation in the different treatments.

1982 Season: The 1982 mean yields are presented in Table 7. The treatments
with 7.5, 15, and 22.5 cm of topsoil (A horizon) were significantly higher
than the T4 treatment with no topsoil (Bt1 horizon). The mean yields of
treatments T1 and T2 were almost twice the mean yields of T4 treatment. Soil
moisture did not appear to be a limiting factor due to evenly distributed
precipitation during the growing season (42 cm precipitation).

Table 7. Mean Soybean Yields and Statistical Relationships for the Dif-
          ferent Topsoil Thickness Treatments in 1982.
===
Treatment   Mean Yields
                                                              (kg/ha)

T1 (22.5 cm A horizon)   2,426 a
T2 (15 cm A horizon)   2,386 a
T3 (7.5 cm A horizon)   2,009 a
T4 (Bt1 horizon)   1,324 b
===
     Means not having a letter in common differ significantly at the 5% (P
     = 0.05) level according to the Newman Keul's Multiple Range Test.

1983 Season: The 1983 mean yields are presented in Table 8. The highest
yield was 1,787 kg/ha for treatment T1 (22.5 cm A horizon) and the lowest
yield was 1.068 kg/ha for the no topsoil T4 treatment (Bt1 horizon).
Although treatments T2 (15 cm A horizon) and T3 (7.5 cm A horizon) had
slightly higher yields than T4 (Bt1 horizon), the differences were not
statistically significant (P = 0.05). Soybean yields in 1983 were severely
affected by very dry weather during critical bloom and pod filling stages.
The research plots received only 20 mm precipitation during August and 276
mm during the four month growing season.

Table 6. Soil Chemical Characteristics of Research Plots After Two Cropping Years.

Treatment	pH	Organic Matter (%)	Exchangeable Cations ————(cmol (p+)/kg)————						Total[b]	Base Saturation (%)
			Ca	Mg	K	Na	H	Al[a]		
T1 (22.5 cm A Horizon)	6.2	3.7	9.6	0.71	0.42	0.05	4.1	0.08	14.88	72
T2 (15 cm A horizon)	5.7	3.0	6.7	0.56	0.37	0.05	5.1	0.10	12.78	60
T3 (7.5 cm A horizon)	6.0	1.7	7.7	0.56	0.31	0.06	4.5	0.17	13.13	66
T4 (Bt1 horizon)	6.2	0.9	9.4	0.51	0.34	0.06	3.3	0.06	13.61	75

[a]Not included in the summation of exchangeable cations.
[b]Summation of exchangeable cations.

Table 8. Mean Soybean Yields and Statistical Relationships for the
          Different Topsoil Thickness Treatments in 1983.

Treatment	Mean Yields
	(kg/ha)
T1 (22.5 cm A horizon)	1,787 a
T2 (15 cm A horizon)	1,263 b
T3 (7.5 cm A horizon)	1,155 b
T4 (Bt1 horizon)	1,068 b

There were no significant differences (P = 0.05) in K, Na, Ca, Mg and P
levels in the plant tissue at the first bloom period for the different
treatments (Table 9). The plant nutrient levels appear to be well above the
critical values depictive of deficiencies. These data confirm field
observations during the growing season where no deficiency symptoms were
observed.

Table 9. Plant Tissue Analyses of Soybean Leaves at Early Bloom Period,
          August, 1983.

Treatment	K	Na	Ca	Mg	P
			(%)		
T1 (22.5 cm A)	2.47 a	0.04 a	0.62 a	0.35 a	0.59 a
T2 (15 cm A)	2.44 a	0.05 a	0.67 a	0.36 a	0.59 a
T3 (7.5 cm A)	2.31 a	0.05 a	0.74 a	0.37 a	0.56 a
T4 (Bt)	2.29 a	0.04 a	0.69 a	0.37 a	0.52 a

Means not having a letter in common differ significantly at the 5% (P =
0.05) level according to the Newman Keul's Multiple Range Test.

The combined 1982 and 1983 yields and statistical relationships are presented in Table 10. The effect of topsoil thickness is clearly reflected in
the yields for the two growing seasons with diverse climatic conditions.
Yields in all the topsoil (A horizon) treatments were significantly higher
than in the zero topsoil (Bt1 horizon) treatment. Yields in the thickest
topsoil treatment (22.5 cm A horizon) were almost double the yields of the
zero topsoil (Bt1 horizon) treatment.

Table 10. Combined 1982-1983 Mean Soybean Yields and Statistical
           Relationships for the Different Topsoil Thickness Treatments.

Treatment	Mean Yields
	(kg/ha)
T1 (22.5 cm A horizon)	2,110 a
T2 (15 cm A horizon)	1,821 ab
T3 (7.5 cm A horizon)	1,579 b
T4 (Bt1 horizon)	1,196 c

SUMMARY

Soybean yields were markedly affected by topsoil thickness over a two year
period in a virgin soil limed and fertilized for optimum production. Plants
grown in the subsoil (Bt horizon) were delayed in germination and emergence,
and they were shorter throughout the growing season than plants in topsoil
(A horizon). Soil textures were silt loam in both topsoil and subsoil plots

with no textural restrictions. No soil physical restrictions were indicated by bulk density levels. No plant nutrient deficiencies were observed. As suggested by the 1982 versus 1983 cropping season rainfall, the effect of topsoil (A horizon) thickness on soybean yields may be partly related to available soil moisture. The study will continue for several years to evaluate soil temporal changes.

REFERENCES

1. Adams, F. and B. L. Moore. 1981. Chemical factors affecting root growth in subsoil horizons of Coastal Plain soils. Soil Sci. Soc. Am. J. 47:99-102.

2. Adams, W. E. 1949. Loss of topsoil reduced crop yields. J. Soil and Water Cons. 4(3): 130.

3. Allison, L. E. 1935. Organic soil carbon by reduction of chromic acid. Soil Sci. 40:311-320.

4. Blake, G. R. 1965. Bulk density: Core method. In C. A. Black (ed.) Methods of Soil Analysis, Part I. Agronomy 9:375-377. Am. Soc. of Agron., Madison, Wis.

5. Day, P. R. 1965. Particle fractionation and particle size analysis. In C. A. Black (ed.) Methods of Soil Analysis, Part I, Agronomy 9:545-566. Am. Soc. of Agron., Madison, Wis.

6. Latham, E. E. 1940. Relative productivity of the A horizon of Cecil sandy loam and the B and C horizon exposed by erosion. Am. Soc. Agron. J. 34:12.

7. Millar, C. E. 1923. Studies on virgin and depleted soils. Soil Sci. 16:433-438.

8. Peech, M. 1965. Exchange acidity. In C. A. Black (ed.) Methods of Soil Analysis, Part I, Agronomy 9:914-926. Am. Soc. Agron., Madison, Wis.

9. Science and Education Administration - Agricultural Research Task Force. 1981. Soil erosion effects on soil productivity: A research perspective. J. Soil and Water Cons. 36(2):82-90.

10. Uhland, R. E. 1949. Crop yields lowered by erosion. SCS-TP-75. U. S. Dept. Agr., Washington, D. C.

11. Yuan, T. C. 1959. Determination of exchangeable hydrogen in soils by a titration method. Soil Sci. 88:164-167.

INTERRELATIONSHIPS AMONG SOIL EROSION, LANDSCAPE POSITION
AND SOIL PRODUCTIVITY IN THE NORTH CAROLINA PIEDMONT

J. W. Gilliam, D. K. Cassel, R. B. Daniels, and J. R. Stone

The southern Piedmont extends from Virginia into Alabama. It is an erosional landscape with gently rolling uplands and moderate to steep valley slopes that grade to the adjacent stream system. The soils have developed from residuum and the saprolite is several meters thick in most places. Most of the weatherable minerals originally present in the igneous and metamorphic rock are gone from the upper saprolite and nutrient content is low. The surface horizons of the predominant soil order (Ultisols) are 8- to 10-cm-thick loamy sand to sandy loams, even under mature forests. The B horizons are clayey in essentially all soils.

There is strong evidence that much erosion occurred in the Piedmont before European settlement (unpublished manuscript, R. B. Daniels). The land mass is several million years old and erosion during this period, even though a very low mean rate of erosion occurred, resulted in large amounts of soil movement. After settlement, the Piedmont became one of the most severely eroded areas in the United States. Because of this, the Piedmont was chosen as a site for one of the ten original national soil erosion experiment stations in the early 1930's (Copley et al., 1944). Soil erosion is still severe in many Piedmont areas and a potential problem throughout the area whenever sound conservation practices are not followed.

Even with all of the previous work on erosion in the North Carolina Piedmont, there was little definitive information on the effects of previous accelerated erosion on soil productivity under modern management practices. Thus it was impossible to predict the effects of current erosion upon future productivity. We began our work in 1981 with the objectives of quantitatively determining the effects of erosion on soil productivity and what factors contributed to any measured yield differences.

LANDSCAPES

As a result of the long-term erosion and natural topography, it is necessary to consider the total landscape when attempting to quantify the effects of erosion on productivity. The interfluves (Fig. 1) have broad gently convex to narrow cross sections. The shoulders are the areas between the interfluves and valley slopes. The valley slopes are subdivided into linear, head and foot slopes. The linear slopes have linear water flow downslope. Head slopes are bowl-shaped areas with converging water flow. Foot slopes occur at the base of the linear slopes. Because of their location, the head and foot slopes are generally the wettest areas of the fields.

In essentially all Piedmont fields, there are at least two and usually three erosion classes within one soil mapping unit. Criteria of the National Cooperative Soil Survey indicates that 0 to 25% mixing of the B horizon into

The authors are J. W. Gilliam, Professor; D. K. Cassel, Professor; R. B. Daniels, Visiting Professor; and J. R. Stone, former Research Assistant. Soil Science Department, North Carolina State University.

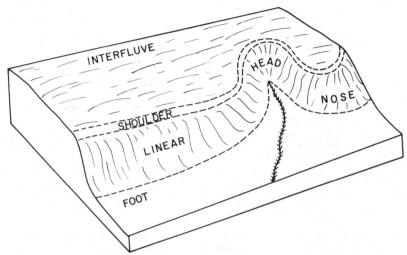

Figure 1. Landscape positions

the A horizon is "slight" erosion, mixing of 25 to 75% is "moderate"
erosion and greater than 75% mixing is "severe" erosion. Although several
erosion classes may be found in a given landscape position, a definite
relationship exists between landscape position and degree of erosion.
Daniels et al. (1985) investigated the areal relationship between erosion
class and landscape position for 10 fields of Cecil soil. They found that
the interfluve was the only topographic position which, on the average,
contained about equal areas of slightly and severely eroded soil (Table 1).
Within each individual field, the interfluve areas tended to be mostly

Table 1. Average Relationship Between Erosion Class and Landscape
Position for 10 Fields Mapped as Cecil. (Data From
Daniels et al., 1985)

Landscape Position	Area Occupied	Area in Each Erosion Class		
		Slight	Moderate	Severe
		%		
Interfluve	12	37	21	42
Shoulder	10	12	31	57
Valley Slope				
Linear	44	13	37	50
Head	14	44	43	13
Foot	15	50	46	4

severely eroded or mostly slightly eroded so that average areas of each
erosion class across all 10 field was about equal. All other topographic
positions were either mostly severely eroded or slightly eroded. Eighty to
90% of the areas contained in the shoulder and linear slopes were moderately
to severely eroded, whereas 85 to 95% of the areas in head and foot slopes
were slightly to moderately eroded. Thus, in a given field, randomly

selected experimental areas of severely eroded soil are likely to be situated on a shoulder or linear slope whereas randomly selected areas of slightly eroded soil would probably be situated on head and foot slopes. When grouped by erosion class, 27% of the total area in the 10 Cecil fields was slightly eroded and the remaining areas were approximately equally divided between the moderately and severely eroded classes. However, erosion class and landscape position form an intricate pattern within each field. The mean contiguous width of soil falling within an individual erosion class-landscape position in eight fields ranged from 6 to 27 m (Table 2). The mean width of area falling within an individual erosion class was approximately 35 m. Within all the fields which we have observed (including the 10 Cecil fields discussed here) no field was found with large areas of any particular erosion class-landscape position. This greatly complicates research designed to determine the effects of past soil erosion on soil productivity.

Table 2. Mean Width of Soil in Each Erosion Class on Each Landscape Position in Eight Cecil Fields. (From Daniels et al., 1985)

Soil Landscape Position	Erosion Class (Munsell Hue)		
	Slight(10YR)	Moderate(7.5YR)	Severe(5YR)
	------------------------ m ----------------------		
Cecil			
Interfluve	6	18	21
Shoulder	15	10	9
Slopes			
Linear	14	21	14
Nose		18	21
Head	27	21	--
Foot	25	16	--

PHYSICAL AND CHEMICAL CHARACTERISTICS

The most obvious effect of differential erosion in cultivated fields of Cecil soil is the patchwork of colors from red to brown. This presumably results from differential incorporation of the red subsoil into the Ap. There is a very definitive relationship between Ap color and Ap clay content (Table 3). Within individual fields, surface soil color gives a very good indication of the clay content. The combination of color and clay content is the primary information used by the field soil mapper to distinguish among erosion classes.

With the increase in clay content from slight to severe erosion, there are concurrent expected changes in other soil parameters which sometimes have an influence upon soil productivity. For example, there was a relatively large decrease in available P levels as estimated by soil testing for all five locations examined by Stone et al. (1985). However, even on the severely eroded sites with the lowest available P levels, a response to P fertilization would not be expected because research has shown that extractable P levels above 10-12 mg/dm^3 provide sufficient P for maximum corn production on these Piedmont soils (Kamprath, 1967). This viewpoint was confirmed for these five fields because no differences in P content of corn leaves was found between the severely and slightly eroded areas. Moreover, linear regression analysis of corn yields on soil extractable P levels was not significant. Thus even though erosion did result in lower available P levels on the more eroded areas, we do not believe this contributes to decreases in productivity because previous cultural practices have overcome this limitation.

Significant differences among erosion classes were also noted for other soil test measured parameters (Mn, Cu, Zn, pH, K, O.M.) but none of these were significantly correlated with measured differences in yields. The organic matter contents are relatively low in all areas but when significant differences existed between erosion classes, the severely eroded areas had the highest organic matter contents as determined by the Walkey-Black proce- dure procedure (Table 3). Even though the eroded areas tended to have higher organic matter contents, the differences were not considered suf- ficiently large to be of practical significance with regard to soil produc- tivity. Regression analysis confirmed this evaluation.

Table 3. Selected Chemical and Physical Properties of Soils by Erosion Class at two Piedmont Locations. (Data from Stone et al., 1985)

	Rockingham County			Wake County		
	Slight (10YR)	Moderate (7.5YR)	Severe (5YR)	Slight (10YR)	Moderate (7.5YR)	Severe (5YR)
Ap Clay (%)	11.7 (3.3)[a]	16.6 (4.15)	30.4 (5.5)	13.2 (5.2)	22.9 (6.7)	38.1 (5.2)
Ap Organic Matter (%)	0.65 (0.2)	1.05 (0.3)	1.2 (0.2)	1.9 (0.4)	1.9 (0.3)	2.2 (0.3)
Ap Depth (cm)	27.0 (5.2)	27.7 (14.4)	19.0 (3.7)	28.1 (3.1)	25.7 (2.1)	25.7 (3.3)
Soil Test P (mg/dm)	138 (56)	41 (35)	17 (10)	140 (48)	80 (22)	41 (14)
pH	5.0 (0.4)	5.1 (0.5)	5.4 (0.5)	6.3 (0.25)	6.3 (0.3)	6.4 (0.2)
Water content at 1500 kPa (g/g)	0.053 (0.013)	0.085 (0.035)	0.146 (0.025)	0.078 (0.025)	0.112 (0.019)	0.178 (0.029)
Available H_2O in Ap (g/g)	0.069 (0.021)	0.083 (0.020)	0.092 (0.015)	0.059 (0.011)	0.063 (0.011)	0.079 (0.008)

[a] Standard deviations.

The available water capacity in the Ap horizon increased with erosion severity in the same manner that clay content and organic matter content increased. Available water capacity was estimated as the difference between the -33 kPa (-0.33 bar) and the 1500 kPa (15 bar) water contents. It is possible that the rooting depth might vary with erosion class or landscape position, or with an interaction of the two. Unfortunately, no data are available for these Piedmont soils to evaluate total available water holding capacity of the entire rooting zone as functions of erosion class or landscape position.

CORN YIELDS

The corn grain yields by erosion class across all landscape positions at two Piedmont locations as measured by Stone et al. (1985) are given in Table 4. There were significant differences among erosion classes: the moderately

Table 4. Corn Grain Yield by Erosion Class at Two Piedmont Locations.
(Data from Stone et al., 1985)

Year	Rockingham County			Wake County		
	Slight	Moderate	Severe	Slight	Moderate	Severe

-------------------------- (Mg/ha) ----------------------------

Year	Slight	Moderate	Severe	Slight	Moderate	Severe
1981	4.72	5.80	4.16	2.43	2.66	3.03
1982	4.84	5.74	4.58	6.57	6.38	6.17

Relative Yields

Year	Slight	Moderate	Severe	Slight	Moderate	Severe
1981	0.81ab*	1.00a	0.71b	0.80b	0.88ab	1.00a
1982	0.84ab	1.00a	0.80	1.00a	0.97a	0.94a

*Relative yields within a location-year not followed by the same letter
are significantly different at the 95% level of probability by the t
test.

eroded sites in Rockingham County consistently had the highest yield as
compared to the other two erosion classes. In Wake County, the severely
eroded sites had the highest yield in 1981 but no differences were observed
in 1982. The 1981 growing season in Wake County was very dry and is
reflected in the low grain yields during that year. The higher yield which
occurred on the severely eroded site is probably a reflection of the
slightly higher available water holding capacity or deeper rooting depth of
the heavier textured soils on these sites (Table 3). The 1982 growing
season in Wake County was near ideal with regard to rainfall and no yield
differences among erosion classes were observed.

The highest average yields were not obtained on slightly eroded plots as
compared to moderately and severely eroded plots at any of the five sites
studied by Stone et al. (1985). When significant differences existed,
the moderately eroded sites most often had the highest yields. It must be
remembered that the yields obtained on the erosion classes were averaged
across all landscape positions. Thus many of the slightly eroded sites
would be found in depositional areas which sometimes contain deeper sandy A
horizons and sometimes E horizons. The water relations in these areas would
most likely not be as favorable for plant growth during dry seasons.
Perhaps a better evaluation of effects of erosion on productivity can be
made by comparing moderately eroded areas to severely eroded areas.

A comparison of grain yields among landscape positions across all erosions
classes shows that landscape position also affects corn grain yield (Table
5). The only exception was in 1982 in Wake County which had near ideal
moisture during the growing season. There was a very strong tendency for
the landscape position that received converging water flow (head and foot
slopes) to have higher yields than areas with diverging water flow. In
fact, differences among plots in plant available water in the Ap horizon at
the initiation of tasseling at the Rockingham location explained 50% of the
observed yield variation (Yield = 2.39 + 2.73 PAW; R^2 = .50 where PAW = cm
of available water in the Ap horizon on 8 July, 1981). This soil content
measurement followed a very intense rainfall event of 51 mm which would have
been expected to result in significant runoff. We believe that the crest
position had the lowest yield because more water was lost to surface runoff
at this position. This viewpoint is consistent with observations by others
(Kirkby and Chorley, 1967; Carson and Kirkby, 1972) who observed that

Table 5. Corn Grain Yield by Landscape Position. (Data from Stone et al., 1985)

===

Position	1981		1982	
	Yield Mg/ha	Relative Yield	Yield Mg/ha	Relative Yield
		Rockingham County		
Interfluve	3.6	0.69	3.9	0.67
Shoulder	4.6	0.88	4.7	0.81
Linear	5.2	1.00	5.5	0.95
Head	4.8	0.92	5.0	0.86
Foot	5.2	1.00	5.8	1.00
PR>F	0.06		0.05	
		Wake County		
Interfluve	2.2	0.71	6.3	0.93
Shoulder	2.9	0.94	6.5	0.96
Linear	2.5	0.81	6.4	0.94
Head	3.1	1.00	6.8	1.00
Foot	3.0	0.97	6.4	0.94
PR>F	0.03		0.84	

===

differences in overland flow, throughflow and subsequent redistribution of soil water result in different soil water contents among landscape positions.

The data in Table 5 indicate that effect of variation in landscape position on grain yield may be equally as important as variation in erosion. Unfortunately, the experiments of Stone et al., (1985) were not designed to adequately separate the effects of landscape position and erosion class upon soil productivity. However, a few comparisons of yields within an erosion class across all landscape positions can be made as well as some comparisons of yield within one landscape position across the erosion class (Table 6). This data indicate that the variations among yields within an erosion class across landscape position is greater than variations in yields among erosion classes within a single landscape position.

The above discussion is not intended to minimize the potential importance of erosion upon soil productivity. It does, we believe, however, demonstrate the extreme difficulty in quantitatively determining these effects because of the interrelation between erosion and landscape position. Some Piedmont landscape positions are more likely to be eroded than others. These same landscape positions would likely have lower yields even if no erosion had occurred because of differences in the water regime or water balance. Much of the data frequently cited to support the idea that soil erosion results in large decreases in soil productivity were obtained without consideration of landscape position. We do not believe such date are quantitatively correct although they are probably qualitatively accurate.

Table 6. Corn Grain Yields Within an Erosion Class Across Landscape Positions and Within a Landscape Position Across Erosion Classes.

	Moderately eroded sites in Davidson County			
	1981		1982	
Landscape Position	Yield	Relative Yield	Yield	Relative Yield
	Mg/ha		Mg/ha	
Interfluve	6.67	0.77	6.61	0.93
Shoulder	6.64	0.76	5.10	0.71
Linear	6.22	0.71	4.80	0.68
Head	8.71	1.00	7.03	0.99
Foot	6.87	0.79	7.10	1.00

	Severely eroded sites in Rockingham County			
	1981		1982	
Landscape Position	Yield	Relative Yield	Yield	Relative Yield
	Mg/ha		Mg/ha	
Interfluve	3.58	0.67	3.94	0.70
Shoulder	3.99	0.74	4.44	0.79
Linear	4.54	0.84	4.82	0.86
Head	3.15	0.68	4.88	0.87
Foot	5.37	1.00	5.60	1.00

	Interfluve landscape positions in Davidson County			
	1981		1982	
Degree of Erosion	Yield	Relative Yield	Yield	Relative Yield
	Mg/ha		Mg/ha	
Slight	5.91	0.88	6.49	1.00
Moderate	6.68	1.00	6.41	0.99

	Linear landscape positions in Wake County			
	1981		1982	
Degree of Erosion	Yield	Relative Yield	Yield	Relative Yield
	Mg/ha		Mg/ha	
Slight	2.35	0.83	6.02	0.91
Moderate	2.33	0.82	6.61	1.00
Severe	2.83	1.00	6.49	0.98

REFERENCES

1. Carson, M. A., and M. J. Kirkby. 1972. Hillslope Form and Processes. Cambridge Univ. Press. 475 p.

2. Copley, T. L., L. A. Forest, A. G. McCall, and F. C. Bell. 1944. Investigations in erosion control and reclamation of eroded land at the Central Piedmont Conservation Experiment Station, Statesville, N.C. U.S.D.A. Agr. Tech. Bull. No. 873. 66 p.

3. Daniels, R. B., J. W. Gilliam, D. K. Cassel, and L. A. Nelson. 1985. Relationship between erosion class and landscape position of some eroded North Carolina Piedmont soils. Submitted to Soil Sci. Soc. Am. J.

4. Kamprath, E. J. 1967. Residual effect of large applications of phosphorus on high phosphorus fixing soils. Agron. J. 59:25-27.

5. Kirkby, M. J., and R. J. Charley. 1967. Throughflow, overland flow and erosion. Bull. Intern. Assoc. Sci. Hydrol. 12:5-21.

6. Stone, J. R., J. W. Gilliam, D. K. Cassel, R. B. Daniels, L. A. Nelson, and H. J. Kleiss. 1985. Effect of erosion and landscape position on productivity of Piedmont soils. Submitted to Soil Sci. Soc. Am. J.

CHARACTERIZING PRODUCTIVITY OF ERODED SOILS IN THE SOUTHERN PIEDMONT

A. W. White, Jr.   R. R. Bruce   A. W. Thomas
                                     Member ASAE

G. W. Langdale   H. F. Perkins

Soil erosion is reported to be the main conservation problem on about half of the cultivated cropland in the USA (Larson, 1981). Progressive soil erosion over a period of time usually results in reduced crop yields. Evidence of productivity losses caused by erosion can be found throughout the country (Williams et al. 1981). A National Soil Erosion - Soil Productivity Research Planning Committee (Williams et al. 1981) named loss of plant available soil water capacity as the major reason erosion reduces productivity. Available soil water can be reduced by changing the soil water holding characteristics or by reducing the depth of the rooting zone. They also listed loss of nutrients, degradation of soil structure, and nonuniform removal of soil within a field as ways that erosion reduces productivity.

The effect of erosion on soil productivity varies by physiographic region and with climate, and with different soils depending on the nature of the soil pedon. The Southern Piedmont area of the Southeast is historically recognized as one of the most severely eroded regions of the nation (Hendrickson et al., 1963; Trimble, 1974). The soils are predominantly Ultisols with relatively thin sandy or loamy surface horizons (if only slightly eroded) overlying loamy or clayey subsurface horizons (Perkins et al., 1973). The soils are generally infertile with low base saturation and have problems associated with subsoil acidity. Research between 1930 and 1950 on Southern Piedmont soils showed large yield reductions on severely eroded or desurfaced plots (Collins, 1935; Copley et al. 1944; Latham, 1940). However, this was during a time before extensive use of fertilizer and lime and yield reductions were due in large part to nutrient deficiencies and acid subsoils. More recent information compiled by Langdale et al. (1985) from studies conducted throughout the South over the last 40 years, indicates that yield reductions on severely eroded Ultisols averaged near 38% for soybeans and 37% for corn. During the same period, yield reductions resulting from severe erosion on Alfisols averaged 16% for soybeans and 17% for corn. In contrast with the Ultisols, Alfisols are not as highly weathered and have higher contents of Ca, Mg and K (Slusher and Lytle, 1973). Apparently more favorable physical and chemical properties of the Alfisol argillic horizons resulted in less yield reduction due to erosion than on the Ultisols. Langdale et al. (1985) observed that deep medium textured soils generally showed less crop yield reduction from soil erosion than those with a medium- to coarse-textured surface over clayey subsoils. Frye et al. (1982) also reported that erosion substantially decreases the productivity of soils,

The authors are: A. W. WHITE, JR., Soil Scientist; R. R. BRUCE, Soil Scientist; A. W. THOMAS, Agricultural Engineer; G. W. LANGDALE, Soil Scientist, USDA-ARS, Southern Piedmont Conservation Research Center, Watkinsville, Georgia 30677; H. F. PERKINS, Professor, University of Georgia, Athens, Georgia 30602.

such as the Maury and Crider soils, with strongly developed pedons. Effects of erosion on soil productivity may be more critical and difficult to alleviate on thin-surface Ultisols because of the adverse physical and chemical condition associated with subsoils exposed by erosion (Winters and Simonson, 1951; Langdale and Shrader, 1982).

Much of the available information on the relationship between erosion and productivity comes from early research that is of little value for predicting crop yields on eroded soils today. Specific information is unavailable for accurately defining levels of erosion and productivity of eroded soils, and there is no accepted method for determining production potential of these lands. Recent reports emphasize that current information is inadequate for defining the effects of erosion on soil productivity and indicate an urgent need for research to "quantify the relationship between plant growth and those soil attributes affected by erosion" (Larson et al. 1981; Langdale and Schrader, 1982; Williams et al. 1981).

The purpose of this paper is to describe the methods used in evaluating the effects of erosion degree on soybean yields in the Southern Piedmont of Georgia and to identify soil properties associated with different degrees of eroded soils and related to crop production levels.

EXPERIMENTAL PROCEDURES

A study was conducted in 1982 and 1983 on 40 farm fields located within a 40 km radius of Watkinsville, Georgia. Fields were chosen to meet the following conditions: (1) soils were classified predominantly in the Cecil or Pacolet series (clayey, kaolinitic, thermic, Typic Hapludults); (2) each field was planted in conventionally tilled soybeans; and (3) each field exhibited degrees of erosion ranging from slight to severe. Slope and field size were not critical factors for selection purposes. Management practices, fertilization, and choice of cultivars were determined by the grower.

The same basic approaches were followed each year in selecting the fields and in conducting the studies. District Conservationists of the Soil Conservation Service made initial contact with farmers and screened potential sites. Soil scientists then made final selection of the fields based on soil series and degrees of erosion present in each field. In 1982, 24 fields were selected. In 1983, for various reasons (crop rotation or ownership change) 16 new fields were selected along with 8 fields from 1982.

Within each field slightly, moderately, and severely eroded sites were selected using Soil Conservation Service guidelines (Soil Survey Staff, 1980). Three plots were established in each site or erosion level for measurement purposes. Each plot consisted of three rows 3-m long. Spacing between plots varied from one to three rows and the three plots were located within about a 15 x 15 m area.

Pedon descriptions were made to a 1.5-m depth on each erosion site in each field at a single point centrally located in the three plot area. Soil samples were taken from the Ap and from 0.2-0.3 and 0.45-0.55-m depths of each plot for physical and chemical determinations. Soil chemical analyses on plow-layer samples were made for available P, K, Ca, and Mg using the double-acid extraction method (Donohue and Isaac, 1983). Soils from different horizon depths were extracted with neutral $\underline{N}$ ammonium acetate and exchangeable K, Ca, and Mg were determined by atomic absorption (Donohue and Isaac, 1983). Soil pH was determined in 1:1 soil-water and total C was determined with a Leco CR12* carbon analyzer.

Rain gauges were installed in each field. Electrical resistance units (Delmhorst Instrument Co.)* for soil water measurement were installed in each plot at 0.10-, 0.25-, and 0.50 m depths in 1982 and at an additional 0.75-m depth in 1983. Rainfall and soil water were measured twice weekly from mid-July to the end of the growing season in 1982 and from June 20 to the end of the 1983 growing season. Plant height was measured weekly.

At harvest, plant heights were measured and stand counts made for each plot. Soybean plots were clipped by hand, air dried and samples were processed through a small plot combine. Bean yields were computed at 13% moisture. Plant residue separated by combining was weighed, corrected for moisture content, and reported as dry matter yield of stover.

Data were analyzed as a randomized complete block with subsampling using fields as blocks.

CROP INFORMATION AND GROWING CONDITIONS

Table 1 summarizes some of the variations in growing conditions and management practices that existed between fields.

Table 1. Crop Information, Fertilization, and Rainfall for 24 Soybean Fields in 1982 and 1983.
==
1. Soybean cultivars (number): 5 (1982), 6 (1983). Maturity groups VI and VII.

2. Row spacings (range): 0.76 to 1.02 m.

3. Planting dates: May 6 to June 12.

4. Rainfall, mean and range for all locations (July 15 to October 5)
   1982 - mean 255 mm, range 176 to 301 mm.
   1983 - mean 210 mm, range 136 to 310 mm.

5. Fertilization rates:

Element	1982 Number of fields	1982 Range in rates (kg/ha)	1983 Number of fields	1983 Range in rates (kg/ha)
N	8	13 - 20	17	7 - 28
P	13	10 - 25	19	13 - 24
K	14	39 - 98	21	42 - 98
==

Most plantings were in mid-May. In 1982, 10 of the 24 fields received no fertilizer and in 1983 3 fields were unfertilized. Some farmers fertilized based on soil test recommendations; others did not. Rainfall among locations showed a large variation. Lowest rainfall locations received 42% less in 1982 and 56% less in 1983 than the highest rainfall areas. Rainfall records at Watkinsville showed that for the period covering the major portion of the growing season for soybeans (June-Aug.) rainfall was 147 mm in 1982,

---

*Mention of a trade name, proprietary product or specific equipment does not constitute a guarantee or warranty by the USDA and does not imply its approval to the exclusion of other products that may be suitable.

slightly above the 98-year average of 135 mm, but below average in 1983 (110 mm). Also, a severe drought occurred in 1983 extending throughout July and the first half of August.

SOIL AND FIELD DESCRIPTIONS

Soils classed as Cecil or Pacolet were chosen for the studies to reduce variability unrelated to erosion degree as well as to provide information for an important benchmark soil (Cecil). These and closely related soils occupy about two-thirds of the total land area in the Southern Piedmont (Hendrickson et al., 1963). Cecil and Pacolet are closely related series differing mainly in depth and thickness of the Bt horizon. Thickness of the clayey Bt in the Cecil series ranges from 0.61 to 1.12 m, and the Bt extends to a depth of 0.76 to 1.52 m below the surface. Pacolet has a clayey Bt at least 0.30 m thick but is shallower than 0.76 m. The Pacolet soil is sometimes referred to as a "shallow Cecil". Depth to bedrock is more than 1.52 m in each series.

The processes of erosion involve gradual removal of topsoil over a period of time from certain areas. As this process continues, tillage implements extending through the original A horizon mix soils from the underlying horizons into the surface soil thus imparting some of the subsoil characteristics into the plow layer. The slightly, moderately, and severely eroded sites in each field were picked with this concept in mind and in conformance with SCS descriptions for these soils (Soil Survey Staff, 1980). Slightly eroded sites were judged to have lost less than 25% of the original surface soil with little or no subsoil mixing evident. Moderately eroded sites were those that showed definite signs of subsoil mixing into the plow layer with estimated soil losses of 25 to 75% of the original A horizon. Severely eroded sites had plow layers consisting mainly of material that was below the original A horizon and were estimated to have lost 75% or more of the original surface soil.

Field sites chosen on upland positions were mainly on nearly level to gently sloping ridge tops and side slopes having slopes mostly less than 8% (Table 2). Foot slope positions and alluvial soils were avoided in selecting the slightly eroded sites. Generally, eroded sites had slightly steeper slopes (averaging about 4%) than slightly eroded sites which averaged under 3%.

Stage of erosion effected differences in Munsell hue (Table 2) and topsoil clay content (Table 3). Munsell hues ranged from 7.5YR for most slightly eroded soils to the redder 2.5YR on severely eroded sites. Plow layer textures ranged from sandy loam on slightly eroded sites to mostly sandy clays on the severely eroded sites. Conditions were similar in both 1982 and 1983 (Tables 2 and 3) even though 16 new fields were included in 1983.

Soil depth measurements for major horizons were summarized from pedon descriptions and indicate that the average pedons for the different erosion levels were similar each year (Table 4). Moderately and severely eroded sites had thinner surface horizons with increased clay content and the overall depth through the Bt horizon was less with increased degree of erosion. Average Ap thickness decreased from about 190 to 110 mm with increased erosion. Using depth to the bottom of the Bt as a reference point, average depths for the severely eroded soils were 340 and 360 mm shallower than slightly eroded soils in 1982 and 1983, respectively. Slightly eroded pedons typically had a BE horizon (transition from Ap to Bt which was mixed in some cases) which was absent in most cases on the more eroded soils.

86

Table 2. Slope and Topsoil Munsell Hue for Slightly, Moderately and Severely Eroded Sites on 24 Farm Fields in 1982 and 1983.

Erosion Level	Slope, (%) Mean	Range	Std. Dev.	Topsoil Munsell hue and no. of fields
			1982	
Slight	2.8	1- 7	1.9	7.5YR (18), 5YR (6)
Moderate	4.2	1- 9	2.1	5YR (7), 2.5YR (17)
Severe	4.3	1-10	2.5	2.5YR (23), 10R (1)
			1983	
Slight	2.5	1- 7	1.7	7.5YR (12), 5YR (12)
Moderate	3.9	1- 6	1.3	5YR (10), 2.5YR (14)
Severe	4.1	1- 6	1.4	2.5YR (23), 10R (1)

Table 3. Topsoil Textures on Slightly, Moderately, and Severely Eroded Sites on 24 Farm Fields in 1982 and 1983.

Erosion level	Sand(%) Mean	Range	Std.Dev.	Silt(%) Mean	Clay(%) Mean	Range	Std.Dev.	Texture Class
				1982				
Slight	76	53-86	7.8	16	8	4-16	3.5	Sandy loam
Moderate	63	47-76	8.5	14	23	14-36	6.4	Sandy clay loam
Severe	49	30-62	8.3	12	39	27-53	7.5	Sandy clay
				1983				
Slight	74	58-87	6.9	18	8	3-20	3.9	Sandy loam
Moderate	63	50-78	6.8	16	21	10-31	4.5	Sandy clay loam
Severe	50	42-63	6.1	15	35	26-46	6.6	Sandy clay

Table 4. Mean Depths of Soil Horizons on Slightly Moderately, and Severely Eroded Sites for Farm Fields Included in 1982 and 1983 Studies.[a]

Horizon description	Year	Slight Mean	Std.Dev.	Moderate Mean	Std.Dev.	Severe Mean	Std.Dev.
		(mm)		(mm)		(mm)	
Ap depth	1982	188	35	121	19	105	25
	1983	191	26	120	13	110	15
BE or B/A thickness	1982	(21)[b] 128	34	(5) 81	21	(4) 95	32
	1983	(23) 126	44	(6) 97	25	-	-
Depth to bottom of Bt	1982	858	122	678	239	518	171
	1983	946	169	632	252	589	226

[a]Mean of 22 fields in 1982 and 24 fields in 1983. Two fields in 1982 did not have clearly defined Bt horizons and were omitted from averages.
[b]Indicates number of fields having indicated horizon. Not all pedons had an intermediate horizon between the Ap and Bt horizons.

EFFECTS OF EROSION ON PLANT POPULATION, HEIGHT, STOVER, AND SOYBEAN YIELDS

Averages for the 24 fields each year indicate that erosion resulted in reductions in plant population, height, stover yields, and soybean yields
(Table 5). However, results varied considerably from field to field and
some fields had greater differences between erosion levels than others.
Overall, 45 and 63% of the fields in 1982 and 1983, respectively, had best
stands on slightly eroded sites, while 63 and 58% had poorest stands on the
severely eroded sites for the same years. The tallest plants were measured
on slightly eroded sites on 88 and 79% of the fields in 1982 and 1983,
respectively, and also smallest plants occurred on severely eroded sites 88%
of the time (21 of 24 fields) each year.

Yields differed among fields as would be expected with differences in
cropping, fertility, management, landscape positions, and rainfall among
the locations. In 1982, stover and bean yields were highest on slightly
eroded sites on 96% of the fields (23 of 24 fields). Severely eroded sites
had lowest stover yields in all cases and lowest bean yields on 20 of the 24
fields (83%). Results were similar in 1983 although yields were generally
lower as a result of dry weather. Stover yields were highest on slightly
eroded sites on 83% of the fields (20 of 24 fields), and lowest on severely
eroded sites on 22 of the 24 fields (92%). Slightly eroded sites produced
highest bean yields on 21 of 24 fields (88%) while severely eroded sites had
lowest yields on 20 of 24 fields (83%).

Table 5. Effects of Erosion on Plant Population, Height, Stover, and
          Soybean Yields on 24 Farm Fields in 1982 and 1983.

Erosion level	Population (plants/ha)		Plant height		Stover yield dry matter		Soybean yield	
	1982	1983	1982	1983	1982	1983	1982	1983
	(1000)		(m)		(kg/ha)		(kg/ha)	
Slight	296	295	1.02	.88	3267	2169	2775	1996
Moderate	276	278	.91	.81	2359	1715	1888	1503
Severe	255	268	.75	.67	1568	1124	1330	997
LSD 5%:								
Erosion	31	22	6	5	276	209	228	208
Significance levels, probability >F:								
Erosion	0.04	0.05	0.01	0.01	0.01	0.01	0.01	0.01

Because 1983 was a drier year than 1982, stover and bean yields averaged
about 30 and 25% lower, respectively, in 1983 than in 1982. The reductions
on slightly eroded land were slightly higher than on eroded sites. However,
percent differences between erosion levels were about the same each year.
Both stover and bean yields were reduced 52% in 1982 on the severely eroded
sites compared to slightly eroded sites. In 1983, the reductions were 48
and 50% for stover and bean yields, respectively. Yield reductions for the
moderately eroded sites were intermediate between slight and severe.

EFFECTS OF EROSION ON SOIL WATER AND CROP YIELDS

Considerable variation in amount and distribution of rainfall during the
growing seasons of 1982 and 1983 was found among the selected field locations
(Table 1). Rainfall occurring between July 14 and Oct 5 each year on each
field was examined in relation to soybean yield. A similar relationship
existed each year. When the two years of data were combined (Fig. 1), yield
was positively related to rainfall on the slightly eroded sites (highly

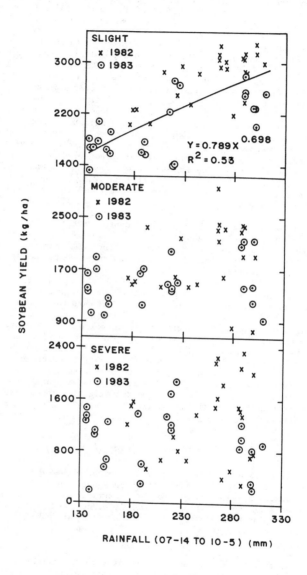

Fig. 1 Soybean Yields on Slight, Moderate and Severely Eroded Sites on All Fields in 1982 and 1983 in Relation to Rainfall Amount on Those Sites Between July 14 and October 5.

significant at the 0.01 level). Data for the moderately and severely eroded sites showed greater scatter and a confident relationship is not shown, i.e. $R^2=0.12$ for moderate erosion and $R^2=0.02$ for severe erosion. Considerable uncertainty is associated with the effect of increasing rainfall amounts on soybean yield on the moderately and severely eroded sites.

Soil water tension as a function of time from day 195 to 265 (July 14 to Sept. 22, 1982) is shown in Fig. 2 for slightly, moderately and severely eroded sites on one field (Oc 9). This field had 243 mm of rainfall during the July 15 to October 5 period, which was close to the mean of all fields. In Fig. 2A the mean soil water tension at 0.10 and 0.25 m is shown. Rainfall events were more effective in reducing the soil water tension on the slightly eroded site than on the moderately and severely eroded sites. Therefore, the soil water tension regime for the slightly eroded site was distinctly lower and more favorable for crop growth than that on the moderately and severely eroded sites. For example, following the rainfall events on day 221, 222, and 223 the moderately and severely eroded sites rapidly returned to about 15 bar soil water tension whereas the slightly eroded site maintained a tension less than 0.25 bar until day 231. These data suggest that the slightly eroded site was recharged more completely by the rainfall than the other sites and was more affected by the rainfall on day 229 and 231. This pattern was repeated several times during the season. Soil water tension data shown in Fig. 2B for the 0.5-m depth indicate that by day 195 the moderately and severely eroded sites were between 6 and 8 bars and remained at greater than this tension throughout the remainder of the period. In contrast, the slightly eroded site indicated recharge to the 0.5-m depth by several rainfall events.

Although each field site exhibited somewhat unique soil water tension patterns in response to the rainfall input, the response described above for Oc 9 was predominant. On Oc 9 the P level of the Ap horizon was medium or higher on all plots. On fields where low to very low P levels occurred on the severely eroded plots the soil water regime effect on yield was masked. On a few sites the presence of high Al levels in the subsoil may have modified soil water extraction. Although infiltration measurements were not made, the soil water tension data accompanied by rainfall data over the season strongly suggest that the infiltration on the moderately and severely eroded sites is considerably lower than on the slightly eroded sites and may be primarily responsible for the yield differences. Certainly landscape position of the sites may contribute to the difference in infiltration.

EFFECTS OF EROSION ON SOIL CHEMICAL PROPERTIES

Results of soil tests on plow layer samples in 1982 showed differences in some of the available nutrients (Table 6). Phosphorus availability was markedly influenced by severity of erosion. Extractable P was high in slightly eroded soils and very low in severely eroded soils. In contrast, K and Mg averaged in the medium range on the slightly eroded soils, but showed higher levels with increased degree of erosion. Erosion had no significant effect on soil pH or total C.

Analyses of exchangeable K, Ca, and soil pH at three depths in the soil pedon in 1982 present a more complete view of soil fertility conditions deeper in the soil (Table 7). Although the same soil depths were sampled for each erosion class, different horizons were dominant in some cases, depending on the erosion class. For example, on slightly eroded soils the 0.2-0.3 m depth was in the BE horizon, and the 0.45-0.55 m sample was from the Bt horizon. In the moderately and severely eroded sites, samples from these depths were mainly in the Bt horizon.

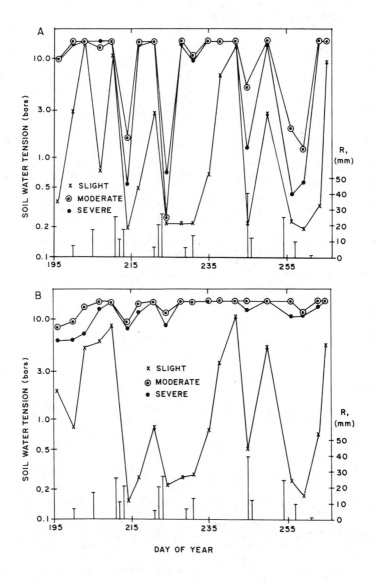

Fig. 2 Soil Water Tension on the Slight, Moderate, and Severely Eroded
Sites on One Field (Oc 9) as a Function of Time and Rainfall (R)
in 1982.   (a) Mean Soil Water Tension at 0.10- and 0.25-m Depth
(b) Soil Water Tension at 0.5-m Depth. Rainfall for the Period
was 243 mm.

Table 6. Available Nutrients, pH, and Carbon Concentration of Topsoils from Slightly, Moderately, and Severely Eroded Sites on 24 Soybean Fields in 1982.[a]

Erosion level	Soil pH	P	K	Ca	Mg	C
		(µg/g)	(µg/g)	(µg/g)	(µg/g)	(%)
Slight	6.4	54	118	620	68	0.68
Moderate	6.3	17	158	551	92	0.71
Severe	6.2	9	180	593	112	0.75
LSD 0.05	NS	12	20	NS	13	NS
Significance levels, probability >F						
Erosion	0.25	0.01	0.01	0.58	0.01	0.14

[a]Extractable P, K, Ca, and Mg determined by double acid extraction method. Low and high levels are P<10 low, >20 high; K<60 low, >125 high; Ca<200 low, >200 adequate; Mg<60 low, >120 high.

Table 7. Ammonium Acetate Extractable K, Ca, and Soil pH at Three Soil Depths on Slightly, and Severely Eroded Sites on 24 Soybean Fields in 1982.

Soil depth	Erosion level		LSD 0.05	Prob.>F
	Slight	Severe		Erosion
(m)	pH			
0-0.10	6.4	6.2	NS	0.26
0.20-0.30	5.9	5.3	0.2	0.01
0.45-0.55	5.5	5.0	0.2	0.01
	K(µg/g)			
0-0.10	84	176	17	0.01
0.20-0.30	99	87	NS	0.23
0.45-0.55	92	53	12	0.01
	Ca(µg/g)			
0-0.10	311	451	56	0.01
0.20-0.30	253	324	43	0.01
0.45-0.55	344	202	49	0.01

The results indicate greater movement of bases into the soil pedon on slightly eroded soils with deep sandy loam surface than into the clayey severely eroded soils. Soil pH was higher at all depths in these soils compared to the more eroded soils. Both K and Ca, although lower in the slightly eroded surface soils, were higher at the lowest depth than in the more eroded soils. In contrast, on the severely eroded soils, highest K and Ca concentrations were in the surface soil and decreased with depth. These differences may be attributed to less water movement through the severely eroded soils as well as the fact that the higher clay contents with higher exchange capacities of the more eroded soils would tend to retain cations nearer the surface more readily than the sandy loam surface soils. Also, because of lower yields on eroded soils there was less removal of K and Ca.

DISCUSSION

When comparing sites with different degrees of erosion, interpreting crop performance differences associated with erosion levels can sometimes be confounded by other factors. Stone et al. (1982) demonstrated that land-scape position affected corn yields. Severely eroded sites tended to be in positions of diverging water flow and were more droughty than uneroded sites which occurred more in positions of converging flow and less runoff. Also, it has been pointed out that in some cases sites identified as "eroded" very likely were initially thinner or shallower than other soils (Langdale, et al., 1985). Thus, in comparing sites with different degrees of erosion it would be inaccurate to attribute yield differences totally to soil loss by accelerated erosion. A complexity of factors, not all of which are asso-ciated with soil loss, contribute to observed production differences on soils classed as eroded.

The results of our studies show measureable differences in crop yield levels and in soil properties related to soil erosion levels, or more specifically as related to soil erosion classes as presently classified in the field. It is reasonable to conclude that yield differences between erosion classes were influenced in some cases by factors other than soil loss by erosion. Slightly eroded sites were located most frequently on ridge top areas and eroded sites were predominantly on side slopes. Position would thus con-tribute to more favorable soil moisture on the less eroded soils. Another factor contributing to production difference, and perhaps favoring the slightly eroded soils, would be management practices used in this area of the Southeast. The disk harrow is widely used in land preparation on these soils. A disk harrow usually penetrates deeper into the slightly eroded sandy loam soils than into the more clayey eroded soils. This practice re-sults in a shallower Ap layer on eroded soils which is due to a management practice. Also, the problem of optimum management for different degrees of eroded soil in the same field becomes evident in our studies. Soil P levels on slightly eroded soils were in the high fertility range indicating little or no need for P fertilizer on these soils. At the same time P availability levels on severely eroded sites were almost all in the low range indicating insufficient P fertility levels. Yet farmers were applying low to moderate rates of P uniformly over the fields which were probably not needed on the slightly eroded soils and insufficient for correcting P deficiencies on the more eroded soils.

It is clear that a multiplicity of factors contribute to soil productivity, but because of confounding it is not possible to isolate specifically which of these factors has the greatest effect on crop production. In general, the overall results in this study on Cecil-Pacolet soils indicate that crop production is lower on soils classified as eroded and that a range of measureable soil properties and characteristics have application in describ-ing differences in productivity of these soils. This kind of information is useful in more clearly understanding the factors that affect soil producti-vity.

SUMMARY

Field investigations were conducted in 1982 and 1983 on 40 farm fields in a seven-county area in the Southern Piedmont region of Georgia to evaluate the effects of erosion on soil productivity. All fields (24 each year) were planted in conventionally tilled soybeans on Cecil-Pacolet soils (Typic Hapludults). Replicated plots were established in three areas of each field classified as slightly, moderately, and severely eroded for characterizing differences in soil properties and to measure erosion effects on soybean yields. Results indicated that the range of crop production effected by soil erosion on these soils can be reliably determined. The effects of past erosion reduced plant growth, yields, and stands in 1982 and 1983. Highest yields were measured both years on slightly eroded sites averaging 2775 and 1996 kg/ha for 1982 and 1983, respectively. Yields on severely eroded sites were about 50% of those on slightly eroded sites each year. With more severe erosion, surface horizons were thinner, clay contents higher and hues redder. Sites classified as most eroded had shallower rooting depths and were more infertile and acid in the subsoil than the less eroded sandy loam surface soils. Analysis of rainfall data from all locations showed that rainfall was not as effective in increasing yields on the more eroded soils. Soil water data from over the season also indicated that on many occasions slightly eroded sites were more completely recharged by rainfall than the more eroded sites suggesting that infiltration is lower on the more eroded soils and is a major factor influencing yield differences. Overall results indicate that a number of interrelated factors are involved and influence productivity of eroded soils. These procedures have proven satisfactory in evaluating the effects of erosion on productivity.

ACKNOWLEDGEMENTS

This contribution is from cooperative investigations conducted by the Southern Piedmont Conservation Research Center, USDA-ARS, Watkinsville, Georgia, the Department of Agronomy, University of Georgia, Athens, Georgia and the Soil Conservation Service, USDA, Athens, Georgia. Special appreciation is due the cooperating farmers and L. W. Frost, Soil Scientist, SCS, for his assistance in locating sites and making pedon descriptions for the fields used in the study.

REFERENCES

1. Adams, W.E. 1949. Loss of topsoil reduces crop yields. J. Soil and Water Cons. 4:130.

2. Collins, W.O. 1935. Soil erosion experiments. Col. Agr. Bul. No. 30(106): Serial No. 613. Univ. GA. Athens.

3. Copley, T.L., L.A. Forest, A.G. McCall, F.C. Bell. 1944. Investigattions in erosion control and reclamation of eroded land at the Central Piedmont Conservation Experiment Station, Statesville, N.C. U.S. Dept. Agr. Tech. Bull. No. 873. 66 p.

4. Day, P.R. 1965. Particle fractionation and particle-size analysis. In C.A. Black et al. (ed.) Methods of soil analysis, part 1. Agronomy 9:545-569. Amer. Soc. of Agron., Madison, Wisconson.

5. Donohue, S.J., and R.A. Isaac (Comm. Chairmen). 1983. Reference soil test methods for the southern region of the United States. Sou. Coop. Series Bul. 289. Univ. of Ga. Coll. Agric. 40 p.

6. Frye, W.W., S.A. Ebelhar, L.W. Murdock, and R.L. Blevins. 1982. Soil erosion effects on properties and productivity of two Kentucky soils. Soil Sci. Soc. Am. J. 46:1051-1055.

7. Hendrickson, B.H., A.P. Barnett, J.R.Carreker, and W.E. Adams. 1963. Runoff and erosion control studies on Cecil soil in the Southern Piedmont. U.S. Dept. Agr. Tech. Bul. No. 1281. 33 p.

8. Langdale, G.W., and W.D. Shrader. 1982. Soil erosion effects on soil productivity of cultivated cropland. pp. 41-51. In B.L. Schmidt, R.R. Allmaras, J.V. Mannering, and R.I. Papendick (eds.) Determinants of soil loss tolerance. Amer. Soc. of Agron. Spec. Publ. No. 45. Madison, Wisconsin. 153 p.

9. Langdale, G.W., H.P. Denton, A.W. White, Jr., J.W. Gilliam, and W.W. Frye. 1985. Effects of soil-erosion on crop productivity of southern soils. Chap. 15. In R. F. Follett (ed.) Soil erosion and crop productivity. Amer. Soc. of Agron. Spec. Publ. Madison, Wisconsin. (Accepted for publication in 1985).

10. Larson, W.E. 1981. Protecting the soil resource base. J. Soil and Water Cons. 36(1):13-16.

11. Larson, W.E., L.M. Walsh, B.A. Stewart, and D.H. Boelter (ed.) 1981. Soil and water resources: research priorities for the nation. Soil Science Society of America Inc., Madison, Wisconsin. 229 p.

12. Latham, E.E. 1940. Relative productivity of the A horizon of the acid sandy loam and the B & C horizons exposed by erosion. J. Am. Soc. Agron. 32:950-954.

13. Perkins, H.P., H.J. Byrd, and F.T. Ritchie, Jr. 1973. Ultisols - light-colored soils of the warm temperate forest lands. p. 73-86. In S.W. Buol (ed.) Soils of the southern states and Puerto Rico. Southern Cooperative Series Bull. No. 174. 105 p.

14. Slusher, D.F., and S.A. Lytle. 1973. Alfisols - light-colored soils of the humid temperate areas. p. 61-72. In S.W. Buol. (ed.) Soils of the southern states and Puerto Rico. Southern Cooperative Series Bull. No. 174. 105 p.

15. Soil Survey Staff. 1980. Soil Survey Manual. USDA. Soil Conser. Ser. Chap. 5 (NSH-Appendix 1 - 9/11/80):17-18.

16. Stone, J., R. Daniels, J. Gilliam, J. Kleins, and K. Cassel. 1982. Relationship among corn yields, surface horizon color and slope form in some clayey North Carolina Piedmont soils. Agron. Abs. 74:257.

17. Trimble, S.W. 1974. Man-induced soil erosion on the Southern Piedmont, 1700-1970. Soil Cons. Soc. Am., Ankeny, Iowa. 180 p.

18. Williams, J. R., R.R. Allmaras, K.G. Renard, L. Lyles, W.C. Moldenhauer, G.W. Langdale, L.D. Meyer, W.J. Rawls, G. Darby, R. Daniels, and R. Magleby. 1981. Soil erosion effects on soil productivity: A research prospective. J. Soil and Water Cons. 36(2):82-90.

19. Winters, E., and R.W. Simonson. 1951. The subsoil, Adv. Agron. 3:1-92.

SOIL PROPERTIES AND PRODUCTIVITY CHANGES ALONG A SLOPE

R. D. Williams   J. W. Naney   L. R. Ahuja
                                                 Member ASAE

Crop yields vary from one field to another and from one location to another
in a field. Such variations are due to differences in physical and chemical
soil properties among and within the fields (see for example Costigan et
al., 1983; Costigan and McBurney, 1983). Soil erosion can affect physical
and chemical soil properties, and principally affects crop production by
reducing nutrient supply, water infiltration and soil water holding capacity
(Langdale and Shrader, 1982). Previous studies have shown that crop
response to eroded soils may vary significantly (Adams, 1949; Baver, 1950;
Buntley and Bell,1976); severe erosion, however, is not a prerequisite to
significant variation in crop yield.

The effects of erosion on productivity have been studied either by comparing
crop yields on different eroded sites and then using multiple regression
techniques to determine the significant soil parameters with regard to
yield, or by incrementally removing soil layers at one site and observing
the effects on crop yield (Langdale and Schraider, 1982). In the present
study, a simple watershed, in wheat and grain sorghum, with a gradual slope
was selected, and the change in soil properties and crop yields along the
slope were determined. Relationships between soil properties and yield were
determined using stepwise multiple regression techniques.

MATERIALS AND METHODS

The area selected for study was a 1.6 ha watershed at El Reno, OK. The
watersheds upper boundary is the remnants of terrace deposits of the
Quaternary system. These deposits have been described as a mixture of sand,
silt and clay, reddish in color, and nearly indistinguishable from the
underlying redbeds of Permian age (Mogg, et al. 1960). Since the deposition
of the terrace deposits, the North Canadian River channel has migrated
northward 3 km, leaving the sloping terrace face exposed to weathering and
erosional forces for perhaps as long as 10,000 years. The effect of this
long term weathering and soil formation activity has been to redistribute
the finer material along the slope to the lower elevation of the terrace.
Five soil series have been identified along the 200 m length of 3-4% slope
(Fig. 1). On the upper one third of the watershed, Milan loam (fine-loamy,
mixed, thermic, Udic Argiustoll), Aydelotte silt loam (fine, mixed, thermic,
Udertic Paleustalf), Renfrow silt loam (fine, mixed, thermic, Udertic
Paleustoll) and Bethany silt loam (fine, mixed, thermic, Pachic Paleustoll)
are found. The lower two thirds of the watershed has been classified as
Kirkland silt loam (fine, mixed, thermic, Udertic Paleustoll). Prior to
1978, the watershed was in native grass; since that time, it has been
planted yearly to winter wheat using management practices typical for the
area. Further description of the watershed and management, including
fertilizer rates, has been published elsewhere (Sharpley et al. 1982; Smith
et al. 1983).

The authors are: R. D. Williams, Plant Physiologist, J. W. Naney,
Geologist, and L. R. Ahuja, Soil Physicist, Water Quality and Waterhsed
Research Laboratory, USDA-ARS, Durant, Oklahoma.

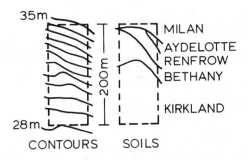

Figure 1. Watershed Topography and Soil Series

A line transect was established in the fall of 1981 down the center of the
watershed, parallel to the main slope. Soil core samples (3.5 cm dia. x 137
cm) were taken at 20 sites at 10 m intervals along the transect using a
Giddings core sampler. Care was taken not to compact the soil during
sampling. Immediately after sampling, the core was divided into 15 cm
segments; each segment was stored in a sealed PVC tube. The cores were
taken to the laboratory and bulk density, texture, macroporosity,
gravimetric soil water content, organic matter, pH and available phosphorus
(P) were determined for each segment. Soil bulk density of each core was
used to calculate volumetric soil water content.

In the laboratory, the edges of each core were trimmed, and the length and
weight of the remaining intact sample were determined. From the intact
portion, two 3-cm lengths were cut and placed in two open-ended brass
containers (4 cm dia. x 3 cm deep). Molten paraffin wax was used to fill
the gap between the soil and the container walls. The rest of the sample
was weighed and dried in the oven at 60° C for 48 h to determine the soil
moisture content. Drying at 60° C for 48 h resulted in the same moisture
level as attained by drying at 105° C for 8 h. The lower temperature was
used to avoid changes in chemical properties that were subsequently measured
on the dried subsamples.

Soil bulk density of the core sample was determined from the above
measurements. The two 3-cm cores from each 15-cm segment were used to
determine the soil water content-potential relationships for each layer. A
pressure-plate apparatus was used for successive pressure steps of 10, 33,
66 and 100 kPa; a pressure membrane apparatus was used for 1500 kPa. A thin
filter paper was placed between the soil and the pressure plate to retain
the soil in the core when removed for weighing after equilibration at each
step. Only the volumetric soil water content at 33 kPa and 1500 kPa, and
the potentially available water (the difference between 33 kPa and 1500 kPa)
were used in the analysis. Macroporosity was defined as the difference
between saturation and 33 kPa for each core sample.

Soil texture (percent sand, silt and clay) was measured on a portion of
oven-dried sample using the hydrometer method (Day, 1965). The remainder of
the subsample was used to make duplicate measurements of pH, organic matter
content and available P. Organic matter content was estimated from weight
loss after ashing a representative 2 g subsample in a muffle furnace

at 50°C for 3 h, following oven-drying (105° C) and weighing. The pH was estimated using a soil-water paste (1:1 wt/wt). Available P was determined by the method of Bray and Kurtz (1945), by extracting 2 g soil with 20 ml 0.03 M NH_4F and 0.025 M HCl for 5 min.

Wheat yield in 1982 was estimated by clipping the plants at ground level from 1 m^2 quadrats adjacent to the soil core sampling sites along the transect. Biomass, the combined ear and straw weight, was determined after air drying for 2 weeks. Grain sorghum yield in 1983 was estimated by clipping the plants at ground level along 1 m of row length at each soil core sampling site and 10 m to each side of the site along the transect. Total biomass was determined after the material was dried at 75° C for 48 h. In 1984, the sampling pattern was similar to that used in 1983, except two row lengths of 1 m each were sampled for grain sorghum yield. Biomass was determined for each sample after plants had been separated into heads and shoots, and dried at 75° C for 24 h. Total dry weight (g/m) was determined from head and shoot weights.

Regression of yield on individual soil parameters and a forward stepwise multiple regression analysis (SAS Institute Inc., 1982) were used to determine which soil parameters affected yield. Data from individual soil cores were pooled to obtain averages for 0-30 cm, 30-76 cm and 76-137 cm soil depth intervals; these averages were used in the analysis. The multiple regression analysis was performed for individual soil layers, as well as for all soil layers combined. When the soil layers were combined, pH, organic matter available P, and volumetric water content at 33 kPa and 1500 kPa suctions were not used in the analysis. Grain sorghum yield samples were averaged for each site (3 and 6 yield samples for 1983 and 1984, respectively). The cutoff probability level for inclusion of a parameter in the multiple regression model was 0.50.

RESULTS AND DISCUSSION

As suggested by the different soil series identified along the slope, the physical and chemical soil properties varied along the slope and with soil depth. Regression analysis indicated significant correlations between several parameters and position along the slope (Table 1). Among the more significant correlations were the texture parameters.

Table 1. Simple correlation coefficients for soil parameters with position along the slope.[a]

Parameter	Soil layer (cm)		
	0-30	30-76	76-137
		r	
Bulk density	.339	.008	-.168
Texture			
sand	.898**	.885**	.910**
silt	-.907**	-.780**	-.813**
clay	-.309	-.234	-.813**
Macroporosity	.379+	.635+	.496*
Organic matter	-.522**	-.254	-.187
pH	-.534	-.599**	-.500*
Available P	.275	-.287	-.585**
Volumetric water content			
33 kPa	-.050	-.157	-.034
1500 kPa	-.107	-.211	-.005
Available water	.048	.057	-.049

[a] **, * and + indicate the 0.01, 0.05 and 0.10 probability level respectively.

Sand content increased with distance upslope and was significantly correlated with position along the slope for each soil layer (Table 1, Fig. 2). The increase in sand content was more gradual in the lower two-thirds than in the upper one-third of the watershed. Although the differences in sand content between soil layers were small, percent sand generally decreased with soil depth (Table 2, Fig. 2).

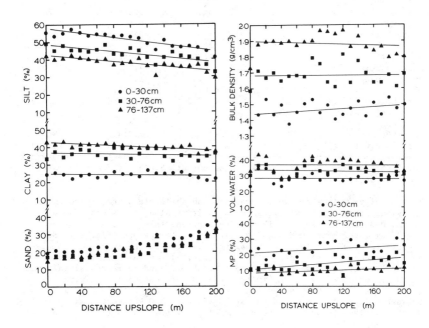

Figure 2.   Texture, Bulk Density, Volumetric Water Content at 33 kPa, and Macroporosity (MP) Along the Slope and with Depth

Silt content was significantly correlated with position along the slope (Table 1) and decreased with distance upslope and soil depth (Table 2, Fig. 2). Clay content was also negatively correlated with position along the slope, but the correlation coefficient was significant only for the 76-137 cm soil layer (Table 1). As with the silt content, clay content decreased with distance upslope, but, unlike sand and silt, increased with soil depth (Table 2, Fig. 2).

In addition to texture, macroporosity, organic matter, pH and available P at certain soil depths were significantly correlated with position along the slope (Table 1). Macroporosity increased with distance upslope and decreased with soil depth (Table 2, Fig. 2). Organic matter content was significantly greater in the surface layer than in the deeper layers (Table 2), and decreased with distance upslope (Table 1). Within each soil layer, pH decreased with distance upslope, but only in the 30-76 cm and 76-137 cm soil layers was pH significantly correlated with distance upslope (Table 1). Soil pH increased with soil depth, from 5.3 in the surface layer to 7.9 in the 76-137 cm layer. Available P in the surface layer increased, while that in the subsurface layers decreased, with distance upslope (Table 1). Greater variability in available P was observed in the surface layer, due to fertilizer application, immobility of P in the soil, and predominance of chemical and biological activity at the surface. For example, available P ranged from 4.6 to 113.8 µg/g in the surface layer, but only from 6.2 to 7.9 µg/g in the 76-137 cm layer.

Table 2. Means and standard deviation of physical and chemical soil
          properties.
===

Parameter	Soil layer (cm)		
	0-30	30-76	76-137
Bulk density (g/cm^3)	1.466±.052	1.681±.061	1.879±.061
Texture			
sand (%)	25.0±5.1	20.8±4.4	22.1±4.9
silt (%)	51.1±4.5	43.4±4.2	37.1±3.6
clay (%)	23.9±1.5	38.8±2.6	40.2±1.9
Macroporosity (%)	23.7±4.0	14.5±3.8	10.0±1.9
Organic matter (%)	2.9±0.4	1.9±0.4	1.3±0.4
pH	5.6±0.3	6.2±0.3	6.9±0.5
Available P (μg/g)	16.1±23.3	2.9±1.5	1.6±0.6
Volumetric water content (%)			
33 kPa	28.2±3.0	32.8±3.2	36.6±4.4
1500 kPa	15.2±4.0	22.3±4.0	26.0±4.9
Available water (%)[a]	12.5±4.2	10.3±4.4	10.6±3.7

===
[a]Available water = volumetric water content at 33 kPa - volumetric water
content at 1500 kPa.

Bulk density, volumetric water content, and available water did not display
any significant trends with regard to position along the slope (Table 1).
In the 0-30 cm soil layer bulk density increased slightly, and in the
76-137 cm layer decreased sightly, with distance upslope (Fig. 2). Bulk
density remained fairly constant along the slope in the 30-76 cm soil layer
and increased with soil depth (Table 2, Fig. 2). Volumetric water content
at 33 kPa suction increased with depth (Table 2) and decreased slighly with
distance upslope. (Fig. 2). Similar results were obtained for volumetric
water content at 1500 kPa suction. Available water content, the difference
between volumetric water content at 33 kPa and 1500 kPa suctions, varied
only slightly with position along the slope or soil depth (Tables 1 and 2).

Growing conditions were normal in 1981-1982 for wheat and in 1984 for grain
sorghum production. Good stands of both crops were established at planting,
and an excellent weed and insect control were obtained during the season.
Production and condition of both crops were typical of the area. In 1983,
however, although a good stand of grain sorghum was established, dry weather
in late summer caused water stress in the crop, reducing its growth and
yield. Signs of water stress, including leaf tip burning, were first
apparent at the top of the slope. Head formation was incomplete and
infrequent. For this reason only the total dry weight was obtained in
1983. Regardless of crops or growing season, yields displayed the same
trend with position along the slope: yield decreased with distance upslope
Fig. 3.

Wheat yield was significantly correlated with position along the slope [r =
-.449 at the 0.05 probability level (p)]; for each 10 m increase in distance
upslope, yield decreased by approximately 10 g/m^2 (Fig. 3). Wheat yield was
significantly and negatively correlated with sand content and macroporosity
(Table 3). Silt content, pH and volumetric water content at 33 kPa suction
for the 0-30 cm soil layer were positively correlated with wheat yield.
None of the correlation coefficients was significant for the 76-137 cm soil
layer (Table 3). Based on correlations the surface layer (ie. 0-30 cm)
appeared to be more related to wheat yield than the deeper soil layers.
Similar results were indicated by the stepwise multiple regressions.

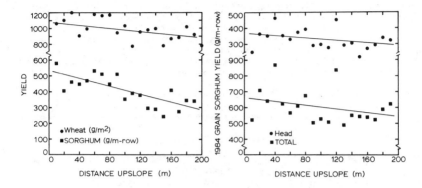

Figure 3. Wheat and Grain Sorghum Yield.

Table 3. Simple correlation coefficients for wheat yield with soil parameters.[a]

Parameter	Soil layer (cm)		
	0-30	30-76	76-137
		----r----	
Bulk density	.342	.355	.293
Texture			
sand	-.459*	-.404+	-.348
silt	.515*	.349	.341
clay	-.003	.112	.251
Macroporosity	-.467*	-.392+	-.284
Organic matter	.231	-.090	-.009
pH	.384+	.313	.267
Available P	-.414+	-.011	.324
Volumetric water content			
33 kPa	.460*	.364+	.202
1500 kPa	.232	.179	.003
Available water	.085	.144	.266

[a]**, * and + indicate the 0.01, 0.05 and 0.10 probability level, respectively.

For the individual soil layers, the stepwise multiple regression of wheat yield with soil parameters of only the 0-30 cm soil layer was significant (0.05 p or less). Results for this soil layer indicated that 26% of the variation in yield was attributed to silt content alone; 50% to bulk density and silt content; 75% to bulk density, silt content, pH and volumetric water content at 33 kPa suction; and 82% to bulk density, macroporosity, pH, volumetric water content at 33 kPa suction and texture (sand, silt and clay content). At the 30-76 cm soil layer 24% (0.08 p) of the variation in yield was attributed to bulk density and sand content, and 34% (0.23 p) attributed to bulk density, volumetric water content at 33 kPa and texture. Thirty eight percent (0.26 p) of the variation in yield for the 76-137 cm soil layer was attributed to sand content, macroporosity, available P, volumetric water content at 33 kPa and 1500 kPa suctions, and available water. The maximum yield response accounted for the stepwise regression model used was 82%, 34% and 38% for the 0-30 cm, 30-76 cm and 76-137 cm soil layers, respectively. The surface layer contributed more to the variation in wheat yield along the slope than the deeper soil layers.

When the individual depths were combined, the first parameters selected by the model were similar to the selections made for 0-30 cm layer (Table 4). The final model (not shown) accounted for 91% (0.04 p) of the variation in wheat yield. The following parameters were selected: bulk density, texture, macroporosity and available water from the 0-30 cm layer; bulk density, sand and clay content, and available water from the 30-76 layer; and sand and clay content, macroporosity and available water from the 76-137 cm layer. By combining the soil layers, 91% of the variation in wheat yield could be explained. This was an increase of only 9% over that attributed to the surface layer alone, however.

Table 4. Stepwise regression model for effects of soil physical properties on wheat yield.

No. Variables	Regression Equation [a]	R^2
1	y = 186.5 + 1555.8 SL-15	.266
2	y = -1899.5 + 1295.2 BD-15 + 1922.5 SL-15	.499
3	y = -3163.9 + 999.3 BD-15 + 4240.0 SL-15 + 2324.6 SD-105	.562
4	y = 2922.1 + 687.5 BD-15 + 4787.5 SL-15 -1212.5 MP-15 + 3330.9 SD-105	.653
5	y = -4187.1 +635.4 BD-15 + 5286.8 SL-15 -1374.1 MP-15 +4488.0 SD-105 + 2162.0 C-105	.681

[a] Abbreviations SL, SD, C, BD, MP and AW refer to silt, sand, clay, bulk density, macroporosity and available water, respectively; and 15, 52, and 105 refer to the 0-30 cm, 30-76 cm and 76-137 cm soil layer, respectively.

Grain sorghum yield in 1983 was significantly correlated with position along the slope (r = -.759, at the 0.0001 p), for each 10 m increase in distance upslope, yield decreased by approximately 13 g/m-row (Fig. 3). Yield was significantly and negatively correlated with sand content for all three soil layers, as it was with macroporosity at both the 30-76 cm and 76-137 cm layers, and available P at the surface layer (Table 5). Silt content (all three soil layers), clay content (76-137 cm layer) and available P (76-137 cm layer) were positively correlated with grain sorghum yield (Table 5).

Stepwise regressions for all the individual soil layers were significant. Results for the 0-30 cm soil layer indicated that 51% (0.0004 p) of the variation in the 1983 grain sorghum yield was attributed to silt content and that 69% (0.009 p) was attributed to bulk density, silt content, organic matter, available P, volumetric water content at 1500 kPa suction and available water. For this soil layer, only 69% of the variation was accounted for and no other parameters were selected by the model. For the 30-76 cm soil layer, only sand content and volumetric water content at 1500 kPa suction were selected by the model which accounted for 48% (0.004 p) of the variation in yield. Similarly, for the 76-137 cm soil layer, only bulk density, sand content and available water were selected which accounted for 58% (0.003 p) of the variation in yield.

Table 5. Simple correlation coefficients for 1983 grain sorghum yield and soil parameters.[a]

Parameter	Soil layer (cm)		
	0-30	30-76	76-137
	--------------------r--------------------		
Bulk density	-.213	.085	.038
Texture			
sand	-.666**	-.682**	-.679**
silt	.711**	.492*	.605**
clay	.037	.322	.556**
Macroporosity	-.293	-.509*	-.416+
Organic matter	.372	-.199	-.152
pH	.305	.357	.196
Available P	-.407+	-.121	.407+
Volumetric water content			
33 kPa	.107	.116	-.019
1500 kPa	-.118	-.050	-.244
Available water	.169	.163	.315

[a]**, * and + indicate the 0.01, 0.05 and 0.10 probability level, respectively.

When the individual soil layers were combined the first parameter selected by the model was silt content of the 0-30 cm layer, which again accounted for 51% (0.0004 p) of the variability in the 1983 grain sorghum yield (Table 6). The final model accounted for only 66% (0.002 p) of the variation in the yield.

Table 6. Stepwise regression model for effects of soil physical properties on the 1983 grain sorghum yield.

No. Variables	Regression Equation [a]	R^2
1	y = -466.8 + 1698.9 SL-15	.381
2	y = -504.4 + 1643.0 SL-15 + 625.3 AW-105	.568
3	y = 155.0 + 1783.6 SL-15 - 398.5 BD-105 +799.9 AW-105	.622
4[b]	y = 118.8 + 1756.9 SL-15 + 885.7 C-52 - 524.4 BD-105 + 518.9 AW-105	.657

[a]Refer to Table 4 for abbreviations.
[b]Only four variables were selected. No other variable met the 0.50 significance level for entry into the model.

Both the 1984 total and head grain sorghum yield were not significantly correlated with position along the slope (r = -.309 at p = 0.20 and r = -.321 at p = 0.18, respectively). Yet both yields decreased with increased distance upslope (Fig. 3). Total yield decreased approximately 5.9 g/m-row with each 10 m increase in distance upslope. Head yield decreased approximately 3.7 g/m-row with each 10 m increase in distance upslope. This decrease in yield with position along the slope was less than that observed for either the wheat or 1983 grain sorghum crop.

Macroporosity was significantly and negatively correlated with both total and head yields (Table 7). Other significant correlations were indicated at various depth for sand and clay content, pH, available P and volumetric water content at 1500 kPa suction (Table 7). Although yield was negatively correlated with sand content (Table 7), the response was not as extensive as that observed for wheat (Table 3) or 1983 grain sorghum (Table 5). Similar differences were noted for silt and clay contents.

Table 7. Simple correlation coefficients for 1984 grain sorghum yield with soil parameters.[a]

Parameter	Soil layer (cm)					
	0-30		30-76		76-137	
	Total	Head	Total	Head	Total	Head
			r			
Bulk density	.178	.242	.296	.288	.135	.212
Texture						
sand	-.314	-.343	-.351	-.396+	-.286	-.279
silt	.284	.351	.138	.125	.262	.251
clay	.151	.056	.338	.417+	.214	.210
Macroporosity	-.503*	-.488*	-.568**	-.636**	-.617**	-.616**
Organic matter	.268	.168	.221	.136	.351	.298
pH	.057	.242	.435+	.553+	.201	.267
Available P	-.102	-.393+	-.160	-.205	.414+	.388+
Vol. water cont.						
33 kPa	-.212	-.228	.035	.021	-.258	-.254
1500 kPa	-.292	-.369	-.053	-.145	-.309	-.423+
Available water	.113	.149	.107	.242	.085	.239

[a]**, * and + indicate the 0.01, 0.05 and 0.10 probability level, respectively.

Results from the stepwise regression for the 0-30 cm soil layer indicated that 25% (0.03 p) of the variation total in the 1984 grain sorghum yield was attributed to macroporosity. Sixty one percent (0.09 p) of the variation in yield was attributed to bulk density, clay content, organic matter, macroporosity, pH, volumetric water content at 1500 kPa suction and available water. The maximum variation explained by the model was 70% (0.02 p) and the parameters selected were bulk density, silt and clay content, organic matter, macroporosity, pH, available P, volumetric water content at 33 kPa and 1500 kPa suctions, and available water. For the 30-76 cm layer, only macroporosity and volumetric water content at 1500 kPa suction were selected by the model which accounted for only 37% (0.02 p) of the variation in yield. For the 76-137 cm soil layer, a maximum of 85% (0.001 p) of the total variation in yield was attributed to bulk density, sand and clay content, organic matter, macroporosity, pH and available P. In the deeper layer 38% of the variation in yield was due to macroporosity alone. When the individual layers were combined, the parameter selected were similar to those for the individual depths (Table 8). The final model (not shown) accounted for 95% (0.02 p) of the variation in the 1984 grain sorghum total yield. The following parameters were selected: bulk density, sand content and macroporosity from the 0-30 cm soil layer; texture, macroporosity and available water from the 30-76 cm layer; and texture, bulk density and macroporosity from the 76-137 cm layer.

Table 8. Stepwise regression model for effects of soil physical properties on the 1984 grain sorghum total yield.

No. Variables	Regression Equation [a]	R^2
1	y = 936.6 - 3346.4 MP-105	.381
2	y = 2059.3 - 2435.1 C-105 - 4795.0 MP-105	.462
3	y = 1894.4 + 1058.3 C-52 - 2996.8 C-105 - 4689.5 MP-105	.518
4	y = 3201.3 + 1496.5 C-52 - 721.3 BD-105 - 3066.7 C-105 - 5413.7 MP-105	.590
5	y = 2124.2 + 523.5 BD-15 + 1693.8 C-52 - 6291.BD-105 - 2954.4 C-105 - 5242.0 MP-105	.637

[a]Refer to Table 4 for abbreviations

Table 9. Stepwise regression model for effects of soil physical
properties on the 1984 grain sorghum head yield.

No.	Variables	Regression Equation [a]	R^2
1		y = 483.4 - 1046.6 MP-52	.405
2		y = 905.2 - 1572.2 C-15 - 1352.2 MP-52	.502
3		y = 910.4 - 1756.5 C-15 - 1394.1 MP-52 + 428.8 AW-52	.587
4		y = 1184.7 - 2457.7 C-15 - 1784.9 MP-52 + 1684.4 AW-52	
		- 1662.2 AW-105	.714
5		y = 1545.7 - 2337.7 C-15 - 1986.0 MP-52 + 1898.4 AW-52	
		- 896.5 C-105 - 1869.8 AW-105	.751

[a]Refer to Table 4 for abbreviations.

Generally the regression analysis for the 1984 head yield were quite
similar to the total yield as reported above. For the individual soil
layers, macroporosity was selected as the first parameter and accounted
for 23%, 40% and 38% (0.01 or greater) of the variation in yield at the
0-30 cm, 30-76 cm and 76-137 cm soil layer, respectively. When the
individual layers were combined the regression model indicated that
macroporosity at the 30-76 cm soil layer in combination with texture and
available water from the other soillayers attributed to the majority of the
variation in head yield (Table 9). The final model (not shown) accounted
for ninety nine percent (0.0003 p) of the variation in 1984 grain sorghum
head yield. The following parameters were selected: bulk density, texture
and available water at the 0-30 cm layer; macroporosity, sand and clay
content, and available water at the 30-76 cm layer; and texture and
available water at the 76-137 layer.

Actual soil erosion from this watershed has been monitored since 1976.
Under native grass average soil loss was 17 kg/ha/yr; under wheat, 490
kg/ha/yr. Extensive soil loss was not detected until grain sorghum was
planted in 1983. In that year, soil loss was 13,159 kg/ha. The SCS
"T-value" (acceptable annual soil loss) for this site is approximately
11,100 kg/ha/yr. Erosion under native grass and wheat was not excessive,
but changes in texture along the slope, are probably due to long term
erosion - ie. several hundred years. Over time, the finer materials have
been repositioned downslope, and left the coarser material behind. Changes
in texture along the slope would also affect the other soil properties such
as bulk density, macroporosity, nutrient availability and water holding
capacity. Infiltration and drainage rates were higher on the upper end of
the slope than on the lower end (data not presented). In addition less
water was available at 1500 kPa suction at the upper end of the slope than
the lower. Such differences would affect crop growth and yield.

In each case reported here, yield was positively correlated with silt and
clay content, and negatively correlated with sand content, indicating the
influence of soil texture on crop growth and yield. Wheat yield appeared to
be affected by the 0-30 cm soil layer more than to the subsurface layers.
Over half of the variation in yield was attributed to the effects of the
0-30 cm layer. In contrast, the 1984 grain sorghum responded to the deeper
soil layers. There were slight differences between the head and total
yield. Clay content from the the 0-30 cm, macroporosity from the 30-76 cm
layer and available water were indicated by the regression procedure for
inclusion in the model for head yield, while available water was not
indicated for total yield. In the dry year (1983), 51% of the variation in
grain sorghum yield was attributed to the silt content of the 0-30 cm layer;
the remainder of the variation in yield was attributed to the deeper soil.
The reduction in crop yield upslope then is a function of these changes in
soil properties along the slope as well as the growth habit of the crop and
growing conditions.

Although the changes in soil properties along the slope were gradual and over a short distance, these changes did influence crop yield. Since the surface properties would be altered by erosion first, such changes would be more apparent in a shallow rooted crop, such as wheat. In addition, slight erosional affects, as those demonstrated here, would be more apparent under less than optimumal growing conditions, as grain sorghum in 1983. Regardless of crop or growing season this study demonstrated a decrease in productivity related to gradual changes in soil properties along the slope.

ACKNOWLEDGMENTS

We thank S. C. Bingaman, Jr., R. R. Huckleberry, R. Watson, J. L. McLemore, C. G. Hunt, B. B. Barnes, J. Story, G. C. Heathman and W. E. Lonkerd for their technical assistance.

REFERENCES

1. Adams, W. E. 1949. Loss of topsoil reduced crop yield. J. Soil. Water Conserv. 4:130.

2. Baver, L. D. 1950. How serious is soil erosion. Soil Sci. Soc. Am. Proc. 42:1-5.

3. Bray, R. H. and L. T. Kurtz. 1945. Determination of total, organic, and available forms of phosphorus in soils. Soil Sci. 59:39-45

4. Buntley, G. S. and F. F. Bell. 1976. Yield estimates for the major crops grown on the soils of west Tennessee. Tenn. Agric. Exp. Stn. Bull. 561. 124 p.

5. Costigan, P. A., D. J. Greenwood and T. McBurney. 1983. Variation in yield between two similar sandy loam soils. I. Description of soils and measurement of yield differences. J. Soil. Sci. 34: 621-637.

6. Day, P. R. 1965. Particle fractionation and particle size analysis. In Methods of Soil Analysis, Part I. C. A. Black (ed.). Agronomy 9:545-567. Am. Soc. Agron., Madison, Wisconsin.

7. Mogg, J. L., S. L. Schoff, and E. W. Reed. 1960. Oklahoma Geological Survey Bull. No. 87. pp. 39-41.

8. Costigan, P. A. and T. McBurney. 1983. Variation in yield between two similar sandy loam soils. II Causes of yield variation in cabbage and lettuce crops. J. Soil. Sci. 34:639-647.

9. Langdale, G. W. and W. D. Shrader. 1982. Soil erosion effects on soil productivity of cultivated croplands. In Determinants of Soil Loss Tolerance. ASA Special Publication 45. 153 p.

10. SAS Institute Inc. 1982. SAS User's Guide:Statistics, 1982 Edition. SAS Institute Inc., Cary, NC. 584 p.

11. Sharpley, A. N., S. J. Smith and R. G. Menzel. 1982. Prediction of phosphorus losses in runoff from southern plains watersheds. J. Envir. Qual. 11:247-251.

12. Smith, S. J., R. G. Menzel, E. D. Rhoades, J. R. Williams and H. V. Eck. 1983. Nutrients and sediment discharge from southern plains grasslands. J. Range Manage. 36:435-439.

CHEMICAL AND PHYSICAL ENRICHMENTS OF SEDIMENT FROM CROPLAND

R. A. Young   A. E. Olness   C. K. Mutchler   W. C. Moldenhauer
Member ASAE   Member ASAE   Mech. Assoc. Member
                                                 ASAE

The United States is losing soil from its agricultural lands at excessive rates, averaging nearly 10.75 tons of soil per hectare per year by water erosion and 7.4 t/ha-yr by wind erosion from cultivated cropland (Lee 1984). Soil loss tolerances are exceeded on about 44% of the total cropland in the country. Effects of erosion are twofold -- first, erosion reduces soil productivity by removing soil nutrients, reducing soil water holding capacity, degrading soil structure, and destroying cropland by gullying. Second, soil erosion contributes to offsite damages in the form of impaired water quality and channel and reservoir sedimentation.

Little change in erosion rate from farmland has occurred from 1977 to 1982. About 4.59 billion tons of soil are removed from cropland, rangeland, pasture and forest land each year. About 37% of this is by wind erosion and 63% by water erosion (Lee 1984). About 20 to 30% of the eroded soil ultimately ends up in the nation's waterways with the remainder depositing somewhere on the landscape. Much of this erosion takes place on a relatively small portion of intensively cultivated land.

Excessive erosion reduces the productive capacity of the soil but much of this reduction in productivity is currently masked by improved technology and management. According to a study conducted by Resources for the Future (Crosson 1984), the growth of potential corn and soybean yields were reduced by about 4% from 1950 to 1980 as a result of erosion; nevertheless, yields increased as a result of technological advancements. Deficiencies of nitrogen, phosphorous and potassium are chiefly responsible for reduction in crop yields on subsoils in the great plains (Eck et al. 1967), although reductions in plant available soil water capacity, degradation of soil structure, and nonuniform soil removal by erosion are also factors affecting soil productivity (Williams et al. 1981).

The problem today is to maintain a balance between controlling erosion and employing new technology and management methods in order to overcome losses due to erosion. This balance should provide for continuous soil productivity and yet be cost effective for today's farmer. To do this we must assess the affects of erosion on soil productivity.

We can do this by using enrichment ratios as an index of erosion severity. An enrichment ratio is defined as the content of a given soil or chemical fraction in sediment divided by the content of that fraction in an equal mass of soil. The erosion process is recognized as being selective in both physical and chemical properties. Erosion tends to remove the smallest and the lightest or least dense particles. Chemicals are carried primarily by

The authors are: R. A. YOUNG, Agricultural Engineer, A. E. OLNESS, Soil Scientist, C. K. MUTCHLER, Agricultural Engineer, and W. C. MOLDENHAUER, Soil Scientist, ARS-USDA, Morris, MN, Oxford, MS, and West Lafayette, IN.

organic matter and the finer soil particles. This selectivity, or discrimination, often causes sediment to show very different physical and chemical characteristics relative to the soil from which it originated. The selectivity of erosion is more pronounced for the more numerous but less severe hydrologic events since these events result in a disproportionate amount of smaller particles being transported from a site. As erosion severity increases, all enrichment ratios tend to converge to a value of 1. This occurs when the entire soil matrix is uniformly detached and transported. Thus, nutrient enrichments are complex and tend to vary inversely with suspended sediment concentration.

Our main concern with agricultural soils is erosion loss of plant nutrients and soil materials which enhance plant yield. Total Kjeldahl nitrogen (TKN), organic carbon (OC), cation exchange capacity (CEC), phosphorus (P), and available nitrogen as autoclave available nitrogen (A-AN) or potentially mineralizable nitrogen (PM-N) are all important soil productivity characteristics. Among these, PM-N or A-AN probably rank among the better measures of soil productivity because they measure the most commonly deficient nutrient -- nitrogen. PM-N is that fraction of soil organic N which is susceptible to mineralization according to first order kinetics (Stanford and Smith 1972).

PROCEDURE

We examined soil and nutrient losses from simulated rainstorms on texturally similar soils at three widely separated locations in the upper, mid, and lower Mississippi River watershed. There was one site on Barnes loam (Udic Haploborolls) located near Morris, Minnesota, one on Russell silt loam (Typic Hapludalfs) near West Lafayette, Indiana, and one on Lexington silt loam (Typic Paleudalfs) near Oxford, Mississippi.

Test plots at all three locations were subjected to simulated rainfall with a rainulator (Meyer and McCune 1958) to induce runoff and soil loss. All plots on the Minnesota site were 4.1 m by 10.7 m, on a 7% slope, and were conventionally tilled (fall plow, spring disk, and harrow). Rainulator runs were made shortly after planting and consisted of a "dry" run of 6.35 cm/h for 1 h at existing soil moisture content followed 24 h later by a "wet" run of the same intensity and duration. Since all plots were treated alike, and since the rainulator tests were made early in the year, before significant crop canopy had developed to influence soil loss, differences between treatments are due primarily to the influence of the previous year's crop.

The Indiana plots were on a 6% slope. Rainulator tests were made at different crop growth stages so soil losses were significantly influenced by the amount of vegetative cover present at the time of testing. Rainulator runs consisted of 60 min at 6.35 cm/h followed 1 h later by two 30-min periods at the same intensity separated by 15 min.

In Mississippi, the plots were on an approximately 3% slope on land which had been in soybeans the previous year. They were in a fallow condition with all residues removed and had undergone tillage 2 days before the rainulator runs. Rainulator runs consisted of 60 min of "dry" run at 7.62 cm/h followed 4 h later with 30 min of "wet run" at the same intensity, followed 30 min later with a 30-min "very wet" run also at the same intensity.

At all sites, tillage and crop rows were parallel to the slope. Soil losses and runoff were measured, sediment sizes and chemical characteristics were determined, and enrichment ratios calculated. Sediment size was determined by directing runoff through a nest of sieves which retained suspended sediment aggregates.

Primary particle size determinations were made using the hydrometer method described by Day (1965), using sodium hexametaphosphate as a dispersing agent and without H_2O_2. Total Kjeldahl nitrogen (TKN) analyses were made using macro Kjeldahl digestion and distillation methods (Bremner 1965). Total carbon was determined using the Walkley-Black method (Allison et al. 1965) and cation exchange capacity was obtained by sodium saturation and determination with atomic absorption spectrophotometry (Chapman 1965). Ammonium (NH_4^+-N) concentrations were determined using a Technicon II Autoanalyzer[1] for the incubation and autoclave methods. Potentially mineralizable nitrogen (PM-N) was determined by the aerobic incubation procedure of Stanford et al. (1974) except that 30 g of 20 mesh silica sand and 15 g of $\leq$ 20 mesh soil were used. The method of Smith and Stanford (1971) was used to determine autoclavable available nitrogen (AA-N). We determined ammonium released in the autoclave method directly on supernatant solution aliquots after centrifuging rather than by distillation as in the Smith and Stanford method (1971). Ammonium-N (NH_4^+-N) was determined by the alkaline phenol method (USEPA 1979).

RESULTS AND DISCUSSION

Chemical characteristics of the three soils change significantly as one goes from north to south (Table 1). Soil organic matter and nutrient concentrations are generally greater in the cooler North Central States where

Table 1. Soil Characteristics

	Sand	Silt	Clay	CEC	C	TKN	NH$_4$-N	NO$_3$-N	AA-N	PM-N
	- - -(%)- -			(mM(P$^+$)/kg)	(g/kg)		- - - - -(mg/kg)- - - - -			
Barnes l.	48	34	18	140.2	28.5	2.22	13.4	25.1	74.5	157.4
Russel sil.	24	59	17	90.3	9.3	.79	5.0	6.2	43.0	---
Lexington sil.	10	75	15	57.4	7.3	.73	8.5	28.12	44.7	90.8

the intensity of weathering is less than that in warmer climates. These differences can affect erosion patterns and subsequent losses in soil productivity. Determination of PM-N was done by an incubation procedure. This is a biological method which more closely represents a natural environment since the biological response of a soil is a function of the relative effects of many chemical and environmental factors. Thus, PM-N would seem to be a more appropriate indicator of the state of productivity of a soil than any single chemical parameter.

Since test conditions varied at the different locations, we were unable to compare soil losses and nutrient losses directly. Instead, we compared enrichment ratios for TKN, OC, CEC, autoclave available nitrogen (AA-N) and potentially mineralizable nitrogen (PM-N) obtained from incubation experiments. Where sufficient sediment samples were available, we also examined clay enrichment ratios.

Enrichments of AA-N were relatively low for sediments (Table 2 and Fig. 3). However, we noted that enrichments of ammonium-N (NH_4^+-N) were rather large. Since NH_4^+-N is adsorbed as a fraction of the CEC, we expected enrichments of

---

[1]Trade names are included for the benefit of the reader and do not imply endorsement or preferential treatment of the product by the USDA.

Table 2. Barnes Loam -- Minnesota Site

	Soil loss	CEC	C	TKN	AA-N	PM-N	Clay
	t/ha	- - - - - - - -Enrichment ratio- - - - - - - - -					
Corn 1[a]	20.58	1.35	1.66	1.76	1.03	2.26	1.09
Corn 2[b]	17.96	1.55	1.50	1.55	.97	2.37	1.31
Soy beans[c]	13.47	1.73	1.96	2.02	1.12	2.50	1.30
Fallow[d]	14.45	1.83	1.93	1.84	1.10	2.53	1.48

[a]First year corn in a corn-corn-soybean rotation.
[b]Second year corn in a corn-corn-soybean rotation.
[c]Soybeans in a corn-corn-soybean rotation.
[d]Continuous fallow.

NH_4^+-N to equal those of CEC; however, in all instances they were much larger than those of CEC. This led to the speculation that a portion of the AA-N may have mineralized as a result of the processing procedure, possibly during drying of the sediment samples. If this had occurred, then a fraction of the NH_4^+-N equal to the excess of the CEC enrichment ratio should probably be considered as part of the AA-N. When NH_4^+-N equal to the excess of the CEC enrichment ratios was combined with AA-N, the sum was termed total autoclave available-N (TAA-N). In all cases, enrichment ratios of TAA-N were not different ($p \leq 0.05$) from those of PM-N except for the Minnesota site.

Smith et al. (1980) noted large losses of soluble TKN in incubation determinations of PM-N from some soils. They also found that inclusion of the soluble TKN with inorganic nitrogen mineralized changed the calculated PM-N values by large amounts in several instances. When we included soluble TKN from the incubation experiments in determinations of PM-N, we found the total potentially mineralizable N (TPM-N) enrichment ratios were not different ($p < 0.05$) from PM-N enrichment ratios. This result suggests a proportionate fraction of soluble TKN was lost from both soil matrix and eroded sediment samples during incubation.

Soil losses and some calculated enrichment ratios from the Minnesota site (Table 2) are averages of two replications and 3 years. The results agree with past studies showing that erosion losses after soybeans are generally greater than erosion following corn (Oschwald and Siemens 1976). It can also be seen from Table 2 that enrichment ratios of most productivity indicators increased with successive years out of soybeans. While soil losses were 50% greater from plots the first year out of soybeans compared with plots 3 years out of soybeans, losses of PM-N were only 39% greater, as illustrated in Fig. 1.

Enrichments of PM-N were significantly greater than those of CEC, OC, or AA-N in sediments obtained from the Minnesota site. Enrichment ratios for PM-N averaged 2.42 compared with average values of 1.76, 1.79, and 1.62 for enrichments of OC, TKN and CEC, respectively. These measurements suggest a much greater difference in productivity loss than would normally be indicated by the chemical indices which are often preferred because of their simplicity.

Soil losses and the enrichment ratios from different tillage practices on row crops from the Indiana sites are averaged by tillage practice -- four moldboard plow, six no-till, and six chisel (Fig. 2). The relatively large soil losses from the chiseled plots compared to the moldboard plowed and no-till plots can be attributed to lower amounts of vegetative cover present (8% average cover compared to 31% and 33% for moldboard plowed and no-till

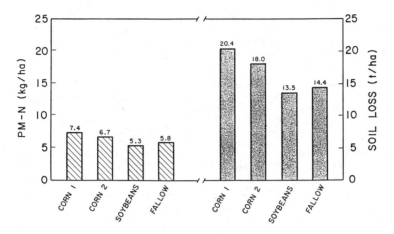

Fig. 1. Soil Losses and Losses of PM–N from Barnes Loam

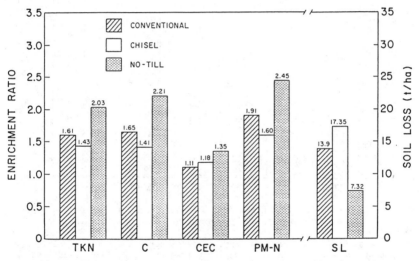

Fig. 2. Soil Losses and Enrichment Ratios from Three Tillage Practices on
Row Crops on Russell Silt Loam

plots, respectively) at the time of testing.   The cover difference was due to
the fact that rainulator runs were made at different times during the season.
The chiseled plots also had the lowest enrichment ratios of TKN and OC.

Sediments from Russell silt loam were more enriched with PM–N (ER = 2.5) than
with TKN (ER = 1.67) or   CEC (ER = 1.15); OC (ER = 1.77) enrichments were
intermediate to those of PM–N and TKN but not significantly different from
either observation.   In all cases, enrichments were greatest and soil losses
were least on no-till treatments compared to conventionally tilled or chiseled
plots. From, the standpoint of soil productivity, no-till, while effective in
reducing soil loss, is relatively less effective in reducing the loss of plant
nutrients or those soil   constitutents that   are related to   a soils
productivity. For example, no tillage reduced total soil loss by 47% compared
to   conventional tillage but only reduced losses of TKN by 33.6%,

111

organic C by 29.5%, CEC by 36% and PM-N by 32.4%. Similar results have been found in Mississippi where soil losses from conservation tilled corn and soybeans were reduced 90 and 99%, respectively, while corresponding total losses of N and P were reduced only 70 and 80%, respectively from corn and 90 and 84%, respectively, from soybeans (McDowell and McGregor 1980; McDowell and McGregor 1984).

Total soil loss and enrichment ratios from a fallow Lexington silt loam (Mississippi) are compared in Fig. 3 with the fallow plot results from the Barnes loam (Minnesota) site. Soil losses from the Lexington soil were 2.3 times greater than those from the Barnes soil. This may be partially due to the fact that northern soils are generally higher in montmorillonitic clays than soils in the South. Past research has shown that, all other things being equal, soil loss varies inversely with the amount of swelling type clays present in the clay fraction (Young and Mutchler 1977).

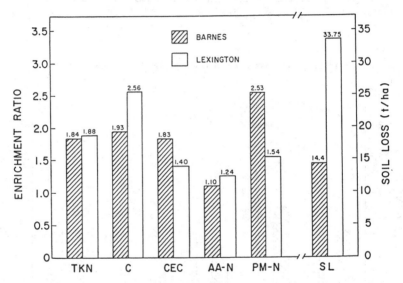

Fig. 3. Comparison of Soil Losses and Enrichment Ratios from Fallow Plots of Barnes Loam (Minnesota) and Lexington Silt Loam (Mississippi)

The greatest differences in enrichment ratios between the two locations were in percent carbon and PM-N. While enrichment of C, AA-N, and TKN were slightly higher on Lexington soil than Barnes, the Barnes sediment was significantly enriched in PM-N compared with Lexington sediment. On the average, three times as much PM-N per ton of sediment (0.4 kg PM-N/t) was lost from the Barnes loam plots compared with the Lexington silt loam plots (0.14 kg PM-N/t). Thus, while fallow plots in Mississippi had 2.3 times as much soil loss as fallow plots in Minnesota, they lost only 82% as much PM-N as the Minnesota plots.

A similar relationship exists between the Russell silt loam in Indiana and the Barnes loam in Minnesota under similar cropping and rainfall conditions (Fig. 4). While soil losses from Russell soil were 22% greater than from Barnes soil for the same amount of rainfall, losses of PM-N were less than half (43%) those from Barnes soil. Apparently, while physically similar soils under similar conditions may undergo less soil loss in Minnesota, from the standpoint of the productive capacity of the soil, these losses may be more damaging.

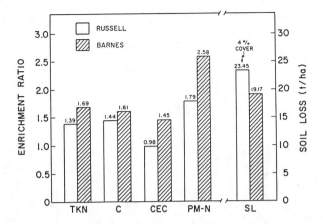

Fig. 4. Comparison of Soil Losses and Enrichment Ratios from Conventionally Tilled, Row Cropped Plots of Barnes Loam (Minnesota) and Russell Silt Loam (Indiana)

Smaller size particles tend to adsorb and transport large quantities of nutrients due to their relatively greater specific surface areas. Table 2 shows the enrichment ratios of primary clay particles in the sediment from the Minnesota site. Enrichments of clay averaged 1.12 while enrichments of PM-N averaged 1.91, or 1.7 times greater. Most of the chemical parameters correlated to some degree with clay enrichment, but the enrichment of PM-N correlated most closely (r = 0.9).

Aggregate size appeared to have little or no influence on the enrichment ratios of any chemical or biological indicators measured (Figs. 5 and 6) with

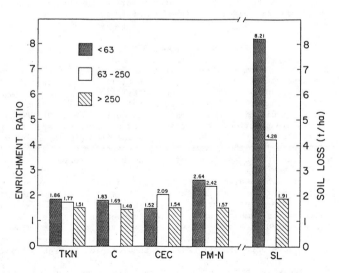

Fig. 5. Soil Losses and Enrichment Ratios of Various Size Classes of Eroded Aggregates on a Barnes Loam.

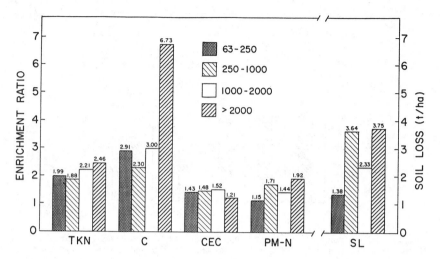

Fig. 6. Soil Losses and Enrichment Ratios of Various Size Classes of Eroded
Aggregates on a Lexington Silt Loam

the exception of carbon on the Lexington soil.   Past research has shown that
primary particle size distribution within aggregates of a matrix soil differs
only slightly from one size class to another and only slightly from the
primary particle size distribution of the matrix soil, depending on the soil
texture (Young 1980).   However, the particle size distribution of eroded
aggregates does vary with aggregate size class.   Larger aggregates are
enriched in both sand and clay compared to the matrix soil particle size
distribution, which may account for the generally higher enrichment ratios in
the larger aggregates (Fig. 6).   From the standpoint of soil productivity,
those size groups which make up the largest portion of the sediment are the
same ones which have the highest enrichments of PM-N.

SUMMARY AND CONCLUSIONS

Soil and water losses from simulated rainstorms on texturally similar soils at
three widely separated locations in the upper, mid, and lower Mississippi
watershed were measured.   Physical characteristics of the sediment were
determined and enrichment ratios of several selected chemical and biological
properties were calculated. Organic matter and nutrient content of the matric
soils and the sediment enrichment ratios of crop nutrients were greatest in
the North and least in the South.   Soil losses from similar rainstorms and
soil conditions were just the opposite being greatest in Mississippi and least
in Minnesota, a fact which may be related to soil mineralogy.

Potentially mineralizable nitrogen (PM-N) is a better indicator of a soil's
productivity than most chemical indicators.   It is a biological process more
representative of processes occurring in a natural environment.   Although the
enrichment of PM-N was almost double the enrichment of clay particles in the
sediment from the Minnesota site, this parameter correlated most closely with
clay enrichment ratios of the sediment.   The enrichment ratios of most
chemical indices were only slightly greater than clay enrichment ratios.

Because the selectivity of the erosion process is more pronounced for those
hydrologic events resulting in lower soil losses, reductions in soil loss
accomplished by conservation tillage or cropping management practices do not
necessarily bring about comparable reductions in losses of crop nutrients.

Sediment enrichment ratios of plant nutrients tend to increase the further north one goes. As a result, the productivity of Minnesota soils is apparently more sensitive to degradation resulting from erosion than soils in Mississippi. Thus, enrichment ratio relationships that are currently being used in sediment and chemical yield modeling may be improved by tailoring them to specific geographic areas.

REFERENCES

1. Allison, L.E., W.B. Bollen and C.D. Moodie. 1965. Chap. 89. Total carbon. In C.A. Black (ed.) Methods of soil analysis: Part 2. Chemical and microbiological properties. Agron. Monograph No. 9. pp. 1346-1366. Amer. Soc. Agron., Madison, WI.

2. Bremner, J.M. 1965. Chap. 83. Total nitrogen. In C.A. Black (ed.) Methods of soil analysis: Part 2. Chemical and microbiological properties. Agron. Monograph No. 9. pp. 1149-1170. Amer. Soc. Agron., Madison, WI.

3. Chapman, H.D. 1965. Chap. 57. Cation-exchange capacity. In C.A. Black (ed.) Methods of soil analysis: Part 2. Chemical and microbiological properties. Agron. Monograph No. 9. pp. 891-901. Amer. Soc. Agron., Madison, WI.

4. Crosson, P. 1984. Soil erosion: production vs protection. American Forests. May.

5. Day, P.R. 1965. Chap. 43. Particle fractionation and particle-size analysis. In C.A. Black (ed.) Methods of soil analysis: Part I. Physical and mineralogical properties. Agron. Monograph No. 9. pp. 545-567. Amer. Soc. Agron., Madison, WI.

6. Eck, H.V., R.H. Ford and C.D. Fanning. 1967. Productivities of horizon of seven benchmark soils of the southern Great Plains. USDA, ARS, Conservation Research Report No. 11.

7. Lee, L.K. 1984. Land use and soil loss: a 1982 update. J. Soil & Water Conserv. 39(4): 226-228.

8. Meyer, L.D. and D.L. McCune. 1958. Rainfall simulation for runoff plots. Agric. Eng. 39: 644-648.

9. Oschwald, W.R. and J.C. Siemens. 1976. Soil erosion after soybeans. In Lowell D. Hill (ed.) World Soybean Research. Interstate Printers and Publishers, Inc. Danville, Illinois. pp. 74-81.

10. Smith, J.G., R.R. Schnabel, B.L. McNeal and G.S. Campbell. 1980. Potential errors in the first-order model for estimating soil nitrogen mineralization potentials. Soil Sci. Soc. Amer. J. 44: 996-1000.

11. Smith, S.J. and G. Stanford. 1971. Evaluation of a chemical index of soil nitrogen availability. Soil Sci. 111: 228-232.

12. Stanford, G. and S.J. Smith. 1972. Nitrogen mineralizing potential of soils. Soil Sci. Soc. Am. Proc. 36: 465-472.

13. Stanford, G., J.N. Carter and S.J. Smith. 1974. Estimates of potentially mineralizable soil nitrogen on short-term incubations. Soil Sci. soc. Am. Proc. 38: 99-102.

14. U.S. Environmental Protection Agency. 1979. Ammonia nitrogen: Method 350.1 (colorimetric, automated phanate). In Methods for chemical analysis of water and wastes. EPA-600, 4-79-020. pp. 350.1-1 to 350.1-6. Environmental Monitoring and Support Laboratory, Office of Research and Development, U.S. EPA, Cincinnati, Ohio 45268.

15. Williams, J.R., Chairman, National Soil Erosion - Soil Productivity Research Planning Committee, USDA-ARS. 1981. Soil erosion effects on soil productivity: A research perspective. J. Soil & Water Conserv. 36: 82-90.

16. Young, R.A. and C.K. Mutchler. 1977. Erodibility of some Minnesota soils. J. Soil & Water Conserv. 32(4): 180-182.

17. Young, R. A. 1980. Characteristics of eroded sediment. TRANS. of the ASAE 23(5): 1139-1142, 1146.

AMOUNT AND NUTRIENT CONTENT OF PARTICLES PRODUCED

BY SOIL AGGREGATE ABRASION

L. J. Hagen   Leon Lyles
Assoc. Member ASAE   Member ASAE

From studies of wind erosion in wind tunnels and on farm fields, much practical knowledge about the physics of wind erosion has been amassed (Chepil and Woodruff 1963). During wind erosion, saltating particles abrade the surface aggregates. Typically, both the aggregates and the saltating particles ($\approx$ 100 to 840 μm diameter) break down under impact and contribute to the suspension-size particles (< 100 μm diameter), which are transported beyond stable field boundaries. The fine suspension-size particles (< 50 μm in diameter) can be transported tens of kilometers by the wind. However, much is still unknown about the relative importance of the various factors which control the creation and emission of fine particles during wind erosion.

Because many variables, such as impacting particle velocity, are usually unknown in the field, a laboratory study of aggregate abrasion was designed where many of the variables could be controlled. One objective of the study was to determine the amount of suspension-size particles produced, as influenced by velocity, impact angle, diameter, and texture of the impacting saltation-size particles and the stability of the target aggregates. A second objective was to determine the nutrient content of the saltation-size and fine suspension-size particles created, compared to their parent aggregates to check for nutrient enrichment. Soil samples trapped in field saltation catchers also were checked for available phosphorus enrichment.

REVIEW OF LITERATURE

In the field, the factors that control soil aggregate production and degradation include cropping systems, microorganisms, earthworms, cultivation, and climate (Harris et al. 1966). Soil aggregates > 1.0 mm in diameter, which occur at a given location, show little variation in either chemical composition or texture (Tabatabai and Hanway 1968). However, at aggregate sizes below 1.0 mm in diameter, differences appear among aggregate size fractions when soil is fragmented in water using agitation or ultrasonic dispersion to reduce aggregate size (Chichester 1969, Cameron and Posner 1979).

Differences in texture between the parent soil and suspension-size particles created by wind erosion also have been reported. From observations of wind-eroded fields, Chepil (1957) found that silt was more readily depleted from eroding soil than were the sand or clay portions. He also found that wind erosion caused little textural change in loess soils but tended to remove the fine constituents from coarse-textured soils, leaving the sand behind.

Contribution from the U.S. Department of Agriculture, Agricultural Research Service, in cooperation with the Dept. of Agronomy and the Kansas Agricultural Experiment Station. Contribution 85-139-A.

The authors are: L. J. Hagen, Agricultural Engineer, and Leon Lyles, Research Leader, USDA, ARS, Kansas State University, Manhattan, Kansas.

Gillette (1977) measured the vertical (suspension) flux of particles < 20 μm diameter caused by wind erosion and the total horizontal (saltation and creep) soil flux on several fields. He found that ratios of the vertical to horizontal flux had great scatter on sandy soils and there was little evidence of a trend with windspeed. For loamy soils there was a large increase in the flux ratio as windspeed increased. In general, he found that finer textured soils produced a higher ratio of vertical to horizontal flux than coarse-textured soils, except for a clay soil where the small aggregates were stable enough to resist impact breakage.

Nutrient enrichment of wind-eroded suspension or saltation-size particles has been little studied. However, in some preliminary work, Merva and Peterson (1983) reported that total phosphorus measured in wind-eroded material deposited on snow was very large compared to total phosphorus in waterborne sediment. They suggested further study of this phenomenon.

Although the creation and emission of fine particles are complicated processes, there is a need to determine how various factors control these processes so that creation and emission of fine particles can be calculated in simulation models on a field scale for a wide variety of soils. Earlier, Hagen (1984) reported how impact particle factors and target aggregate stability controlled total abrasive erosion from target aggregates. This report is a continuation of the earlier analysis, with emphasis on the production of fine suspension-size particles during abrasion.

EXPERIMENTAL PROCEDURES

A commercial sandblasting nozzle was used to abrade individual soil aggregates (4 to 8 cm diameter) with weighed amounts of abrader. The aggregates were placed inside a cyclone separator during abrasion and both the abrader and abraded soil were collected in various parts of an abrasion sampling apparatus (Fig. 1). The abrasion apparatus was designed to aerodynamically separate particles < 100 μm diameter and trap them in the largest cyclone, while finer particles were trapped in both cyclone separators, as well as on the impaction plates.

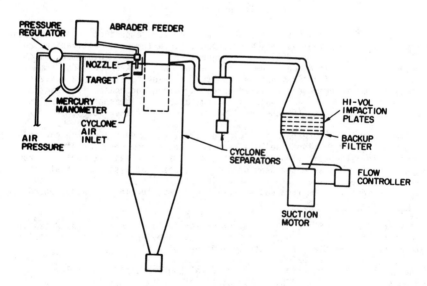

Fig. 1 Abrasion Apparatus Schematic

Because of the probability of creating new fine particles during sieving small amounts of fine particles (< 53 μm diameter) from the large amounts of sand abrader trapped in the large cyclone, 10 calibration tests with small amounts of soil abrader were performed to relate total production of fine particles to those trapped in the small cyclone and on the impaction plates. A regression equation with coefficient of determination (R^2) of 0.97 then was used in subsequent abrasion tests to predict total fine particle production, based on the subsamples collected in the small cyclone and on the impaction plates. During both calibration and abrasion tests, a steady flow of 9.44 L/s (20 ft^3/min) at STP was maintained in the abrasion apparatus by the flow controller. The sandblasting nozzle also was calibrated using procedures described elsewhere (Hagen 1984).

For the abrasion tests, soil samples of Haynie very fine sandy loam and Wymore silty clay loam were collected from the surface of tilled fields and air-dried. The soil samples then were rotary sieved to separate the fractions to be used as targets and abrader. In addition, local quartz river sand also was washed and sieved for use as an abrader. The three sieved size fractions used for abrader were 100 to 150, 290 to 420, and 590 to 840 μm in diameter. One side of the target aggregates was leveled with a knife for use as the impaction surface.

Four impact velocities (V_p) were used for each abrader size. The various V_p were obtained by varying the nozzle air pressure and ranged from 400 to 1200 cm/s for the smallest abrader particles to 300 to 900 cm/s for the largest. Two to 6 g of soil were abraded from target aggregates. Soil abrader was always the same texture as the target aggregate, while sand abrader was used on targets of all textures. Three abrader impact angles (α) of 15, 30, and 90 degrees were obtained by changing the angle of the nozzle relative to the impact surface.

After abrasion, each target aggregate was subjected to a drop-shatter test similar to that described by Farrell et al. (1967). The aggregates were dropped inside a tube onto a concrete floor from a height of 2 to 3 m, and the resultant particle size distribution was determined by sieving. Energy input to the aggregate was calculated from the drop height. New surface area created by the drop was calculated from the size distribution, assuming that the particles were spherical. The ratio of energy input to new surface area created was used as a measure of aggregate stability (S_a).

The amount of fine particles (WF) created during abrasion of aggregates was analyzed using multiple regression of the following primary variables:

$$WF = f(\alpha, d_p, V_p, S_a, AM, W) \tag{1}$$

where WF is the ratio of fine suspension-size particles (< 53 μm diameter) in g per kg of abrader, α is angle of abrader impact in degrees, d_p is average abrader diameter in μm, V_p is average particle impact velocity in cm/s, S_a is average stability of 4 aggregates in J/m^2, AM is abrader mass in g, and W is the ratio of total predicted abrasive erosion from the targets in g per kg of abrader. Regression equations for W were presented in an earlier report (Hagen 1984).

Secondary variables constructed from the primary variables and their interactions also were added to the data set. Each data observation of WF was based on collection of fine particles from four target aggregates. Because no single equation produced a satisfactory fit, separate regression equations for WF were calculated for three data sets: (a) 67 observations of sand abrader on both soil textures, (b) 53 observations of soil abrader on very fine sandy loam, and (c) 18 observations of soil abrader on silty clay loam aggregates. Most of the observations in the latter data set were made with α = 15 degrees.

119

From the two soils studied in the abrasion tests, composite samples of seven
size fractions (treatments) of each texture were prepared for chemical and
textural analysis. These fractions included suspension-size (< 53 µm diameter) trapped in small cyclone, three saltation sizes used as abrader, parent
oil aggregates, and < 53 µm and 53 to 250 µm particles created by crushing
and sieving parent aggregates. In addition, four similar size fractions
(treatments), excluding the three saltation sizes, of a Keith silt loam soil
also were prepared. Each soil fraction was analyzed for nitrate nitrogen
(NO_3-N), ammonium nitrogen (NH_4-N), available phosphorus (P), potassium (K),
and organic matter (OM). Duncan's multiple range tests were used to test for
differences in nutrient contents among the various size fractions.

Eroded saltation-size soil particles/aggregates collected in wind erosion
(Bagnold) catchers (1977-78) located in Major Land Resource Areas (MLRA) 72
and 77 (Nebraska, Colorado, Kansas, Oklahoma, New Mexico, and Texas) were
analyzed for available phosphorus. The erosion catchers were located on both
cropland and rangeland sites according to soil wind erodibility groups (WEG)
(Table 1). To make comparisons with the eroded material, residual (parent)
soil samples to 5.1 cm depth obtained within 15 m of each catcher also were
analyzed for available P. All the nutrient analyses were performed at the
Kansas State University Soil Testing Laboratory.

Table 1. Soil Wind Erodibility Groups (WEG)

WEG	Predominant soil texture class of surface layer	Dry soil aggregates over 0.84 mm %	Wind erodibility index (I) t/(ha·yr)
1	Very fine sand, fine sand, sand, or coarse sand.	1 2 3 5 7	695 561 493 404 359
2	Loamy very fine sand, loamy fine sand, loamy sand, loamy coarse sand, or sapric organic materials.	10	300
3	Very fine sandy loam, fine sandy loam, sandy loam, or coarse sandy loam.	25	193
4	Clay, silty clay, noncalcareous clay loam, or silty clay loam with more than 35 percent clay content.	25	193
4L	Calcareous loam and silt loam, or calcareous clay loam and silty clay loam.	25	193
5	Noncalcareous loam and silt loam with less than 20 percent clay content, or sandy clay loam, sandy clay, and hemic organic soil material.	40	126
6	Noncalcareous loam and silt loam with more than 20 percent clay content, or noncalcareous clay loam with less than 35 percent clay content.	45	108
7	Silt, noncalcareous silty clay loam with less than 35 percent clay content and fibric organic soil material.	50	85
8	Soils not suitable for cultivation due to coarse fragments or wetness, wind erosion not a problem.	--	--

RESULTS AND DISCUSSION

Suspension-Size Predictions

To find prediction equations for WF, a number of multiple linear regression models were considered. Using a stepwise regression procedure, the best six-variable model found to predict WF for sand abrader was

$$WF = 17.79 + 0.002293\ W^2 - 8.41 \times 10^{-6}\ W^3 - 0.05705\ d_p + 5.97 \times 10^{-5}\ d_p{}^2 -$$
$$0.04 \times 10^{-7}\ d_p\ V_p{}^2 + 4.9 \times 10^{-7}\ \alpha V_p{}^2. \tag{2}$$

The coefficient of multiple determination (R^2) for this model was 0.87. When using sand abrader, the only source of WF was the target aggregates, and the relative proportion of WF to total aggregate abrasive erosion (W) varied with test conditions (Fig. 2). As S_a increased, the relative proportion of WF increased at low velocities. This was probably because the slowest particles did not have enough kinetic energy to remove large fragments upon impact. However, W at an S_a of 8.0 J/m^2 was about 1/4 the value of W at 2.0 J/m^2 (Hagen 1984), so the absolute value of WF decreased as S_a increased using sand abrader.

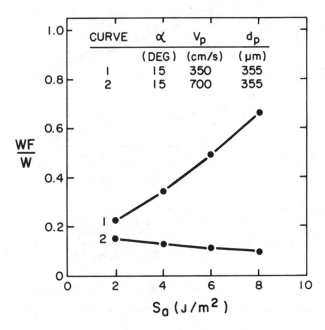

Fig. 2   Predicted Ratio of Suspension-Size (< 53 μm Diameter) to Total Erosion from the Target for Sand Abrader as a Function of Aggregate Stability and Abrader Velocity

For very fine sandy loam, the best seven-variable model found was

$$WF = 73.85 + 44.623\ S_a - 4.9476\ S_a{}^2 - 2.794\ \alpha + 0.03169\ \alpha^2 -$$
$$0.03653\ S_a\ d_p + 3.8 \times 10^{-7}\ \alpha V_p{}^2 - 0.04569\ AM. \tag{3}$$

121

The R^2 for the preceding model was 0.79. The decrease in WF as Am increased suggests that the target surfaces became smoother as abrasion progressed.

For an AM of 200 g per target, WF of both very fine sandy loam and sand abrader increased with V_p but decreased with d_p as plots of Eq. (1) and (2) show (Fig. 3). Using soil abrader caused a three- to fifteenfold increase in WF over sand abrader for the conditions plotted. A portion of the increased WF may come from the target aggregates, because the soil abrader tends to fragment on impact. However, the majority of the WF came from the soil abrader. Average S_a for the very fine sandy loam target aggregates was 2.3 $\pm$ 1.33 J/m^2.

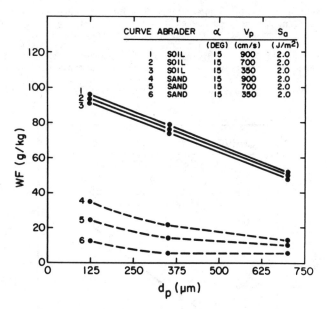

Fig. 3 Predicted Production of Fine Particles (< 53 μm Diameter) from Very Fine Sandy Loam Aggregates Per kg of Impacting Sand (Dashed Lines) and from both Aggregates and Very Fine Sandy Loam Abrader (Solid Lines) as a Function of Abrader Velocity and Diameter

For silty clay loam abrader, the best eight-variable model found was

$$WF = 238.31 - 0.6837 \, W^2 + 0.010155 \, W^3 + 2.9727 \, S_a^2 + 0.6219 \, V_p -$$

$$0.059534 \, S_a \, V_p - 1.49671 \, \alpha \, S_a + 0.187702 \, W^2 \, \alpha - 0.3262 \, AM. \quad (4)$$

The R^2 for the preceding model was 0.81. For typical tests with AM of 500 g per target, the WF of silty clay loam abrader followed trends similar to that of fine sandy loam abrader (Fig. 4). Under similar test conditions, the silty clay loam abrader produced higher WF than the very fine sandy loam abrader. In contrast, the sand abrader on silty clay loam produced lower WF than on the fine sandy loam targets. This effect was probably due to the stability of the silty clay loam targets, which averaged 6.6 $\pm$ 3.7 J/m^2. As V_p and d_p increased, both abrader and abraded material broke into larger fragments (Fig. 4).

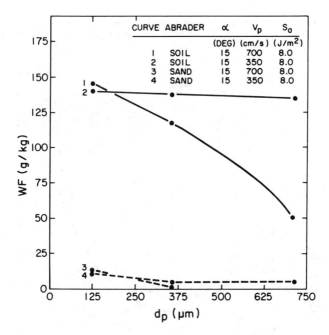

Fig. 4 Predicted Production of Fine Particles (< 53 μm
Diameter) from Silty Clay Loam Aggregates Per
kg of Impacting Sand Abrader (Dashed Lines) and
from both Aggregates and Silty Clay Loam Abrader
(Solid Lines) as a Function of Abrader Velocity
and Diameter

For AM of 200 g per target, the effect of impact angle on very fine sandy
loam targets is shown in Fig. 5. Increasing the angle of sand abrader
increased WF slightly. However, WF for very fine sandy loam abrader decreased
towards a minimum as α increased from 15 to 30 degrees but then increased
sharply towards a maximum at 90 degrees. Evidently, normal impact is the
most effective in breaking down the abrader and target to fine particles
even though Hagen (1984) showed that total erosion from the targets was
largest at 20- to 30-degree impact angles.

As field erosion proceeds, the initial saltation-size particles decrease in
size and change in composition unless they were initially sand particles.
Thus, the production of WF for the soil abrader in Eq. (2) and (3) should be
viewed as maximums produced during the first few impacts. The production
rate of new saltation-size particles by abrasion will determine if WF stays
near the maximum during an erosion event. In contrast, the production of
WF from sand abrader (Eq. 1) likely represents field minimums for impacts on
stationary aggregates of a given stability. We have not studied WF production of saltation-size particles striking surface particles that move on
impact but would speculate that WF production would be less than on stationary aggregate targets.

Mechanical analysis of the three soils showed that the surface of the silty
clay loam soil was actually on the border between a silt loam and a silty
clay loam and that its saltation-size particles became silt loam in texture
after use as an abrader (Table 2). The mechanical analysis also showed that
the suspension-size particles (< 53 μm) obtained by crushing and sieving parent soil aggregates produced a fraction enriched in silt primary particles.

Evidently, silt particles are easier to break down to suspension-size from the soil aggregates than are clay particles, which tend to remain in aggregates larger than suspension-size.

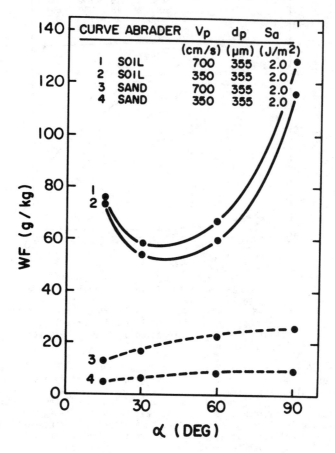

Fig. 5 Predicted Production of Suspension-Size Particles (< 53 μm Diameter) from Very Fine Sandy Loam Aggregates Per kg of Impacting Sand Abrader (Dashed Lines) and from both Aggregates and Very Fine Sandy Loam Abrader (Solid Lines) as a Function of Abrader Impact Angle and Velocity

Whether most coarse silt particles are suspended for long-range transport depends on the windspeeds during erosion events. Gillette et al. (1974) reported that trajectories of soil particles are significantly affected by settling when the ratio of particle sedimentation velocity (V_s) to wind friction velocity (u_*) is above 0.12 and less than 0.68. For a 40-μm-diameter particle, density 2.0 g/cm^3, settling velocity 10 cm/s, and u_* of 70 cm/s, the ratio is about 0.14. Thus, under strong erosive winds the silt fraction would be most likely to be abraded to suspension-size and carried long distances.

Table 2. Primary Particle Composition of Various Size Fractions

Treatment	Primary particle	Very fine sandy loam	Silt loam	Silty clay loam
		(%)		
Eroded soil (μm)				
< 53	sand	0.07	0.01	0.01
	silt	79.16	72.48	75.36
	clay	20.77	27.51	24.63
100 - 150	sand	79.11		4.79
	silt	16.01		73.69
	clay	4.88		21.52
290 - 420	sand	76.36		5.18
	silt	18.87		74.49
	clay	4.77		20.33
590 - 840	sand	46.29		9.79
	silt	41.89		71.29
	clay	11.82		18.92
Parent soil (μm)				
< 53	sand	0.70	0.82	0.16
	silt	89.09	82.12	82.11
	clay	10.21	17.06	17.73
53 - 250	sand	77.86	32.05	15.78
	silt	16.67	49.38	63.88
	clay	5.47	18.57	20.95
Large aggregates	sand	55.78	15.40	5.11
	silt	37.16	65.77	71.17
	clay	7.06	18.84	23.72

For 40 μm diameter particles with u_* of 25 cm/s, the ratio V_s/u_* equals 0.4. Thus, under low erosive winds, particles in the coarse-silt range are subject to considerable aerodynamic separation from the suspended soil. In this study, abrasion followed by selective aerodynamic separation, as typified by the first treatment in Table 2, simulates the effect of low to moderate erosive windspeeds. The first treatment produced a suspension-size mixture enriched in both silt and clay primary particles compared to the parent soil. After abrasion, the two smallest saltation-size fractions of very fine sandy loam were higher in sand but lower in silt than the parent soil.

Nutrient Content

Nutrient concentrations of composite samples were similar for all size fractions except the first one (Table 3). The nutrient content of the < 53 μm diameter soil in the first treatment was significantly greater than the whole parent soil in all cases at the 0.05 level except for NH_4-N, which was significant at the 0.10 level.

One can define enrichment ratios (ER) as the ratio of nutrients in the eroded soil to that in the parent soil. For treatment one, adding NO_3-N and NH_4-N gives an approximate ER for available N of 3.11. The ER for available P is 2.25, for K 1.67, and for OM 1.91. As one moves further from the wind erosion source area, the size distribution of particles tends to become finer than the size distribution in the immediate eroding area (Gillette, 1977). This downwind sorting will likely cause the ERs of suspended particles also to increase with distance from the source.

Table 3. Nutrient and Organic Matter Content of Various Soil Size Fractions

Treatment	No.[a]	NO_3-N	NH_4-N	P	K	OM
			$(\mu g/g)$			%
Eroded soil (μm)						
< 53	3	39.8 a[b]	32.8 c	95.2 e	816.7 g	4.77 i
100 - 150	2	23.5 ab	5.0 d	34.0 f	350.0 h	2.55 ij
290 - 420	2	18.1 b	4.6 d	31.3 f	337.5 h	2.10 j
590 - 840	2	27.7 ab	9.2 cd	39.0 f	395.0 h	2.90 ij
Parent soil (μm)						
< 53	3	16.0 b	9.2 cd	51.5 f	446.7 h	2.37 j
53 - 250	3	17.4 b	9.0 cd	43.5 f	408.4 h	2.67 ij
Large aggregates	3	15.4 b	8.0 cd	42.3 f	490.0 h	2.50 j

[a]Number of soil textures (observations) in each mean

[b]Treatment means followed by the same letter are not different at the 0.05 level using Duncan's multiple range test

Using the t-test to compare differences between P in windblown (eroded) and residual soils indicated significantly more P in windblown cropland samples for three of eight WEGs (Table 4). Results from similar tests on rangeland showed more P in three of seven WEGs. Data from cropland soils were more variable than those from rangeland soils, and 28 percent of P measurements on parent samples were larger than those from windblown samples. That compares to 13 percent for rangeland samples. Apparently, in some cases not enough observations were available to detect differences, e.g., WEG 5 soil on rangeland contained 5.1 times more P in windblown than residual samples but the means were not significantly different at the 95 percent level (only two observations were available).

Pooling all the cropland data without regard to WEG showed significantly larger amounts of P in windblown samples than residual samples, and the enrichment ratio was 1.43. The corresponding value for rangeland was 2.61. The larger ER on rangeland compared to cropland was probably due to a higher concentration of P in the surface because the surface layer was not mixed by tillage, and perhaps the erodible aggregates also contained more fine material on rangeland than on cropland.

These data show that the saltation-size particles moved by wind are often enriched in P relative to residual (parent) soils. The suspendible fraction that leaves the local area likely undergoes further enrichment, as suggested in Table 3.

SUMMARY AND CONCLUSIONS

During wind erosion, saltation particles abrade the surface aggregates. Typically, both the aggregates and saltating particles ($\approx$ 100 to 840 μm diameter) break down and contribute to the suspension-size particles (< 100 μm diameter) which are transported beyond field borders. The fine suspension-size particles (< 53 μm diameter) can be transported tens of kilometers by the wind, but little is known about how various physical variables govern the creation of these fine particles and the final composition of the fine particles. A laboratory study of aggregate abrasion was designed in which many of the variables could be controlled.

Table 4. Available Phosphorus in Windblown and Residual Soil (0 - 5.1 cm) by Wind Erodibility Group (WEG). Windblown Soil Collected in Point Samplers in MLRA 72 and 77 (Colorado, Kansas, New Mexico, Nebraska, Oklahoma, and Texas)

WEG	Number of observations	Available phosphorus		Enrichment ratio (W/R)
		Windblown (W)	Residual (R)	
		--------------- (kg/ha) cropland ---------------		
1	20	33*[a]	21	1.57
2	20	66**[b]	34	1.94
3	14	60ns[c]	43	1.40
4	6	93	99ns	0.94
4L	10	67ns	29	2.31
5	2	44	46ns	0.96
6	34	83*	64	1.30
7	0			
8	2	60ns	33	1.82
Total	108	Av. 66**	46	1.43
		--------------- (kg/ha) rangeland ---------------		
1	12	42**	21	2.00
2	11	47**	21	2.24
3	6	64*	22	2.91
4	0			
4L	3	61ns	21	2.90
5	2	67ns	13	5.15
6	3	157ns	48	3.27
7	0			
8	2	75ns	23	3.26
Total	39	Av. 60**	23	2.61

[a]* - Significant at 95% level

[b]** - Significant at 99% level

[c]ns - Nonsignificant (< 95%)

One objective of the study was to determine the amount of fine particles (WF) produced per unit mass of abrader as influenced by velocity (V_p), impact angle (α), diameter (d_p), and texture of impacting saltation-size particles and the stability (S_a) of the target aggregates. A second objective was to compare the nutrient content of the saltation-size and fine suspension-size particles created to that of their parent aggregates to check for nutrient enrichment. Soil samples trapped in field saltation catchers also were checked for available P enrichment.

Individual aggregates (4 to 8 cm diameter) were placed inside a cyclone separator and a calibrated sandblasting device was used to abrade them with weighed amounts of abrader. Soil of the same textures as the aggregate and sand were used as the two abraders. Three regression equations were developed relating WF to V_p, α, d_p, S_a, AM, and W for sand, very fine sandy loam, and silty clay loam abraders. AM is abrader mass and W is predicted total abrasive erosion from the target aggregates.

The production of WF was influenced most by abrader texture. On very fine sandy loam targets (S_a = 2.0 J/m^2), using soil abrader increased WF 3 to 15 times compared to sand abrader, while on silty clay loam targets (S_a = 8.0 J/m^2), WF was always tenfold or more greater for soil than for sand abrader. Typical predicted values of WF were 5, 75, 4, and 138 g/kg for sand and soil abraders on very fine sandy loam and silt loam targets, respectively, with

d_p = 350 μm, V_p = 350 cm/s, and α = 15 degrees. Clearly, soil abrader was a larger source of WF than the target aggregates.

In general, WF decreased as d_p increased, while WF increased as α increased from 15 to 90 degrees. On very fine sandy loam, WF increased with V_p, but on silty clay loam at large d_p, the particles evidently broke into large fragments so WF decreased as V_p increased. While WF production from both soil abraders was initially large, the available WF in the very fine sandy loam abrader would be exhausted with fewer impacts than in silty clay loam.

The total erosion from the target aggregates decreased as S_a increased, but the proportion of the total that was WF arose at low V_p and remained nearly constant at high V_p. For sand abrader, WF ranged from 15 to 65 percent of the total soil eroded from the targets in typical test conditions.

Composite samples of the parent aggregates, saltation-size, and suspension-size particles for each soil texture used in the abrasion studies were analyzed for available nitrogen (N), available phosphorus (P), potassium (K), and organic matter (OM). If we define enrichment ratio (ER) as ratio of nutrients in particles to those in parent aggregates, then average ERs of particles < 53 μm in diameter derived from the laboratory abrasion studies were 3.11, 2.25, 1.67, and 1.91 for N, P, K, and OM, respectively.

Slightly abraded saltation-size particles in the laboratory tests usually had ERs > 1.0, but they were not statistically different than the large aggregates of their parent soils. However, soil particles trapped in a large number of field erosion catchers often had significantly more P than parent soils, and average ERs were 1.4 and 2.6 for available P on cropland and rangeland sites, respectively. The larger ER on rangeland compared to cropland probably was due to higher concentrations of P near the untilled rangeland surface. The enrichment data show that the saltation-size particles aerodynamically separated by the wind are often enriched in P and, as suspendible particles are created from them, they undergo further enrichment.

REFERENCES

1. Cameron, R. S., and A. M. Posner. 1979. Mineralizable organic nitrogen in soil fractionated according to particle size. J. Soil Sci. 30:565-577.

2. Chepil, W. S. 1957. Sedimentary characteristics of duststorms: I. Sorting of wind-eroded soil material. Amer. J. of Sci. 255:12-22.

3. Chepil, W. S., and N. P. Woodruff. 1963. The physics of wind erosion and its control. Adv. in Agron. 15:1-301. A. G. Norman, Ed., Academic Press, New York.

4. Chichester, F. W. 1969. Nitrogen in soil organo-mineral sedimentation fractions. Soil Sci. 107:356-363.

5. Farrell, D. A., E. L. Greacen, and W. E. Larson. 1967. The effect of water content on axial strain in a loam soil under tension and compression. Soil Sci. Soc. Amer. Proc. 31:445-450.

6. Gillette, D. A. 1977. Fine particulate emissions due to wind erosion. TRANS. of the ASAE 20:890-897.

7. Gillette, D. A., I. H. Blifford, Jr., and D. W. Fryrear. 1974. The influence of wind velocity on the size distributions of aerosols generated by the wind erosion of soils. J. Geophys. Res. 79:4068-4075.

8. Hagen, L. J. 1984. Soil aggregate abrasion by impacting sand and soil particles. TRANS. of the ASAE 27:805-808, 816.

9. Harris, R. F., G. Chesters, and O. N. Allen. 1966. Dynamics of soil aggregation. Adv. in Agron. 18:107-169. A. G. Norman, Ed., Academic Press, New York.

10. Merva, G. E., and G. Peterson. 1983. Wind erosion sampling in the North Central Region. ASAE Paper No. 83-2133, presented at ASAE Annual Meeting, Bozeman, Montana, June 1983, 21 pp.

11. Tabatabia, M. A., and J. J. Hanway. 1968. Some chemical and physical properties of different sized natural aggregates from Iowa soils. Soil Sci. Soc. Amer. Proc. 32:588-591.

SEPARATING EROSION AND TECHNOLOGY IMPACTS ON WINTER WHEAT

YIELDS IN THE PALOUSE: A STATISTICAL APPROACH

D. L. Young   D. B. Taylor   R. I. Papendick

General improvements in agricultural technology, including improved crop
varieties, fertilization advances, and better pest control practices, have
doubled or tripled many U.S. crop yields during the past several decades.
These yield advances have also occurred in areas like the Pacific Northwest
Palouse which have experienced high levels of topsoil erosion. Figure 1
illustrates that average annual wheat yields in Whitman County, Washington,
located in the heart of the highly productive and highly erodible Palouse
River Basin, roughly doubled between 1934 and 1982--from about 25 bu/ac to
more than 50 bu/ac. Progress in average county-wide yields has been erratic
due to fluctuations in weather, disease problems, introduction of technical
improvements, and fluctuations in government wheat programs, as noted in
Fig. 1. Overall, however, the net positive impacts of technical
improvements have more than offset the negative yield impacts of topsoil
loss over the past five decades.

Topsoil loss in the Palouse has been severe over the same period. The
Palouse Cooperative River Basin Study (USDA 1978) estimated that topsoil
loss in the region averaged 14 tons/ac/yr, with losses of 100 to 200 tons/ac
on some slopes in exceptionally severe winter erosion seasons. During the
100 years the Palouse has been under cultivation, all the original topsoil
has been lost from an estimated 10 percent of the cropland (USDA 1978).

The fact that wheat yields have doubled in the Palouse over the past 50
years does not mean that there has been no productivity damage from erosion
in the region. The true yield damage of topsoil erosion is properly
measured as the reduction in potential yields. In other words, how much
higher would yields have been with today's improved technology if there had
been no topsoil erosion? Consequently, correctly measuring the magnitude of
erosion damage, or conversely the payoff to soil conservation, requires
disaggregating the yield impacts through time of improved technology and
topsoil erosion for the particular crops and production regions under
consideration. More specifically, it will be demonstrated in this paper
that when technology and erosion interact multiplicatively over time,
ignoring technology will underestimate erosion damage. Nonetheless, in 10
of 15 long-run soil conservation benefit evaluation studies recently
reviewed by Young (1984), dynamic technology effects were ignored entirely
in assessing the long-run crop yield and economic benefits of topsoil
conservation. Where the interaction was considered, there generally was
scanty empirical support for the nature of the interaction.

The objectives of this paper will be to (1) present a procedure for
disaggregating erosion damage from technology gains on crop yields, (2)

The authors are: D. L. YOUNG, Agricultural Economist, Washington State
University, Pullman; D. B. TAYLOR, Agricultural Economist, Virginia Poly-
technic Institute and State University, Blacksburg; and R. I. PAPENDICK,
Soil Scientist, USDA-ARS, Pullman, Wash.

The major statistical results presented in this paper were originally
drafted as an unpublished working paper by Young, Hoag, and Taylor (1982).

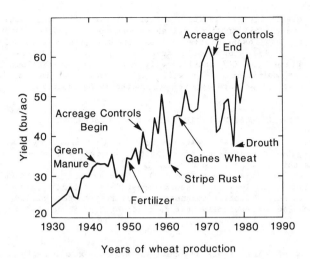

Fig. 1 Wheat Yield Trend for Whitman County, Washington, 1932-82
Source: Papendick et al. (1983).

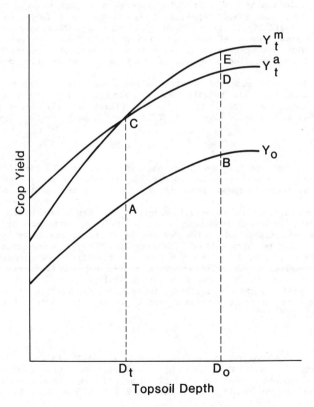

Fig. 2 Comparison of Additive and Multiplicative Technical Progress
Impacts on Crop Yield Response to Topsoil Depth

131

examine theoretically how additive versus multiplicative interaction between technology and topsoil erosion influences measures of erosion damage on crop productivity, (3) present statistical estimates of the relationships between winter wheat yields and topsoil depth in the eastern Palouse region of Washington State, and (4) statistically test whether technology interacted additively or multiplicatively with topsoil depth in influencing winter wheat yields in the Palouse region between the 1950s and 1970s.

DISAGGREGATING EROSION DAMAGE FROM TECHNOLOGY GAINS

The concept of a crop yield response function to topsoil depth will be used to disaggregate the influence of technical progress and topsoil erosion on crop yields through time. In Fig. 2, Y_0, Y_t^a, and Y_t^m represent crop yield response functions in a base period (Y_0), after t years of technical progress with additive technology (Y_t^a), and alternatively after t years of technical progress with multiplicative technology (Y_t^m). For the base period, yield (Y_0) can be expressed algebraically as a function of topsoil depth (D) alone:

$$Y_0 = f(D). \tag{1}$$

For purposes of this simple theoretical model, topsoil depth serves as a proxy for the vector of soil characteristics influenced by erosion. Its use permits convenient two-dimensional graphical exposition of the relationships in Fig. 2. In practice, a multivariable response function, if available, could be substituted for f(D). The concave nonlinear relationship between topsoil depth and yield represented by Y_0 has been found to provide a reasonable statistical fit to crop yield and topsoil measurements in the Palouse region (Pawson et al. 1961; Taylor 1982; Hoag and Young 1983). It conforms with the agronomically reasonable property of diminishing marginal productivity to additional topsoil as the topsoil horizon grows deeper.

Additive technical progress boosts the base year yield curve by a constant absolute amount at all topsoil depths. For example, t years of technical progress might add 20 bu/ac to wheat yields at all topsoil depths as illustrated in the shift from Y_0 to Y_t^a. Algebraically, we can express Y_t^a as:

$$Y_t^a = A(t) + f(D). \tag{2}$$

A(t) is a function representing absolute yield growth as a function of a time index (t), a proxy for technology. Y_t^a is simply a vertical displacement of the base period response function, $Y_0 = f(D)$, by the quantity A(t).

Uniform multiplicative technical progress, on the other hand, shifts the base period response function by a constant proportional or percentage amount at all topsoil depths. Because base yields are lower on shallower soils, a uniform proportional increase in the response function boosts yields more in absolute terms on deeper topsoils. For example, a 50% increase applied to 60 bu/ac grown on a deep topsoil is larger than a 50% increase applied to 30 bu/ac grown on a shallow topsoil. This decreasing absolute yield growth on shallower topsoils is represented by the shrinking of the vertical distance between Y_0 and Y_t^m in Fig. 2. Algebraically, we can express Y_t^m as:

$$Y_t^m = B(t)f(D). \tag{3}$$

B(t) is a uniform multiplicative technology shift factor. In the base period when t = 0, B(0) = 1.0. B(t) will rise over time assuming positive technical progress. For example, if technical progress increased yields at all topsoil depths by 50% after 30 years, B(30) would equal 1.50.

It should be noted that Y_t^a and Y_t^m represent pure cases of uniform

132

additive or uniform multiplicative technical progress shifts, and that empirical relationships for specific crops and soils may depart from these. For example, technology might clearly boost yields more in absolute terms on deeper topsoils, but display nonuniform proportional shifts over different topsoil depths. This case, referred to in this paper as a nonuniform multiplicative shift, is displayed in Table 1.

Table 1. Hypothetical Nonuniform Shift in Topsoil-Yield Response Function

Topsoil depth	Base year yield	Later year yield	Absolute increase	Percentage increase
0	20	30	10	50
4	30	44	14	47
12	40	57	17	43
36	50	70	20	40

We can use the framework provided by the response functions in Fig. 2 to isolate and quantify the yield damage attributable to topsoil erosion under alternative types of technical progress. It should be understood at this point that applied studies that use this framework to quantify the future crop yield benefits (costs) of topsoil conservation (erosion) must necessarily project the impacts of erosion and technology into the future. For example, the 1980 Resource Conservation Act (RCA) appraisal conducted by USDA projected crop yields with and without erosion over 50 years to year 2030 to assess crop productivity losses from uncontrolled soil erosion (USDA 1981, p. 73).

We will illustrate a framework for assessing yield damage from t years of erosion, during which average topsoil depth for a particular land class is projected to fall from D_0 to D_t in Fig. 2. We will assess damage for the following three scenarios: (1) technology is ignored, (2) technology is additive, and (3) technology is multiplicative. In addition to the graphical analysis in Fig. 2, we present a parallel general mathematical proof of the conclusions regarding impacts of different technology assumptions on yield damage projections in the Appendix.

If technology is ignored, the projected cumulative crop yield damage from t years of erosion is simply the yield difference between points B and A in Fig. 2. With additive technical progress, the projected yield reduction is the yield difference between point D, the projected potential yield without erosion given technical progress, and point C, the projected yield with both erosion and technology. Observe, however, that D minus C is identical to B minus A because Y_t^a is a vertical displacement of Y_0 in Fig. 2. Consequently, if technical progress is uniformly additive, ignoring technical progress will not bias projections of cumulative erosion damage. Of course, projections of absolute yields in the future will still be biased if technical progress is ignored.

Finally, we consider the case of multiplicative technical progress. Y_t^m is drawn so as to intersect Y_t^a at its approximate midpoint so that the total increase in yields due to technology--averaged over all topsoil depths--is approximately equal for both types of technology. Furthermore, the ending year yield is assumed to be at point C in both cases. This isolates the impact of type of shift from the general level of the shift. The projected yield damage from t years of erosion with multiplicative technology is the difference between point E, potential yield without erosion, and point C. Because Y_t^m incorporates a greater absolute shift in the response function on deeper topsoils, projected yield damage in Fig. 2 is greater for multiplicative technology than for the cases where technology was additive or ignored. The general mathematical proof in the Appendix demonstrates that these

133

conclusions are not a result of the specific graphical example. The proof shows that ignoring technology, or assuming additive technology, will always underestimate yield damage from erosion if technical progress is either uniformly multiplicative or nonuniformly multiplicative. Conversely, assuming technology is multiplicative when it is additive will overestimate yield damage.

Precision in identifying the nature of the technology-topsoil depth interaction is not inconsequential academic hair splitting. Decisions to target soil conservation funds to areas where economic erosion damage averted is greatest could be strongly influenced by assumptions regarding the interaction between topsoil depth and technical progress. Assumptions about this interaction are made whenever erosion damage is measured as the difference between projected crop yields with and without erosion. In the 1980 RCA Appraisal, for example, the projected erosion damage assessments for all crops, soils, and regions in the nation implicitly assume uniformly multiplicative technical progress (see Young 1984, pp.75-76, for derivation of this conclusion based on documentation of the RCA Appraisal methodology provided in Benbrook 1980). However, this key assumption is neither explicitly recognized nor is any empirical basis for it provided. Indeed, our literature review has uncovered very little empirical research of any kind on this issue.

Of course, no one can project for certain the type of agricultural technology breakthroughs, and their relative crop yield impacts on deep versus shallow topsoils, that are likely to emerge over the next 50 years. A logical first step in gaining insight into this important question would be to examine how improved technology historically has influenced crop yields on deep versus eroded (or naturally shallow) topsoils.

In the next section, we present a statistical comparison of two topsoil depth-wheat yield response functions estimated with data collected in the eastern Palouse during the 1950s and the 1970s. The comparison formally examines the nature of the historical impact of improved technology on wheat yields at different topsoil depths. As shown in Fig. 1, wheat yields in the Palouse increased substantially between the 1950s and 1970s due to introduction of higher-yielding semidwarf wheat varieties, increased use of nitrogen fertilizers, improved chemical weed control practices, and other improvements in agricultural technology.

STATISTICAL COMPARISON

Figure 3 summarizes the estimated historical shift in the yield-topsoil function for winter wheat grown in Whitman County, Washington. The bottom curve in Fig. 3 was derived from relationships estimated by Pawson et al. (1961) from over 800 observations from eastern Palouse farmers' fields collected in 1952 and 1953. The top curve was estimated by Taylor (1982, p. 145) from 89 observations from farmers' fields collected by Wetter (1977) in the same region during 1970-75.

Both Pawson et al.'s and Taylor's relationships were least squares regression estimates of Mitscherlich-Spillman functions fit to the sample observations. Taylor's function was:

$$Y = 38.92 + 40.50 \ (1 - 0.9^D) \qquad (4)$$
$$(3.40) \quad (4.79)$$

where standard errors are in parentheses, $R^2 = 0.4515$; Y = predicted wheat yield in bu/ac; D = topsoil depth in inches. The parameter 0.9 was fixed at this value a priori. A nonlinear least squares regression estimate of this parameter yielded the value 0.92; however, the nearby value of 0.9 was imposed to remain consistent with Pawson et al.'s earlier work (Taylor 1982).

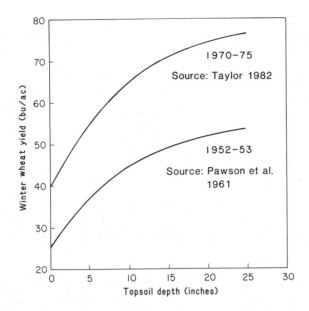

Fig. 3 Comparison of Winter Wheat Yield-Topsoil Depth Relationships
from the 1950s and the 1970s, Eastern Whitman County, Washington

The 89 observations underlying Taylor's function were collected by Wetter
and associates in the years 1970, 1971, 1972, and 1974. Taylor excluded the
1975 observations on the basis of a Chow test that indicated they came from
a different yield pattern, probably due to heterogeneous weather
conditions. There were only two observations for 1973, and these were
deleted due to severe winter damage on the 1973 yields.

Wetter's crop yield and topsoil depth observations were obtained from sites
in the Pine Creek Conservation District in the northeast quarter of Whitman
County. Topsoil was defined as:

> The darkened layer of soil measured from the soil surface to a point
> where the brown organic matter coloring is no longer evident and/or the
> structure or texture changes (Wetter 1977, p. 1).

The lower function in Fig. 3 was derived from the following equation
estimated by Pawson et al. (1961, pp. 66 and 69):

$$Y = 26.4 + 35.1 \ [(1 - 0.90^D)(1 - 0.60^H)].\tag{5}$$

(standard errors and R^2 were not reported by Pawson et al.)

Y and D are defined as in Taylor's equation and H represents the percentage
organic matter in the top 6 inches of soil. Pawson et al. (1961) describe
this function as the best overall relationship showing the impact of
"average depth of soil and soil organic matter content on wheat yields,
except for unfertilized wheat after green manure or hay crops" (p. 66).
Pawson et al. used this equation for projecting future yields under
alternative cropping systems. The intercept term for Pawson et al.'s
equation was estimated separately for different crop rotations, nitrogen
applications, and for south and north slopes. The value of 26.4 was
calculated from information in Pawson et al.'s Table 23 (p. 69) for a
wheat-pea rotation, with nitrogen fertilizer, and no wheat acreage
restrictions. These conditions were considered most comparable, on average,

135

to those underlying Taylor's function. By substituting the yield predictions and topsoil depths listed in Table 23, it was possible to solve algebraically for the value of the intercept associated with the selected conditions.

Unfortunately, detailed documentation on the exact locations and collection procedures for Pawson et al.'s data is very sparse. They write (p. 19):

> To ascertain the relationship of wheat yields to site characteristics, quadrat samples were taken from farmers' fields during 1952 and 1953. In each field, a typical Palouse hill was selected for study. Samples of wheat and soil were taken at various sites over the hill. Data were obtained on the yield of wheat and straw, the depth of topsoil, the soil organic matter content, and the slope of the land. More than 800 samples were taken from 116 fields.

A substantial contribution to better scientific understanding of the interaction between topsoil properties and technology as they have influenced wheat yields in the Palouse could be made if Pawson et al.'s original data and its associated documentation were available. Efforts by the authors to locate the data set or better documentation for it have not been successful to date.

As they stand, Eqs. (4) and (5) are not directly comparable because (5) includes organic matter content as a second independent variable and (4) does not. Unfortunately, data on organic matter content are not available in the more recent data set. However, Pawson et al. (p. 2) do report the following estimated relationships between soil organic matter and depth of topsoil for their data set:

$$\text{S\&W Slopes} \quad H = 0.97 + 3.037\ (1 - 0.92^D), \text{ S.E. Reg.} = 0.67 \qquad (6)$$

$$\text{S\&E Slopes} \quad H = 2.52 + 1.424\ (1 - 0.92^D), \text{ S.E. Reg.} = 0.95 \qquad (7)$$

H and D represent percentage soil organic matter content and inches topsoil depth as before. These equations reveal that organic matter content and topsoil are positively correlated.

In order to adjust Eq. (5) to a form comparable to Eq. (4), we incorporated the systematic correlation between topsoil depth and organic matter reported in Eqs. (6) and (7). We assumed that Pawson et al.'s "overall" Eq. (5) contained an equal representation of S&W and N&E slopes. Consequently, we computed the following equally weighted average of Eqs. (6) and (7).

$$H = 1.75 + 2.23\ (1-0.92^D). \qquad (8)$$

We used Eq. (8) to predict organic matter content for topsoil depths from 0 to 36 inches by 1-inch increments. We then inserted the 37 pairs of topsoil depth and organic matter content into Eq. (5) to obtain 37 predicted wheat yields. These 37 predicted yields were regressed on the 37-element vector equaling $(1 - 0.9^D)$ for all integer values of D from 0 to 36. This linear regression yielded:

$$Y = 24.46 + 31.64\ (1-0.90^D) \qquad (9)$$
$$(.283) \quad (.362) \qquad R^2 = 0.9954.$$

(standard errors in parentheses)

Equation (9) provides a yield equation from Pawson et al.'s relationship which is comparable to Taylor's Eq. (4). Equations (4) and (9) are plotted in Fig. 3. In both equations, the single variable of topsoil depth serves as a proxy for all soil chemistry and structure variables that are altered by erosion. Our procedure for adjusting Pawson et al.'s equation implicitly assumes that Wetter's more recent data upon which Eq. (4) is based also exhibited the typical positive correlation between H and D quantified in Eq. (8).

Even visual inspection of Fig. 3 reveals greater yield growth on the deeper topsoils. On subsoil (0 inches topsoil), the predicted 1970s wheat yield exceeded the predicted 1950s yield by 14.4 bu/ac; on a deep 30-inch topsoil the same margin was 22.9 bu/ac.

Technical progress appears to have boosted yields about 60% more on the deeper topsoil, but is the nonuniform yield shift statistically significant? If the yield-topsoil function shift were uniformly additive, the intercepts of the compared equations would be different but the "slope coefficients," which precede the $(1-0.9^D)$ terms, would remain identical. The coefficients preceding $(1-0.9^D)$ will be referred to as "slope coefficients" for purposes of expositional convenience in this paper. It should be recognized, however, that technically they do not represent the slopes of nonlinear Eqs. (4) and (5). Consider the null and alternative statistical hypotheses:

$$H_O: \quad B_T - B_P \leq 0 \qquad\qquad (10)$$

$$H_A: \quad B_T - B_P > 0 \qquad\qquad (11)$$

B_T and B_P represent the slope coefficients of Taylor's and Pawson et al.'s equations, respectively. Rejection of the null and acceptance of the alternative hypothesis permits the conclusion that technical progress has indeed boosted yields more on the deeper topsoils. To test this hypothesis, an estimate of the standard error of the difference between the two coefficients, $S_{(B_T - B_P)}$, is required. Using Var and Cov to denote variance and covariance, respectively, we utilize the following relationship from statistical theory:

$$\text{Var } (B_T - B_P) = \text{Var } (B_T) + \text{Var } (B_P) - 2 \text{ Cov } (B_T, B_P). \qquad (12)$$

However, the two equations were estimated from independent data sets, so it seems reasonable to assume zero covariance. Consequently, we obtain:

$$S_{(B_T - B_P)} = [\text{Var } (B_T) + \text{Var } (B_P)]^{1/2}. \qquad (13)$$

As noted above, Pawson et al. did not report the standard errors of their equation, so we assume for lack of more precise knowledge that Var (B_T) = Var (B_P), which yields:

$$S_{(B_T - B_P)} = [2 \text{ Var } (B_T)]^{1/2} = (2)^{1/2} (4.79) = 6.77. \qquad (14)$$

Recall from Eq. (4) that 4.79 is the estimated standard error of the slope coefficient in Taylor's regression. Because yields generally increased between the 1950s and 1970s, it seems reasonable to speculate that the standard error of the slope coefficient also increased. Consequently, assuming equality of standard errors for the two equations is probably more likely to overestimate rather than underestimate $(S_{(B_T - B_P)})$. This is a conservative assumption because it makes it more difficult to reject the null hypothesis.

As both B_T and B_P are assumed normally distributed from least squares regression estimation, we use the t-statistic for their comparison as follows:

$$t = \frac{B_T - B_P}{S_{(B_T - B_P)}} = \frac{40.50 - 31.64}{6.77} = 1.31. \tag{15}$$

B_T and B_P are obtained from compared Eqs. (4) and (9). The critical value of t with 174 degrees of freedom (d.f.), twice the d.f. of s.e. B_T, for a one-tailed significance level of 0.10 is 1.29. Consequently, we reject the null hypothesis at the 10% significance level. This lends some statistical support for the alternative hypothesis that technical progress has increased yields more on deeper topsoils.

We next test whether the response curves in Fig. 3 display a uniform proportional shift. Taking the ratio of the intercepts of Eqs. (4) and (9) reveals that a multiplicative factor of 1.59 is required to raise Pawson's intercept to the level of Taylor's intercept:

$$\frac{38.92}{24.46} = 1.59. \tag{16}$$

Applying this same multiplicative shift factor to the slope term of Eq. (9) yields:

$$1.59 \, (31.64) = 50.31. \tag{17}$$

Denoting the shifted slope coefficient in (17) as B_P^*, we test the null hypothesis that Taylor's function reached the required slope to display a uniform multiplicative shift.

$$H_O: \quad B_T - B_P^* = 0 \tag{18}$$

$$H_A: \quad B_T - B_P^* \neq 0 \tag{19}$$

$$t = \frac{B_T - B_P^*}{S_{(B_T - B_P^*)}} = \frac{40.50 - 50.31}{6.77} = -1.45 \tag{20}$$

The calculated t exceeds the critical value of t (174 d.f.) for a two-tailed significance level of 0.20, which is 1.29. This test lends modest statistical support to the conclusion that the technical shift was not uniformly multiplicative. The comparison indicates that technology appears to have increased Palouse region wheat yields by greater absolute amounts on deeper topsoils, but in a nonuniformly multiplicative manner.

In related work, Papendick et al. (1983) have incorporated the historical pattern of nonuniformly multiplicative interaction between topsoil depth and technology observed in Eqs. (4) and (9) into a winter wheat yield forecasting equation. Results of that analysis revealed that continuation of the historical interaction and current erosion rates could lead to winter wheat yields peaking out and eventually declining within the next 50 years on steeply sloped and erodible class IV and class VI land.

We caution readers, however, that projections such as those of Papendick et al. (1983) based on historical patterns are subject to considerable uncertainty. Simply stated, future agricultural technology advances could depart markedly from past patterns. Nonetheless, the multiplicative interaction between technology and topsoil identified in this study for winter wheat in the Palouse seems to us to be consistent with fundamental agronomic principles. For example, plant breeding research, among other objectives, strives to develop cultivars with greater genetic potential for converting available plant nutrients and moisture to harvestable grain. Consequently, new responsive cultivars will likely produce relatively greater yield increases in the moisture and nutrient rich environment associated with topsoil than on subsoils which frequently contain fewer plant nutrients and have less available water due to plant-rooting restrictions or to runoff. Furthermore, the greater genetic yield potential of improved varieties will be restricted at the outset if poor seedbed conditions on subsoils impede stand establishment.

Support for the view that the complementary interaction between topsoil depth and technology is likely to continue in the future for winter wheat in the Palouse is available from one important group--namely the farmers in the region. Results of a recent survey of 272 farmers in the southeastern Washington and northern Idaho Palouse showed they expected winter wheat yields to average 12 bu/ac higher over the next 50 years on typical hillslopes, but only by a relatively modest 4 bu/ac on shallow-soil hilltops (STEEP Project, 1980).

CONCLUSIONS AND REMAINING RESEARCH NEEDS

The comparison presented in this paper provides modest empirical support for the contention that recent agricultural technical progress has produced greater yield increases on deeper topsoils for winter wheat grown in the Palouse region. This means, as demonstrated in the Appendix, that technical progress will increase the projected yield damage from erosion. Ignoring multiplicative technical progress in yield projections will underestimate the payoff to soil conservation. The complementary relationship between topsoil depth and technology identified in this paper for winter wheat in the Palouse implies that continued high rates of erosion in this region will stunt the future yield payoff to technical progress. This reinforces the economic justification for soil conservation.

Although the results of this study seem consistent with agronomic principles and also with farmers' expectations of future trends in the region, it should be pointed out that the empirical data base for the results is very limited. The paucity of documentation for Pawson et al.'s data makes it impossible to know the exact degree of similarity between their eastern Palouse data sites and Wetter's eastern Palouse sites. It would be desirable to have yield response functions from two eras that came from the same soil series and topographic hill positions rather than average "overall" functions of the type we compared. Unfortunately, such relationships or the data to estimate them were not available. We were also forced to make specific assumptions in order to obtain an equation from Pawson's relationships that was directly comparable to Taylor's equation. Statistical hypothesis testing required further assumptions. We have argued that the assumptions made were reasonable, but they remain unconfirmed.

Ideally, it would be desirable to base conclusions on technology-erosion interaction on analysis of observations of crop yields and soil characteristics taken from identical sites over a 20-year or preferably longer interval in order to avoid confounding from site differences. Furthermore, it would be desirable to have detailed information on the actual (presumably profit maximizing) adjustments in technology over this time period. The latter information could permit disaggregating the technology shift between management adjustments such as changes in fertilization and introduction of new inputs such as new crop varieties.

We offer this analysis as the most rigorous possible given the sparse available data. However, more complete and detailed data will be required to reach more definitive conclusions. Hopefully, this initial attempt to quantify the historical relationship between technology and erosion through time will stimulate researchers in other regions to make similar comparisons for wheat and other major crops. There is no assurance that the technology-topsoil depth interaction is constant across regions and crops as assumed by the 1980 RCA appraisal (USDA 1981), but little empirical basis presently exists to incorporate regional and crop-specific differences in this interaction.

While a better understanding of how historical technical progress has influenced yields on eroded versus deep topsoils is a logical first step in projecting future trends, these empirical investigations should be followed by systematic future projections from task forces of agricultural scientists as recommended recently by Young (1984, p. 80).

The research question at issue is critical to sound evaluations of the long-run productivity impacts of topsoil erosion, and merits further investigation.

REFERENCES

1. Benbrook, C. 1980. Review of the yield-soil loss simulator. Memorandum for RCA Coordinating Committee Members, Council on Environmental Quality, Washington, D.C.

2. Hoag, D.L. and D.L. Young. 1983. Yield-topsoil depth response functions: Linear versus Mitscherlich-Spillman. STEEP Agric. Econ. Working Paper 82-2. Dept. of Agric. Econ., Washington State University, Pullman.

3. Papendick, R.I., D.L. Young, D.K. McCool and H.A. Krauss. 1983. Regional effects of soil erosion on crop productivity--The Palouse Area of the Pacific Northwest. Paper presented at Soil Erosion and Crop Productivity Symposium, Denver, Colorado, March 1-3. (Proceedings forthcoming).

4. Pawson, W.W. 1961. Economics of cropping systems and soil conservation in the Palouse. Agric. Exp. Sta. Bul. No. 2, Washington State University, Pullman.

5. STEEP Project. 1980. A survey on crop production in the Palouse. Washington State University and University of Idaho, Departments of Agricultural Economics and Rural Sociology, unpublished results.

6. Taylor, D.B. 1982. Evaluating the long run impacts of soil erosion on crop yields and net farm income in the Palouse annual cropping region of the Pacific Northwest. Ph.D. dissertation. Washington State University, Pullman.

7. U. S. Department of Agriculture. 1978. Palouse Cooperative River Basin Study. U.S. Government Printing Office, Washington, D.C. 182 p.

8. U.S. Department of Agriculture. 1981. Soil Water and Related Resources in the United States: Analysis of Resource Trends. 1980 RCA Appraisal, Part II. Washington, D.C.

9. Wetter, F. 1977. The influence of topsoil depth on yields. Tech. Note AGRON-10, and unpublished data underlying report. Soil Conservation Service, Colfax, Wash.

10. Young, D.L. 1984. Modeling agricultural productivity impacts of soil erosion and future technology. pp. 60-85. In English, B.B., J.A. Maetzold, B.R. Holding, and E.O. Heady (Eds.), Future Agricultural Technology and Resource Conservation, The Iowa State University Press, Ames, Iowa.

11. Young, D.L., D.L. Hoag, and D.B. Taylor. 1982. An empirical test of the multiplicative impact of technical progress on the topsoil-yield

response function for winter wheat in the eastern Palouse. STEEP
Agric. Econ. Working Paper 82-3. Dept. Agric. Econ., Washington State
University, Pullman.

APPENDIX

The conclusions concerning the different impact of additive and
multiplicative technology on estimates of the yield damage from erosion can
be proven mathematically as follows. The first part of the proof is adapted
from Young (1984), whereas the extension to nonuniformly multiplicative
technical progress is new.

Define yield damage from t years of soil erosion as:

$$d_t = Y_t^c - Y_t^e \tag{1}$$

where $Y_t^c - Y_t^e$ are projected yields in year t on a topsoil maintained by
conservation and on an eroded topsoil, respectively. Under additive
technology, yield damage (d_t^a) is

$$d_t^a = Y_t^c - Y_t^e = (A(t) + f(D_c)) - (A(t) + f(D_e)) = f(D_c) - f(D_e) \tag{2}$$

where A(t) is the uniform additive yield growth due to technical progress
and f(D) is the topsoil-yield response function for some base period t = 0.
D_c and D_e indicate topsoil depths after t years of erosion with
conservation and erosive practices, respectively. Consequently, $D_c > D_e$
in year t. The "a" superscript on d_t indicates yield damage with additive
technology. The disappearance of the technical progress terms, A(t), in
calculating d_t^a confirms that additive technical progress does not influence
the measure of yield damage. The positive term $d_t^a = f(D_c) - f(D_e)$ simply
measures the reduction in yield from moving down the static positively
sloped topsoil-yield response function.

On the other hand, under multiplicative technology,

$$d_t^m = Y_t^c - Y_t^e = B(t) \, f(D_c) - B(t) \, f(D_e) =$$
$$B(t)[f(D_c) - f(D_e)] = B(t) \, d_t^a \tag{3}$$

where B(t) is the uniform multiplicative technology shift factor. With
positive technical progress, B(0) = 1.0 and B(t) is monotonically increasing
so B(t) > 1.0 for t > 0.

The results show that:

$$d_t^m = B(t) d_t^a > d_t^a . \tag{4}$$

Expressed verbally, the presence of multiplicative technical progress
increases yield damage from erosion. Ignoring multiplicative technical
progress by measuring yield damage along a static reponse function will
result in an underestimate of yield damage.

The proof above applies to the "pure" case of a uniform multiplicative
shift. Consider next the case of a nonuniform shift which still boosts
absolute yields more on deeper topsoils, but by nonuniform proportional
amounts as topsoil depth increases. Define the damage term in this case as:

141

$$d_t^n = Y_t^c - Y_t^e = B(D_c,t) \ f(D_c) - B(D_e,t) \ f(D_e).$$ (5)

Again, $B(D,0) = 1.00$ to set the technology shift factor equal to 1.00 in the base year ($t = 0$). The assumption of positive technical progress implies that $B(D,t)$ is monotonically increasing with respect to t. As before, after t years of erosion, $D_c > D_e$. The assumption that technical progress boosts absolute yields more on deeper soils means that the following relationship holds for all positive t:

$$[B(D_c,t) \ f(D_c) - f(D_c)] > [B(D_e,t) \ f(D_e) - f(D_e)].$$ (6)

To determine whether nonuniform multiplicative technical progress, as defined here, leads to greater erosion yield damage than uniform additive technical progress, consider the difference:

$$d_t^n - d_t^a = [B(D_c,t) \ f(D_c) - B(D_e,t) \ f(D_e)] - [f(D_c) - f(D_e)] =$$ (7)

$$[B(D_c,t) \ f(D_c) - f(D_c)] - [B(D_e,t) \ f(D_e) - f(D_e)].$$ (8)

This difference is positive because the first bracketed term in Eq. (8) is larger than the second as specified in Eq. (6).

This result confirms that any technology shift which boosts absolute yields more on deeper soils with increase the yield damage from erosion. Ignoring technology will result in an underestimate of the payoff from soil conservation whenever technical progress produces greater absolute yield growth on deeper topsoils.

A MODEL OF EROSION AND SUBSEQUENT FERTILIZATION

IMPACTS ON SOIL PRODUCTIVIY

E.M. Craft   S.A. Carlson   R.M. Cruse

The effect of erosion on crop production has been masked by gradual increases in technological inputs. Certain soil properties, such as fertility and water holding capacity can, to some extent, be altered by fertilizer additions, irrigation, or tillage. Other effects of erosion, such as changes in soil texture, bulk density, and soil structure cannot readily or economically be corrected by technology. Estimating the degree to which soil management can compensate for losses in soil fertility, tilth, or water holding capacity is difficult.

The objective of this study was to develop a model which estimates soil productivity based on simulated root growth and potential nutrient and water uptake for a corn crop through the growing season.

The simulated root growth in this model is sensitive to the soil environment. As topsoil is lost due to erosion a new soil environment is encountered. This environment may alter the root system. The potential for nutrient and water uptake then depends on the new level of soil nutrients and available soil water surrounding the root system.

MODEL DESCRIPTION.

Programmed in Fortran IV, the Potential Yield Index (PYI) model was organized in a modular structure to facilitate the incorporation of variables, i.e., additional nutrients, not presently considered in the model. At present, the 11 subroutines contained in the model interact as shown in Fig. 1. The model requires the unput of 8 soil characteristics over the depth of the soil profile. An example of these inputs are shown in Table 1.

A five-step approach was used to predict the PYI for a soil. First, soil physical and chemical properties were utilized to predict the corn root distribution with depth during the growing season. Outputs from this step were used in the second and third steps which predicted the amount of phosphorus (P) and potassium (K) removed from the soil by the plant through the full dent stage. The total uptake of each nutrient was related to separate yield indexes. The fourth step calculated the total water available to a plant for the growing season which was then related to a yield index. The fifth step estimated a PYI based on the three independent indexes for either P, K, or water uptake.

Root Distribution

The rooth growth subroutines ROOTS(Fig. 1) simulated root growth through a soil profile assuming that corn roots adapt to the environment encountered. The root growth submodel from the Nitrogen, Tillage, Residue Management (NTRM)

The authors are: E.M. CRAFT, Research Assistant, S.A. CARLSON, Research Assistant, and R.M. CRUSE, Associate Professor, Dept. of Agronomy, Iowa State University, Ames, Iowa

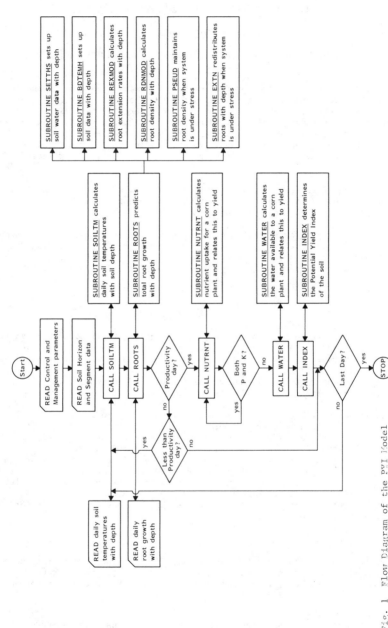

Fig. 1 Flow Diagram of the PYI Model

144

Table 1. Required Inputs for the PYI Model; Adair Soil Series, Aquic
Argiudolls Fine Montmorillonitic, Mesic.

Hori-zon	Depth	Texture			Bulk density	Soil pH	Avail-able water	Available	
		Sand	Silt	Clay				P	K
	(cm)	-------- % --------			(g/cc)		(cm/cm)	-- (kg/ha) --	
Ap	0-16	23	46	31	1.47	6.50	0.18	27	134
A1	16-22	23	46	31	1.48	6.45	0.18	13	49
A2	22-42	23	46	31	1.49	6.45	0.18	12	41
2Bt1	42-64	30	26	44	1.55	5.80	0.11	8	25
2Bt2	64-86	30	26	44	1.60	5.80	0.15	7	18
2Bt3	86-118	30	36	34	1.70	6.70	0.15	7	18
2BC	118-150	30	36	34	1.75	6.70	0.15	7	18

model was selected to predict the root distribution in accordance with
existing soil characteristics (Shaffer and Clapp, 1982). Utilizing a dynamic,
one-dimensional, multilayered approach, the model distributed roots as a
function of seven variables. These variables included soil strength,
aeration, bulk density, water potential, temperature, salinity, and pH. The
prediction and indexing of the first six variables is further described in
the NRTM Manual (Shaffer and Larson, 1982). Soil pH was incorporated into
the rooting subroutine using the method described by Pierce et al. (1983).
The prediction of soil temperature over depth was modified using an amplitude
equation based on average monthly soil temperature with depth (Horton,
Wierenga, and Nielsen 1983).

Predictions of the daily accumulated net and total root length, root weight,
amd root length density within specified increments of the soil profile were
simulated. If any soil conditions restricted root branching or penetration
in a soil depth increment, the roots were redistributed to those soil layers
above it which had more favorable growth conditions. If no such layer was
found the total root growth was reduced.

Nutrient Uptake

The nutrient subroutine, NUTRNT (Fig. 1), uses root growth and soil fertility
over depth to estimate the total amount of a nutrient removed by a corn plant
throughout the growing season. Nutrient uptake was estimated separately for
P and K, assuming that all other nutrients were nonlimiting to plant growth.
The potential nutrient uptake from a soil was assumed to be (1) proportional
to the root length density in each soil layer, (2) dependent on the total
soil volume potentially extractable by a root, (3) limited to the amount of
nutrient available in each soil layer, and (4) restricted to the soil volume
containing roots as dictated by the plant population and root growth
simulation.

The radius of the nutrient depletion zone surrounding each root was
estimated by Newman and Andrews (1973):

$$B = (2 \ Dt)^{\frac{1}{2}} \qquad (1)$$

where
D = effective diffusion coefficient (cm^2/sec. 10^7)
t = time (sec)
B = distance from the root surface to the outer edge of nutrient
depletion zone (cm).

In summarizing previous research, Russell (1977) indicated that P and K
uptake occurred through a given segment of root for a significant time period
of up to several weeks following root development. It was thus assumed that

each root segment effectively absorbed nutrients for 30 days (t in Eq. (1)), after which, nutrient uptake ceased due to root aging.

Assuming a root radius (r) of 0.15 mm and using B as the distance of nutrient depletion from the root surface, the cross sectional area (A), (cm^2 soil extracted) of the nutrient depletion zone was calculated:

$$A = \pi(r + B^2) - \pi r^2 \qquad (2)$$

For each soil layer, the volume of soil extracted of each nutrient (Vn) was determined by:

$$Vn = AL \qquad (3)$$

where
  L = total root length within a given soil layer (cm root/cm^3 soil).
Nutrient uptake per soil layer was then determined by:

$$Nu = VnF \qquad (4)$$

where
  Nu = nutrient uptake per soil layer (Kg nutrient/cm^3)
  F = available nutrient concentration in a given soil layer on a volumetric basis (Kg/cm^3).
F was obtained from reported soil test levels throughout the soil profile.

The quantity of each nutrient removed by each plant was determined by separately summing Nu for each soil nutrient over all soil layers to a depth where roots were simulated. To determine the total removal of each nutrient for a given land area the quantity of each nutrient removed by each plant was multiplied by the plant population in that land area.

Water Uptake

The water subroutine, WATER (Fig. 1), estimates the total amount of water available for plant growth. To determine the water index it was assumed that: (1) the entire soil profile was filled to field capacity at the beginning of the growing season, (2) the soil storage capacity for available water to the depth of rooting was considered to be the potentially available soil water, (3) the average growing season rainfall supplements soil available water in determining total water available for plant growth, and (4) the water available from the soil and rainfall was completely utilized for plant growth. The seasonal distribution of rainfall was not considered directly.

Total water available for a plant was dependent on available rainfall during a growing season and the available soil water in the soil profile. The available rainfall was considered to be the average rainfall during the growing season minus the calculated runoff and percolation. If the runoff and percolation data was not available, it was assumed that 20% of the rainfall was lost to runoff, percolation, and canopy wetting. The total available soil water equals the summation of the known available water over the soil layers where root growth was simulated.

Potential Yield Index

To more effectively identify constraints to productivity, P, K, and water availability were individually related to yield indexes, INDEX (Fig. 1). It was assumed that all factors affecting yield, other than the one variable being considered, were nonlimiting.

Separate, nonlinear regression equations related total predicted P and K

146

uptake to theoretically attainable yield or PYI_p and PYI_k. PYI_w is empirically related to potential yield. The lowest of the three predicted potentials, PYI_p, PYI_k, or PYI_w, is assumed equal to the soil potential productivity.

ANALYZING EROSION IMPACTS ON SOIL PRODUCTIVITY

Procedure

PYIs for 45 soils from 16 major soil associations in Iowa were predicted. These indexes assumed that a moderate soil fertility level was maintained in the plow layer under a conventional tillage system. A maximum profile depth of 150 cm was used for all predictions.

Impact on erosion: The impact of soil erosion on soil productivity was estimated by evaluating changes in the PHY of these soils as 6 and 12 cm of soil were removed from the soil surface. The soil profile depth was maintained by incorporating data for soil layers previously below 150 cm. Within the plow layer only bulk density was restored to a consistent value for each stage of erosion. Changes in all other soil properties were dependent on the value of those soil properties previously below the plow layer and now incorporated into it. Root growth was then simulated in response to the properties in the new soil profile. Nutrient and water uptake were estimated according to the modified root distribution and soil properties. New yield indexes for P, K, and water predicted a PYI for the altered soil profile.

Impact of Fertilization: The impact of fertilizer applications for each stage of erosion was evaluated by restoring the original levels of P and K fertility in the plow layer.

Results

The effect of soil erosion and subsequent restoration of plow layer soil fertility on PYI is shown in Table 2.

6 cm Eroded: When 6 cm erosion was simulated on all soils without fertility restoration, PYI predictions on four of the soils remained within 5% of the original PYI, 23 soils had PYI predictions of 5-10%, and 15 soils had PYI reductions of 10-15%. Three soils had PYI reductions greater than 15%. When the original fertility level was restored to the plow layer all but seven soils had PYI predictions within 5% of the original PYI values.

Table 2. Precentage Reduction in PYI for 45 Soils After 6 and 12 cm Erosion and Under Two Levels of Fertility Management

| Reduction in PYI % | 6 cm erosion | | | | 12 cm erosion | | | |
| | No fertility restored | | Original fertility restored | | No fertility restored | | Original fertility restored | |
	No.	%	No.	%	No.	%	No.	%
+5-10			5	11			4	9
0-5	4	9	33	73			23	51
5-10	23	51	7	16	1	2	16	36
10-15	15	33			11	24	1	2
15-20	2	4			11	24	1	2
20-25	1	2			12	27		
25-30					6	13		
30-35					3	7		
35-40					1	2		

147

12 cm Eroded: Doubling the soil erosion loss, i.e., simulating 12 cm loss,
resulted in further reductions in the predicted PYIs. Only 12 of the 45 soils
were within 15% and 18 of the 45 soils were within 20-30% of the original PYI.
When the original fertility level was restored to the new plow layer of the
eroded surface, 27 of the soils maintained PYIs within 5% of the original PYI.
Only two soils had greater than 10% reduction in PYI.

Five soils exhibited higher PYI values following 6 cm erosion and restoration
of plow layer fertility than those which were predicted for the uneroded
surface. The soil test levels of the most limiting nutrient increases in the
subsoil of each of these soils, resulting in a higher predicted PYI.

Limiting Factors to Production: As erosion proceeds in the field the most
limiting factor(s) to production may change, depending on subsoil properties.
The PYI model, which is sensitive to these changes, appears capable of
identifying the most limiting factor for crop production as well as the
potential interchange among limiting factors as erosion occurs.

The frequency with which each index becomes the most limiting to production
for the 45 soils is illustrated in Fig. 2.

For 36 soils, only one index consistently limited PYI at each stage of
erosion, with and without restoration of plow layer fertility. The limiting
index predicted for the other nine soils changed depending on the stage of
erosion and whether or not the original plow layer fertility was restored.

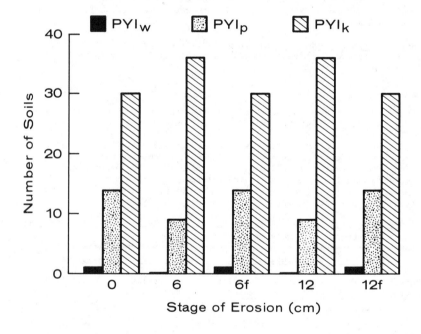

Fig. 2 Number of Soils for Which Each Index is the Limiting Factor For the
PYI at Different Stages of Erosion
(f = original plow layer fertility restored)

The nutrient index which was predicted to be most limiting under noneroded
conditions was in close agreement with known subsoil fertility level for P

and K. There were 10 soils with a subsoil P fertility level significantly
greater than the K fertility level or subsoil K fertility level greater than
the P fertility level. For all these soils the model predicted that PYI was
limited by the nutrient in lowest supply.

The subsoil P and K supplying power of the remaining soils were not distinctly
different. For these soils the factor which limited growth depended on the
distribution of roots and P or K in the soil profile.

Adair Soil Series, a Specific Example: An example of how erosion, with and
without fertility restoration, affects each of the indexes is illustrated for
the Adair soil series (Aquic Argiudoll) in Fig. 3.

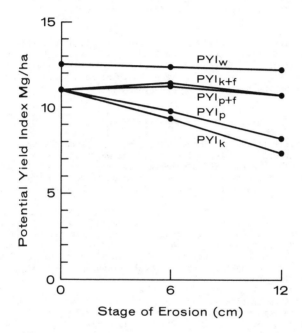

Fig. 3 Change in Yield Indexes for P, K, and Water at Three Stages of
        Erosion, With (+f) and Without Fertility Restored for the Adair
        Soil Series.

PYI_w showed a slight but consistent decline with erosion. PYI_p and PYI_k were
equally limiting when no erosion had occurred. With 6 cm erosion both indexes
are quite sharply reduced to 88 and 85%, respectively, of their original
values with potassium becoming the most limiting factor. Removal of an
additional 6 cm of topsoil (total of 12 cm removed) reduced PYI_p and PYI_k to
74 and 66%, respectively, of their original values. Restoring the plow layer
fertility resulted in index values which nearly matched the original values
prior to erosion.

MODEL EVALUATION

All of the soils evaluated showed a decline in the indexes as erosion
progressed, except those soils in which fertility improves with depth. The

detrimental effect of erosion on soil productivity, as demonstrated in the model, is similar to that established in other research (Frye et al., 1982; Krauss and Allmaras, 1982; Langdale et al., 1979; Langdale and Shrader, 1982; Pierce et al., 1983; Swanson and Harshbarger, 1964). The dramatic increases in PYI when original fertility levels are restored following erosion supports other researchers' theories that technological inputs, such as fertilizer, mask the impact erosion has on soil productivity (Cruse et al., 1983; Krauss and Allmaras, 1982; Langdale and Shrader, 1982; Storie, 1978; Swanson and Harshbarger, 1983; Walker and Young, 1983).

It appears that the impact of erosion on soil productivity is largely determined by subsoil properties as they affect root growth and soil available water, and plow layer fertility. On soils with unfavorable subsoil properties, erosion will have a large effect on productivity if plow layer soil fertility is not restored.

While the economics of controlling erosion and using less fertilizer versus that of increased fertilizer rates with less erosion control is beyond the objective of this study, the topic needs addressing. The approach utilized to estimate soil erosion impacts on productivity of Iowa soils appears adaptable for studying soils of other geographical regions.

SUMMARY

The Potential Yield Index (PYI) model estimates soil productivity based on simulated root growth and potential nutrient and water uptake for a corn crop through the growing season. The simulated root growth is sensitive to the soil environment. A new soil environment is encountered when topsoil is lost due to erosion. This may alter the root system and subsequent nutrient and water uptake.

PYIs for 45 soils from 16 major soil associations in Iowa were predicted. The impact of soil erosion on soil productivity was estimated by evaluating changes in the PYI of these soils as 6 and 12 cm of soil were removed from the soil surface. The impact of fertilization applications on soil productivity was evaluated by restoring the original levels of phosphorus and potassium fertility following erosion.

When simulating 6 cm erosion without fertility restoration PYI predictions on four of the soils remained within 5% of the original PYI, 23 soils had PYI predictions of 5-10% of the original PYI, and 15 soils had PYI predictions of 10-15% of the original PYI. When the original fertility was restored all but seven soils had PYI predictions within 5% of the original PYI.

Doubling the soil erosion loss, simulating 12 cm erosion, resulted in further reductions in the predicted PYIs. Only 12 of the 45 soils were within 15% of the original PYI and 18 of the 45 soils were within 20-30% of the original PYI. When the original fertility was restored 27 of the soils maintained PYIs within 5% of the original PYI.

REFERENCES

1. Cruse, R.M., Diane Tapper and T.M. Crosbie. March 1983. A perspective on developments in biological sciences and their impact on productivity. In Lee A. Christensen (ed.) Perspectives on the vulnerability of U.S. agriculture to soil erosion--an organized symposium. Natural Resources Economics Division, Economic Research Service, USDA, ERS Staff Report AGES830315. Washington, D.C.

2. Frye, W.W., S.A. Ebelhar, L.W. and R.L. Blevins. 1982. Soil erosion effects on properties and productivity of two Kentucky soils. Soil Sci. Soc. Am. J. 46: 1051-1055.

3. Horton, R., P.J. Wierenga and D.R. Nielsen. 1983. Evaluation of methods for determining the apparent thermal diffusivity of soil near the surface. Soil Sci. Soc. Am. J. 47: 25-32.

4. Krauss, H.A. and R.R. Allmaras. 1982. Technology masks the effects of soil erosion and wheat yields--A case study in Whiteman County, Washington. p. 75-86. In B.L. Schmidt, R.R. Allmaras, J.V. Mannering, and R.I. Papendick (eds.) Determinants of soil loss tolerance. Spec. Rep. 45. American Society of Agronomy, Madison, Wisconsin.

5. Langdale, G.W., J.E. Box, Jr., R.A. Leonard, A.P. Barnett and W.G. Fleming. 1979. Corn yield reduction on eroded Southern Piedmont soils. J. Soil Water Conserv. 34(5): 226-228.

6. Langdale, G.W., and W.D. Shrader. 1982. Soil erosion effects on soil productivity of cultivated cropland. p. 41-52. In B.L. Schmidt, R.R. Allmaras, J.V. Mannering, and R.I. Papendick (eds.) Determinants of soil loss tolerance. Spec. Rep. 45. American Society of Agronomy, Madison, Wisconsin.

7. Newman, E.I. and R.E. Andrews. 1973. Uptake of phosphorus and potassium in relation to root growth and root density. Plant and Soil 38: 49-69.

8. Pierce, F.J., W.E. Larson, R.H. Dowdy and W.A.P. Graham. 1983. Productivity of soils: Assessing long-term changes due to erosion. J. Soil and Water Conserv. 38: 39-44.

9. Russell, R. Scott. 1977. The absorption and transport of nutrients. p. 62-89. In Plant root systems: Their function and interaction with the soil. McGraw-Hill Book Company (UK) Limited, London.

10. Shaffer, M.J. and C.E. Clapp. 1982. Root growth submodel. Chapter 10. In M.J. Shaffer and W.E. Larsen (eds.) Nitrogen, tillage, residue, management (NTRM) model technical documentation. USDA-ARS, St. Paul, Minnesota.

11. Shaffer, M.J. and W.E. Larsen. 1982. Nitrogen, tillage, residue, management (NTRM) model technical documentation. USDA-ARS, St. Paul, Minnesota.

12. Storie, R.E. 1978. Storie index soil rating. Univ. California Spec. Pub. 3203.

13. Swanson, E.R. and C.E. Harshbarger. 1964. An economic analysis of effects of soil loss on crop yields. J. Soil Water Conserv. 19: 183-186.

14. Walker, D.J. and D.L. Young. March 1983. A perspective that technology may not ease the vulnerability of U.S. agriculture to erosion. In Lee A. Christensen (ed.) Perspectives on the vulnerability of U.S. agriculture to soil erosion--An organized symposium. Natural Resource Economics Division, Economic Research Service, USDA, ERS Staff Report AGES830315. Washington, D.C.

DYNAMIC IMPACTS OF EROSION PROCESSES ON

PRODUCTIVITY OF SOILS IN THE PALOUSE

A. J. Busacca   D. K. McCool   R. I. Papendick   D. L. Young
                     Member ASAE

The Palouse region is a distinctive geologic terrain of rolling hills of deep loess (windblown silt) which forms approximately 0.7 million ha of highly productive wheatlands in eastern Washington and along the western border of the Idaho panhandle (Fig. 1). The Palouse topography is unusually steep. On most of the land, slopes range from 5 to 17 degrees and on parts of some cultivated fields the steepness exceeds 26 degrees. The Palouse is one of the most rapidly eroding landscapes in the nation, with water erosion rates on some steep slopes of 200 to 450 t/ha of soil in a single winter season (USDA, 1978). The erosion by water is caused by a combination of factors including a winter rainfall maximum, snowmelt on thawing soil, steep slopes, and plow-tillage seedbeds for fall-planted wheat. Tillage erosion caused by repeated downhill plowing also is moving large amounts of soil downslope and accounts for the majority of soil that is being lost from ridges and hilltops in the steeply sloping areas. Since the land was first cultivated about 100 years ago, all of the original topsoil has been lost by erosion from 10 percent of the cropland, and from one-fourth to three-fourths of the original topsoil has been lost from another 60 percent of the cultivated cropland in the region (USDA, 1978).

For many years, farmers and agronomists in the region have spoken of the "Palouse soil", conjuring an image of a homogeneous, equally fertile deposit of loess 30 to 60 m thick. This image is false; there are many buried ancient soils (paleosols) layered within the loess which strongly influence the character of the modern soils. Soil profile characteristics also change markedly from one position on a hillslope to another, and from one part of the Palouse to another. Paleosol horizons, where they occur close to the surface, are very restrictive to both downward water movement and root penetration. On hill summits, and generally on southern exposures, the young, fertile topsoil layer was originally quite thin over clay and hardpan paleosol subsoils, whereas on other parts of each hill such as the north slopes and bottomlands, it was several meters thick. With water erosion and tillage erosion, many of these thin topsoil layers have eroded to the subsoil, and these areas of exposed subsoils of inherently low productivity are becoming larger as a result of the ongoing erosion processes. Soil material eroded from hilltops and sideslopes has covered many fertile bottomlands with silty deposits from 1 to 3 m thick.

Severe erosion has led to the removal of portions of some fields from crop production or to markedly lowered yields on areas where the loess blanket was originally quite thin. The loss of fertile topsoil layers has also created soil management problems associated with farming clay and hardpan

The authors are: A. J. BUSACCA, Assistant Professor, Agronomy and Soils Dept.; D. L. YOUNG, Associate Professor, Agricultural Economics Dept., Washington State University, Pullman; D.K.McCOOL, Agricultural Engineer; and R. I. PAPENDICK, Soil Scientist, USDA-ARS, Pullman, WA.

subsoils, and farming physical mixtures of topsoils and subsoils. These problems include difficulties with tillage operations, seedbeds that are difficult to prepare, severe soil crusting and poor seedling emergence, soil infertility, and higher machinery power requirements.

Fig. 1   View of the Palouse Landscape from Steptoe Butte, near Colfax, Washington

Past research has shown that, as a simple approximation, winter wheat yields across the Palouse landscape decrease with decreasing topsoil depth, and that, per increment of topsoil lost, yields are reduced much more markedly on soils with thin topsoils than on those with thick topsoils (Hoag and Young, 1983; Pawson et al., 1961; Wetter, 1977; Young et al., 1985). The loss of productivity over the past several decades has been least on land classes having moderately low erosion rates (<15.0 t/ha-yr) and relatively thick topsoils (>30 cm) and most severe on classes having high erosion rates (>40 t/ha-yr) and shallow topsoils (<15 cm) (Papendick et al., 1985). For example, it is calculated from data by Papendick et al. (1985) that the decline in winter wheat yield per cm of topsoil loss, for conditions representative of 1975, was 0.011 t/ha for soils with topsoil thicknesses of 55 cm, and 0.094 t/ha for soils with topsoil thicknesses of 7 cm.

Other soil properties besides topsoil depth, principally the nature and degree of development of the subsoil horizons, can cause significant variations in the specific relationship of crop yield to topsoil depth, and hence, can account more directly and completely for the effect of long-term erosion on soil productivity. Fosberg et al. (1983) showed this to be true for three soils in the eastern Palouse that were cropped in a wheat-pea or wheat-lentil rotation. They demonstrated that although there was a significant general relationship between yield and topsoil depth, the exact nature and sensitivity of the relationship was different for each soil series. More research is needed to determine the factors within a soil series or phase that influence erosion-productivity relationships.

In this paper: (1) We describe the Palouse landscape, we place several representative soils in the soil-landscape, and we discuss the features of these soils that have a critical influence on changes in soil productivity as erosion progresses. (2) We calculate differential rates of soil loss from these soils and landscape positions, and we assess the changes in the character of the soil profiles that accompany long-term soil loss. (3) We estimate and discuss the relationships between topsoil depth and winter wheat yield for several soil series subdivided by land use capability class.

UNIQUE LANDSCAPES AND SOILS IN THE PALOUSE

Geologic History

Loessial materials have been accumulating in the Palouse for more than one million, and possibly two million years (Foley, 1982), blown by prevailing southwesterly winds from a sediment source area in the Columbia Basin 50 to 160 km to the west. The climatic fluctuation of the Pleistocene Epoch, along with other geologic events, led to periods of rapid loess accumulation that alternated with periods of landscape stability and soil formation. The fertile topsoil (A horizons) and in some cases the subsoil (B horizons) that are the seat of the tremendous productivity for agriculture, are the result of only the most recent episode of loess accumulation and soil development which has occurred during the last 13,000 yr. Earlier episodes of soil development led to the formation of 10 to 20 or more soils, some of which are very strongly developed. Remnants of these paleosols are now buried and interlayered within the thick loess and play an important role in the decline of productivity as erosion progresses.

Climate and Natural Vegetation

The climate of the Palouse is a Mediterranean type, with cold, wet winters and warm to hot, dry summers. A strong climatic gradient exists across the Palouse; mean annual precipitation increases from 300 mm at the western edge of the Palouse to 600 mm at the eastern edge of the Palouse, east of Moscow, Idaho. Mean annual air temperature decreases from $10^{\circ}C$ to $6^{\circ}C$ along the same transect. The proportion of the mean annual precipitation that falls as snow increases along the transect. Frequency and depth of soil freezing are related in a complex fashion to air temperature and depth of snow cover, and they reach maxima near the Washington-Idaho boundary. The natural vegetation of the Palouse region was a steppe type, with perennial bunchgrasses dominant. Conifer forests existed along the eastern border of the Palouse. Plant density and vigor in the native grassland increased with increasing precipitation across the Palouse.

The Landscape

The Palouse region can be subdivided into several distinct subregions, each with a unique topographic type (Kaiser et al., 1951). Basic hill shapes in each region have resulted from a balance of both depositional and erosional processes. The topographic types differ because of differences across the Palouse in rainfall intensity and quantity, amounts of seasonal snow accumulation, frequency and depth of soil freezing, total loess thickness, and average particle size of loessial parent materials. Each of these vary in a systematic way across the west to east Palouse transect. Generally, in the drier western and southwestern Palouse, the topography is one of long, linear ridges that trend NNE with broad, flat summits and relatively subdued, symmetrical west- and east-facing side slopes. The strong linearity in this part of the Palouse has been attributed to loess accumulation by nearly unidirectional prevailing winds (Lewis, 1960). In the central region, total loess thickness is at a maximum and slopes are very steep; hill summits are narrow and sharp. In the eastern and northeastern Palouse, ridges are irregularly aligned and are shorter. North and northeast facing hillsopes can be very steep, concave, and bowl shaped, the result of soil slips and erosion by meltwater from deep snowdrift accumulation. Both broad-flat and narrow-sharp hill summits are expressed in different subregions of the eastern Palouse.

Modern Soils and Paleosols

Modern soils in the Palouse are classified as Mollisols according to the definitions set forth in Soil Taxonomy (Soil Survey Staff, 1975), except that, where they formed under conifers, some of the soils are Alfisols and Inceptisols. Because of the loessial origin, parent materials for all the soils have silt loam textures. The climatic gradient and dominant prairie vegetation is reflected in both modern soils and in paleosols: Organic matter content and thickness of A horizons before cultivation ranged from 1.3 percent and 25 to 46 cm, respectively, in the drier western Palouse, to 4.2 percent and 50 to 92 cm under grass vegetation in the wetter eastern Palouse (Donaldson, 1980). B horizons in modern soils also reflect the climatic gradient: limited leaching and slow horizon development prevail in the dry western Palouse, where cambic B horizons (color, structure) and weak calcic B horizons (accumulations of $CaCO_3$) are common. Deep leaching, nearly complete removal of $CaCO_3$, and greater subsoil development (weak clay-enriched or argillic B) characterize soils in the youngest loess layer in the eastern Palouse.

Paleosol horizons in the Palouse reflect the existence of a similar climatic gradient during earlier episodes of soil development, but generally they display a much greater degree of development than do the soils in the youngest loess layer. Buried paleosols in the western Palouse are hardpans cemented by calcium carbonate and silica (duripans in Soil Taxonomy), while those in the eastern Palouse are enriched in clay and iron (argillic horizons in Soil Taxonomy). The paleosol layers have a complex and poorly understood spatial relationship with respect to the modern landscape and its thin covering of recent loess. We do know that, in parts of each Palouse hill, paleosol layers originally lay within 0.3 to 1.8 m of the land surface. Where the cover of recent loess was naturally thin, such as on hill summits, and even where recent erosion has removed a thicker layer of recent loess, "clay knobs" and knobs exposing fragmented duripans now are common. Because many paleosol horizons lie within the normal depth of soil profile description (1.5 m), approximately one-half of the upland soil series in Whitman County, Washington, and as much as 30 percent of the upland acres have superimposed profiles, with both modern and paleosol soil horizons in the rooting zone.

DYNAMICS OF LANDSCAPE CHANGE RESULTING FROM ACCELERATED EROSION

In this section we present calculations of soil loss due to water erosion for two representative soil-landscapes in the Palouse. We discuss the effects of tillage erosion in more general terms, for there has been little research to quantify the effects of this form of soil loss. We then discuss the projected, long-term impacts of combined erosion processes on soil properties and on soil-landscape composition. The first soil-landscape is the Walla Walla soil association, which we selected to represent soils in the wheat/fallow cropping rotation area of the dry western Palouse. The second, the Palouse-Thatuna-Naff soil association, is typical of soils in the higher precipitation zone in the eastern Palouse where annual cropping is practiced. Characteristics such as A-horizon thickness described below should be taken as maximal values for each series because accelerated erosion has been occurring in the region for 80 or more years.

The Walla Walla and the Palouse-Thatuna-Naff Soil Associations

The Walla-Walla soil association is in the 300 to 380 mm precipitation zone of western Whitman County, Washington. Walla Walla soils occupy about 82 percent of the association and Risbeck soils occupy 6 percent of the association (Donaldson, 1980). The actual extent of the Risbeck series in this soil association is somewhat larger than 6 percent because it is a common inclusion in map units of the Walla Walla series.

The Walla Walla series soils are weakly developed and formed entirely within the youngest loess layer. They are classified as Typic Haploxerolls. They have dark A horizons approximately 41 cm thick which overlie cambic B horizons. Textures are silt loam throughout the profile. Risbeck soils formed partially in the youngest loess layer, but the young loess has been mixed with fragments of a paleosol duripan. The Risbeck soils are classified as Durorthidic Xeric Torriorthents. They have A horizons that are about 20 cm thick. The content of duripan fragments increases from approximately 5 percent at the surface to 35 percent at 150 cm. These soils are easily recognized on the landscape because the white, lime-enriched soil matrix and duripan fragments contrasts strongly with the dark A-horizons of adjacent Walla Walla soils.

Walla Walla soils occupy most of the linear, NNE-trending hills in this soil association, except for south and southeast facing side slopes, which are occupied by Risbeck soils (Fig. 2). Endicott series soils (Haplic Durixerolls), with hard paleosol calcium carbonate- and silica-cemented duripans at depths of 50 to 100 cm in the profile, occur on some ridgetops in this association.

The Palouse-Thatuna-Naff soil association is one of five upland soil associations in the 460 to 585 mm precipitation zone in the eastern Palouse. The Palouse series is the dominant soil in each of these associations. Soils of the Palouse series make up about 46 percent of the Palouse-Thatuna-Naff association, Thatuna soils about 30 percent, and Naff soils, along with those of the similar Garfield series, make up about 14 percent of the association (Donaldson, 1980). Soils of the Palouse series are moderately developed, and are thought to have formed entirely within the youngest loess layer, although deeper parts of the B horizon in some soils may be a weak paleosol argillic horizon. Soils of the Palouse series (Pachic Ultic Haploxerolls) have A horizons that are approximately 60 cm thick and have strong cambic B horizons to a depth of more than 150 cm which show evidence of slight clay enrichment. Textures are silt loams throughout the profile, but there is a small decrease in permeability, and an increase in clay content in the B horizons. Palouse soils occur on south- and southwest-facing side slopes, and on some broad ridgetops.

Thatuna soils (Xeric Argialbolls) have superimposed profiles and a complex genesis. They have an upper soil profile about 90 cm thick that formed in young loess. This overlies a leached layer (E horizon), formed by lateral soil-water flow, over an impermeable paleosol argillic B horizon that has a texture of silty clay loam. The Thatuna soils occur primarily on north- and northeast-facing side slopes in a moist microclimate with heavy snow accumulation and high potential for soil mass movements (see, for example Garber, 1965; Kardos et al., 1944).

Naff and Garfield soils occur on the crests of flat hill summits in this soil association, and on low-lying secondary knobs and ridges. These soils occur where the young loess layer was originally quite thin, and their profile character reflects this. The Naff soils are classified as Ultic Argixerolls and the Garfield series soils are Mollic Haploxeralfs. Both soils have A horizons less than 20 to 46 cm thick that formed in young loess, overlying strong, silty clay loam paleosol argillic B horizons. Tillage and water erosion has removed the A horizon from the Naff and Garfield soils on many hilltops, exposing the silty clay loam subsoil at the land surface.

Within the Palouse, landscape position and soil profile characteristics are strongly correlated, as are soil characteristics and climate. Soil loss rates due to water erosion differ among soil series because of inherent differences in erodibility, differences in hill shape, different characteristic positions of soil series on the hill slope, and varying rainfall erosivity. Tillage erosion is strongly affecting some soils but is not affecting others, due to differences in landscape position and number and type of tillage operations. Crop yields are reduced much more on some soils than on others as increments of A horizon material are lost, because of major differences in the character of the soil that remains after erosion. Soil profile character and landscape position, then, determine the nature and severity of the erosion problem for each soil series.

Differential Soil Loss Rates for Different Soil Series and Hill Positions

Water Erosion: Water erosion is the dominant form of soil movement from all parts of the hill slopes except perhaps the summit, but it is acting at different rates depending upon relative soil erodibility, slope position, slope steepness, and crop management. We developed a procedure, based on the Universal Soil Loss Equation (USLE), to assess the differential rates of soil loss from the characteristic soil series' and landscape positions in the Walla Walla and Palouse-Thatuna-Naff soil associations. Our analysis is based on idealized, 2-dimensional hillslope cross-sections.

We plotted, on 7.5-minute topographic quadrangle maps, sites of 650 ha each that were originally selected by Gentry (1974) as representative of the two soil associations. In each area we plotted a number of typical water flow paths down the slopes. Water flow paths were laid out in pairs that lie approximately on opposite sides of each hill. Sixteen pairs of flow paths were plotted for each soil association, and from these pairs, average 2-dimensional hill cross-sections were constructed (Figs. 2,3). Flow paths begin near the ridge crests but not at the highest point, and continue downslope only until deposition or concentrated flow channels would be expected to occur. This convention leads to an accentuated "pointiness" of the tops of the cross-sections and does not attempt to represent empheral stream bottoms. This method of creating an average hill cross-section also eliminates extremes of slope. Slopes for all segments range only from 4.7 to 9.1 degrees, considerably less range than that which occurs in the natural landscape.

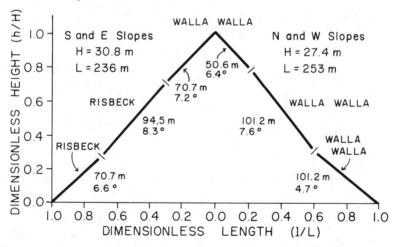

Fig. 2   Idealized Hill Cross-section in the Walla Walla Soil Association

The two representative hill cross-sections were developed by dividing each of the 16 replicate pairs of hillside profiles of total length L and total height H, into 10 equal horizontal segments. From these, dimensionless heights (h/H) and dimensionless lengths (l/L) were calculated for each of the 10 hillslope segments. These were averaged for the 16 hillslope profile pairs to derive the representative cross-sections for each soil association (Figs. 2, 3). Each soil series was located on the cross-sections by transferring map unit delineations from the Soil Survey of Whitman County onto the topographic maps, and generalizing the results from the 16 hillslope pairs. Each slope was divided into 3 segments, upper, middle, and lower, for USLE soil loss calculations.

The USLE adaptation for the Pacific Northwest (McCool and George, 1983) was used to estimate soil loss from each slope segment. Calculations were made for both conventional and reduced tillage. Crop residue production, used to calculate the cover factor (C), was estimated (1) by assuming the common crop rotations in the two soil associations, (2) by estimating crop yields for each soil series, assuming land use capability class III, and (3) from standard grain/total residue ratios (Power and Legg, 1978; Triplett and Mannering, 1978). Erosion estimates were made for 1- and 50-yr periods (Table 1). The decrease in topsoil depth was great enough that, at 50 yr, yield estimates and hence the crop cover factor C should be revised for the calculation of soil loss in a second 50-yr period (we have made such a calculation but do not show the data).

The projected erosion rates for the Walla Walla soil association are less, for either conventional or reduced tillage, than for the Palouse-Thatuna-Naff soil association. The average annual soil loss rate for the Walla Walla association in conventional tillage, all slope segments, is 36.0 t/ha compared to 63.1 t/ha for the Palouse-Thatuna-Naff (Table 1). This is primarily due to differences in rainfall erosivity in the two soil regions. Reduced tillage decreases projected annual soil erosion by 35 to 52 percent compared to conventional tillage, in our calculations for the first 50 years.

Annual erosion rates for conventional tillage on the Walla Walla association range from 15 to 19 t/ha on the upper slope segments to 36 to 53 t/ha on the lower slope segments, depending on aspect. Annual soil erosion for conventional tillage on the Palouse-Thatuna-Naff association ranges from 30 to 37 t/ha on the upper slope segments, to 71 to 75 t/ha on the lower slope segments.

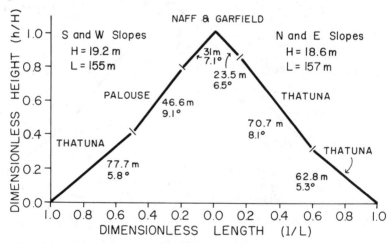

Fig. 3   Idealized Hill Cross-section in the Palouse-Thatuna-Naff Soil Association

When the erosion estimates are reported as cm of soil depth lost (Table 1),

Table 1. Water Erosion Estimates

Slope segment	Soil series	Top-soil depth	K^b	LS^c	P^d	Wheat[e] yield	C^f	Ann. soil loss	50-yr soil loss mass	depth[g]
		(cm)				(t/ha)		(t/ha)	(t/ha)	(cm)

A. WALLA WALLA ASSOCIATION, NORTH AND WEST SLOPES, WINTER WHEAT-SUMMER FALLOW ROTATION
R = 600[a]

Reduced Tillage

Top	WW[h]	41	0.065	1.75	1.0	2.7	0.13	8.7	437	3.4
Middle	WW	41	0.065	4.18	1.0	2.7	0.13	20.8	1 040	8.1
Bottom	WW	46	0.065	4.25	1.0	2.7	0.13	21.3	1 060	8.3

Conventional Tillage

Top	WW	41	0.065	1.75	1.0	2.7	0.22	14.8	740	5.8
Middle	WW	41	0.065	4.19	1.0	2.7	0.22	35.4	1 770	13.8
Bottom	WW	46	0.065	4.25	1.0	2.7	0.22	35.9	1 790	14.0

B. WALLA WALLA ASSOCIATION, SOUTH AND EAST SLOPES, WINTER WHEAT-SUMMER FALLOW ROTATION
R = 600[a]

Reduced Tillage

Top	WW	41	0.065	2.26	1.0	2.7	0.13	11.2	560	4.4
Middle	R	20	0.065	4.82	1.0	2.0	0.17	31.4	1 570	12.3
Bottom	R	20	0.065	5.32	1.0	2.0	0.17	34.8	1 740	13.6

Conventional Tillage

Top	WW	41	0.065	2.26	1.0	2.7	0.22	19.1	953	7.4
Middle	R	20	0.065	4.82	1.0	2.0	0.26	48.2	2 410	18.8
Bottom	R	20	0.065	5.32	1.0	2.0	0.26	53.1	2 660	20.8

C. PALOUSE-THATUNA-NAFF, NORTH AND EAST SLOPES, WINTER WHEAT-SPRING PEA ROTATION
R = 1 060[a]

Reduced Tillage

Top	N & G[h]	23	0.049	1.22	1.0	2.8	0.27	16.9	847	6.6
Middle	T	41	0.042	3.29	1.0	3.8	0.22	32.2	1 610	12.6
Bottom	T	46	0.042	3.63	1.0	3.9	0.21	33.8	1 690	13.2

Conventional Tillage

Top	N & G	23	0.049	1.22	1.0	2.8	0.48	30.0	1 500	11.7
Middle	T	41	0.042	3.29	1.0	3.8	0.45	65.9	3 300	25.7
Bottom	T	46	0.042	3.63	1.0	3.9	0.44	71.1	3 550	27.7

D. PALOUSE-THATUNA-NAFF, SOUTH AND WEST SLOPES, WINTER WHEAT-SPRING PEA ROTATION
R = 1 060[a]

Reduced Tillage

Top	N & G	23	0.049	1.49	1.0	2.8	0.27	20.7	1 030	8.1
Middle	P	61	0.042	3.47	1.0	4.4	0.20	30.9	1 550	12.1
Bottom	T	41	0.042	3.73	1.0	3.8	0.22	36.5	1 830	14.3

Conventional Tillage

Top	N & G	23	0.049	1.49	1.0	2.8	0.48	36.8	1 840	14.4
Middle	P	61	0.042	3.47	1.0	4.4	0.41	63.2	3 160	24.7
Bottom	T	41	0.042	3.73	1.0	3.8	0.45	74.6	3 730	29.2

[a] Erosivity, $\dfrac{MJ \cdot mm}{ha \cdot h \cdot yr}$

[b] Erodibility, $\dfrac{t \cdot ha \cdot h}{ha \cdot MJ \cdot mm}$

[c] Segment length and steepness factor

[d] Erosion control practice factor

[e] Assuming Land Capability Class III

[f] Cover and management factor

[g] Assuming surface bulk density of 1.28 Mg/m^3

[h] WW = Walla Walla, R = Risbeck, P = Palouse, N = Naff, T = Thatuna, G = Garfield

159

soils in the Walla Walla association under conventional tillage may lose 6 to 21 cm of soil at 50 years and 12 to 43 cm of soil at 100 years (data for 100 yr not shown). Risbeck soils on south and east slopes will have exposed B horizons with 5-20 percent duripan pieces in the tillage zone at 50 years. This projection fits with current field observation that duripan fragments and B horizon materials are presently in the tillage zone on many southeast-facing slopes in the dry region. Walla Walla soils on middle and lower slope segments may lose 1/3 of their A horizon at 50 years and more than 2/3 at 100 years.

Soils in the Palouse-Thatuna-Naff association under conventional tillage may lose 12 to 29 cm of soil at 50 years and 24 to 60 cm of soil at 100 years (data for 100 yr not shown). Naff and Garfield soils on ridge tops and knobs will have some exposed clayey B horizons at 50 years and exposure of B horizons by water erosion will be essentially complete for these soils at 100 years. These rates of exposure do not include the tillage erosion that is occurring on these vulnerable hilltop sites. Because the Palouse region has been farmed for more than 80 years, we actually see that clay knobs of exposed B horizons do exist today and their area is increasing with time. For the Palouse and Thatuna soils on middle and lower slopes, the projected erosion losses do not bring clay-rich B horizons to the surface, but they do severely reduce the thickness of the fertile A horizons, and, in the case of the Thatuna, they reduce the effective plant rooting depth (to clayey paleosol B horizons) by more than one-half. The impact of decreasing soil depth on soil productivity will be shown below, as well as the differential impact of topsoil loss on different soil series.

Tillage Erosion: Tillage erosion increases the net soil loss, particularly from upper segments of the slope, from ridge tops, and from mid-slope knobs. In these landscape positions, soil moved downhill is not replaced by soil moving from a higher landscape position. Experimental data on soil movement resulting from tillage are sparse. Its magnitude was recognized by Kaiser (1961), who documented 0.6 m of soil loss from a hill crest over a 31-yr period (1911-1942) and an additional 0.6 m of soil loss in the next 17 years (1942-1959). Its importance can be seen in vertical walls at fence lines that are 0.9 to 2.4 m high, where the farmer upslope has plowed toward the fence and the farmer downslope has plowed away from the fence. Cisterns, well sites, and power poles on ridge tops now protrude above the eroded soil surface.

From a preliminary experiment, we calculated the net soil loss by a single plowing from a ridge top with a slope of less than 5.7 degrees to be 29 t/ha. This is calculated from an observed 18-cm plow depth, and 41-cm lateral movement, by assuming that all plowing is away from the crest, and that 30 m of flatter slope lies immediately beneath the crest. This soil is moved incrementally to the next lower slope segment. If the second segment is steeper than the ridge top, a net loss also occurs from the second segment. The ultimate recipient of this soil is the toe of the slope where there is a flatter gradient.

Long-Term Changes in the Palouse Landscape and Soils

Under the combined effects of water erosion and tillage erosion, the distribution of soils on the Palouse landscape and the properties of the soils are changing rapidly. A-horizon thickness is decreasing on virtually all soils, except those on toe slopes and in valley bottoms. Subsoil materials, both duripans and clay-rich B horizons, are becoming nearer to the surface. On 10 to 20 percent of the Palouse landscape, clay and hardpan horizons exist at the surface today. Map units for the Whitman County Soil Survey (Donaldson, 1980), delineated during mapping in the 1960's and 1970's, in many cases no longer reflect the soils that exist today in those delineations.

Soil deposition in toe slope areas and valley bottoms can bury seedlings and create other management problems. Frazier et al. (1984) estimated that 0.3 percent of the soils in the one creek drainage in Whitman County were heavily impacted by damaging deposition. Individual fields or farms can have much larger affected areas. Another problem that has only recently been recognized is that of clayey B-horizon and duripan materials, eroded from ridge crests and knobs, becoming draped over A horizons on lower slopes by downslope tillage movement. We have observed up to 13 cm of B-horizon material over A horizons. Difficulty in seedbed preparation, poor seedling emergence, and increased water runoff result.

We presently lack the detailed information on soil distribution and on rates of change of the 3-dimensional landscape to be able to accurately predict the rate at which subsoil materials are being exposed and the percentage of the soil area in the Palouse that has or will have limiting subsoil horizons at or near the land surface.

DIFFERING IMPACTS OF EROSION ON PRODUCTIVITY OF DIFFERENT SOILS

In this section we discuss the agronomic and pedologic reasons why different soil series in the Palouse could be expected to respond differently as topsoil is lost by erosion. We then demonstrate statistically significant differences in the shape and position of the response function of wheat yield to topsoil depth for two soil series subdivided by land use capability class.

Erosion-Productivity Relationships as a Function of Soil Characteristics

Numerous authors have discussed the agronomic and pedologic reasons why different soils respond differently to soil erosion (see, for example, Langdale and Schrader, 1982; Schertz, 1983; Schrader, 1980; Winters and Simonson, 1951). Reasons cited most often for the decline in productivity with progressive erosion are (1) loss of soil organic matter, (2) decreased volume of rooting with attendant loss of plant-available water and nutrient storage/supply, and (3) reduced water infiltration. Winters and Simonson (1951) discussed the multitude of ways in which shallow or exposed subsoils can increase the severity of these problems.

In the Palouse each of these problems exist, but the soils most severely affected are those with impermeable, infertile subsoil horizons. The following data, taken from unpublished analyses of the National Cooperative Soil Survey and Washington State University, illustrate some of the important physical and chemical properties of Palouse soils as they relate to crop productivity. Even on sites where erosion has been minimal, continuous tillage has reduced organic matter levels below their levels in the virgin state. The organic matter in most Palouse-area soils is held primarily in the upper 75 cm of the uneroded profile. In the drier western Palouse this means that with the combined effects of tillage and erosion, the organic matter content of surface soils has declined from about 2.0 percent to 1.0 percent today. In the eastern Palouse, where soils originally had higher levels of organic matter but also where higher erosion rates prevail, the organic matter content of surface soils has declined from 4.5 percent to less than 2.0 percent today, depending on slope position. The organic matter content of clay subsoils now at the land surface on ridge tops is less than 0.5 percent. This decline results in poorer aggregate stability, with increased surface crusting and rainfall runoff.

With some soils, such as those of the Palouse and Walla Walla series, plant rooting volume or depth is not reduced appreciably until and unless a paleosol horizon is brought into the effective rooting zone by erosion. In these soils, surface bulk densities average 1.3 Mg/m^3 and subsoil bulk densities are only slightly higher at 1.3 to 1.5 Mg/m^3. With other soils, such as the Risbeck, Endicott, Naff, Garfield, and Thatuna series, plant rooting volume or depth is strongly affected by erosion. In Risbeck soils, erosion increases the percentage of cemented duripan fragments in the rooting zone, effectively reducing rooting volume, and in Endicott soils an intact duripan at 50 to 100 cm acts as a complete barrier to rooting. Paleosol B horizons in Naff, Garfield, and Thatuna soils have silty clay loam and silty clay textures (32 to 48 percent clay) and bulk densities as high as 1.6 to 1.75 Mg/m^3. When these lie near the soil surface, they physically restrict rooting depth, and where they are at the soil surface a severe limitation of plant growth can result.

Infiltration rates for both A and B horizons of Palouse and Walla Walla series soils are similar, 15 to 50 mm/h, so that progressive erosion does not have a strong effect on runoff/infiltration ratios of these soils. However, infiltration rates for paleosol B horizons of Naff, Garfield, Thatuna, and similar soils are as low as 1.5 to 15 mm/h. Water intake and storage is considerably less on these soils and runoff is increased, particularly where the subsoil is exposed, which may increase the erosion hazard. Exceptionally high water storage for crop growth has been a major factor in the success of dryland farming in the Palouse region, yet because of the slow infiltration rate of paleosol horizons we are finding droughtiness to be an increasing problem in soils on selected landscape positions.

The exposure of paleosol horizons has created new problems in crop management such as difficult seedbed preparation and poor seedling emergence in clay and duripan materials. Nutrient deficiencies of P, N, S, and Zn on exposed clay ridges have been observed on an increasing basis. These deficiencies are very difficult to treat because small areas in the irregular Palouse landscape cannot easily be managed separately. In summary, based on the widely ranging characteristics of soil series in the Palouse, both uneroded and eroded, we would predict that the response functions of wheat yield to declining topsoil depth would differ among soil series.

Estimated Topsoil Depth - Wheat Yield Relationships

In Table 2 and Fig. 4 we summarize the relationship between topsoil depth and average winter wheat yield in the eastern Palouse that we estimated for two soil series subdivided by capability class. These predictions are based on a statistical equation fit by regression analysis to 213 observations (Hoag, 1984). The unpublished data utilized were collected by the Colfax, Washington office of the Soil Conservation Service from farmer cooperators' fields over the years 1966-1980. Rod-row samples of wheat yield and topsoil depths were recorded at each site. Wetter (1977) defined the measured "topsoil" as "the darkened layer of soil measured from the soil surface to a point where the brown organic matter coloring is no longer evident and/or the structure or texture changes". The soil series, land use capability class, and sometimes other site characteristics were also recorded for each observation.

The Mitscherlich-Spillman response function below was fit to the sample data by nonlinear least squares regression procedures.

$$Yw = \{[4.264 + 1.411 \text{ (Palouse)} + 1.301 \text{ (CL3)} - 1.432 \text{ (CL6)}]WI + \tag{1}$$
$$\phantom{Yw = \{[}(9.52) (1.53) (2.90) (-1.66)$$

$$(4.083 + 2.787 \text{ (Palouse)} + 4.804 \text{ (Thatuna)})(1 - 0.989 \text{ (TD)})WI\}\exp(-0.01)(T),$$
$$(1.31) (0.79) (1.62) (-44.20) (-1.49)$$

$$R^2 = 0.48$$

The variables in Eq. (1) are: Yw = wheat yield in t/ha; Palouse = one for the Palouse soil series and zero otherwise; Thatuna = one for Thatuna soil series and zero otherwise; CL3 = one for capability class III and zero otherwise; CL6 = one for capability class VI and zero otherwise; WI = an annual weather index, $0 \leq WI \leq 1.00$, indicating the suitability of weather in the region for wheat production in the year the observations were collected (James et al., 1982; Hoag, 1984). Due to the absence of site-specific weather records, weather records from Pullman, WA which is located in the approximate center of the eastern Palouse, were utilized to construct the annual WI series. TD = topsoil depth in cm; and T = (year minus 1966), is an annual time index. The values in parentheses are asymptotic t-statistics.

Table 2. Predicted Average Annual Winter Wheat Yields in the Eastern Palouse
for Varying Topsoil Depths, by Soil Series and Capability Class

Topsoil depth (cm)	Predicted yields (t/ha)					
	Palouse series		Thatuna series		Naff series	
	Class III	Class IV	Class III	Class IV	Class III	Class IV
0	2.96	2.41	2.36	1.81	2.36	1.81
15	3.41	2.86	2.94	2.39	2.63	2.08
30	3.79	3.24	3.44	2.88	2.86	2.30
45	4.11	3.56	3.85	3.30	3.05	2.49
60	4.38	3.83	4.20	3.65	3.21	2.66
75	4.61	4.06	4.50	3.95	3.34	2.79
90	4.81	4.26	4.75	4.20	3.46	2.91

The non-linear Mitscherlich-Spillman functional form employed in Eq. (1) and illustrated in Fig. 4 for the Palouse, Thatuna, and Naff soil series' possesses properties that are theoretically reasonable in an equation that predicts response of crop yield to topsoil depth: It displays diminishing marginal productivity as topsoil depth increases, and it approaches the empirically estimated maximum yield in an asymptotic fashion. In addition, the Mitscherlich-Spillman form used here was found, in related earlier work (Hoag and Young, 1982; Taylor, 1982), to provide a statistically superior fit to the data when compared to other models.

The coefficient of multiple determination, R^2, indicates that the equation explained 48 percent of the variation in yield in the data set. The absence of information in the data set on site-specific management practices, microclimatic conditions, and pest and disease conditions probably account for the unexplained residual variability.

When used to generate the yield predictions in Table 2 and Fig. 4, the WI was held constant at 0.64, its 1966-83 average value in the region, and T was held constant at 4 (for 1970), the median year in the data set. The relationships between wheat yields and topsoil depth could shift upward or downward over time with progress or decline of technology, respectively. Our analysis of the effect of topsoil loss on crop yields in this paper does not attempt to account for the impact of technology. These impacts are discussed elsewhere (Papendick et al., 1985; Young et al., 1985).

The estimated response function for winter wheat (Eq. 1) generated higher yields than the regional average for this period because (1) most of the data used to estimate the function come from the higher-yielding eastern portion of the region which averages 560 to 580 mm of precipitation per year and (2) the farms where data were collected were judged by the SCS scientists to have superior management. For this reason, yields predicted by Eq. (1) were multiplied by 0.69 to derive the values given in Table 2 and plotted in Fig. 4. The 0.69 is a deflator that we used to make the yield predictions consistent with the 1977-1982 regional average winter wheat yields reported by the Washington Crop and Livestock Reporting Service.

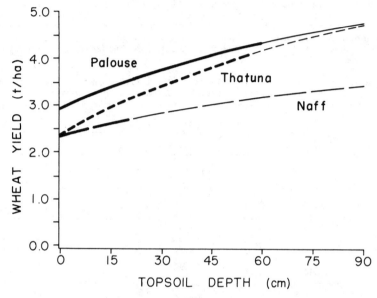

Fig. 4   Topsoil Depth-yield Response Functions for the Palouse, Thatuna, and Naff Soils, Capability Class III Sites. (Heavier line segments represent the natural range of topsoil thickness for undisturbed and eroded sites of each soil; lighter line segments are extrapolations beyond this range using Eq.(1.))

Palouse-Thatuna-Naff Association: The "base soil" in Eq. (1) was taken to be a capability class II site of the Naff series. The positive coefficients on "Palouse" and "Thatuna" variables indicate that the topsoil depth-wheat yield response equation for these soils is shifted upward in comparison to that for the Naff series (Fig. 4). Higher yields are predicted, therefore, at any specified depth for the Palouse and Thatuna soils than for Naff soils (Table 2). This result is consistent with the discussion above that subsoil B horizon characteristics are far more favorable for crop growth and water infiltration in Palouse than in Naff soils.   The statistical support for the upward shift in the response function is not strong, as evidenced by low t-statistics (Eq. (1)), however we feel that this is primarily due to the small numbers of observations for some soil series' and topsoil depths (Table 3). Observed topsoil depths for Palouse and Thatuna soils ranged from 0 to 76 cm. Observations of topsoil depth on Naff soils were less than 46 cm on all but one site, and all 37 Garfield observations had less than 15 cm of topsoil. We feel that the distribution of observed topsoil depths in Table 3 reflects the natural differences in A-horizon thickness both within and among soil series, and not bias in the sampling scheme. The yield predictions for the Naff series above 46 cm of topsoil (Table 2, Fig. 4) should be interpreted with caution because this is an extrapolation beyond the natural maximum thickness for this soil.

The response function is more steeply sloping for the Thatuna series than for either the Naff or the Palouse series (Fig. 4); when its topsoil is deep, the Thatuna series produces wheat yields comparable to the Palouse series, however, when its topsoil is thin, yields drop to levels that are comparable to those for the Naff series. This is consistent with soil characteristics. Palouse soils have deep A horizons and their B horizons offer minimal limitations to crop rooting and water infiltration. A- horizons of Thatuna soils are of comparable thickness, however, they have a dense, impermeable clayey B horizon at about 100 cm. As topsoil is lost from both soils, productivity should decline more markedly on the Thatuna than on the Palouse soils, and, as the subsoil becomes very near the surface, yields on the Thatuna should approach the limiting minimum yield of the Naff series with its clayey subsoil exposed. The slope of the response function for the Naff series is quite low possibly because most of the topsoil depth observations from which the function was calculated were less than 30 cm. Thirty centimeters of topsoil over a very restrictive subsoil may not yield appreciably more wheat than farming directly in the subsoil.

In earlier versions Eq. (1) also had shift variables for the Garfield series, but they were deleted from the equation because of very low t- statistics. Naff and Garfield soils apparently do not differ significantly in their response to declining topsoil depth. This finding is reasonable because Naff and Garfield soils are both dominated by a thick paleosol argillic horizon at shallow depth.

Table 3. Number of Field Observations by Topsoil Depth for Four Soil Series

Soil series	Topsoil depth (cm)				
	0-15	16-30	31-46	47-76	>76
Naff	2	29	9	1	0
Garfield	37	0	0	0	0
Palouse	6	34	44	13	2
Thatuna	2	2	12	10	10

In the loessial soils, the primary variable that has been used to define phases or map units within a soil series is slope steepness. Slope is therefore also the primary determinant of the land use capability class of each map unit. Capability classes within a series may be thought of as subdivisions of the series based on similar hydrologic and microclimatic regimes within each hill.

Class IV soils demonstrated the same topsoil-yield relationship that class II soils did for the 3 soil series; their response functions were not separable and therefore "class IV" does not appear as an explicit dummy variable in the equation. Capability class III imposed a modest positive shift in the response function relative to the class II and IV "base class" (Table 2). The positive impact of class III relative to class II soils was not expected and could have been an artifact of the data set. It may also be that class III soils have the most favorable slope, aspect, and hydrology for crop growth; class II soils have 1.7 to 4.0 degree slopes and can be saturated with water and cold later into the spring than class III soils, which have 4.0 to 14.0 degree slopes. This may provide better early-spring growing conditions for winter wheat. The negative impact of class IV (14.0- 21.8 degree slopes, and some eroded phases of lower slope classes) and class VI soils (21.8-28.8 degree slopes and some eroded phases) may be due to the tendency for these to occur on steeper, more northerly aspects where yields are sometimes reduced by cold soil temperatures and heavy snow accumulation.

Walla Walla Association: We calculated a topsoil-yield response function for the soils in the Walla Walla association (data not shown). Wheat yields on soils with comparable morphologies are substantially lower in the Walla Walla association than in the Palouse-Thatuna-Naff association. For example, a class III Palouse series soil with 60 cm of topsoil was predicted to yield 4.4 t/ha, based on an annual cropping system, while the Class III Walla Walla series soil with 60 cm of topsoil would yield 3.0 t/ha (data for Walla Walla soil not shown), based on a wheat/fallow cropping system. The difference in yield is even larger when the crop rotation differences are considered. The profiles of the two soils are similar, very deep and with no restriction on rooting or moisture storage capacity; the difference in yield is principally a function of precipitation.

Classes III and VI imposed progressively greater negative shifts in the response function for the Walla Walla series, relative to the class II "base class". Class IV imposed a moderate positive shift relative to the class II "base class" and therefore produced the highest yields of the 4 classes. We cannot explain this finding at this time. As an example, the Walla Walla series with 60 cm of topsoil was predicted to yield 3.6, 3.0, 3.8, and 2.0 t/ha on classes II, III, IV, and VI, respectively.

Insufficient data were available for Risbeck and Endicott soils to statistically compare their yield-topsoil depth response to that of the predominant Walla Walla series. It is interesting to note, however, that among the 11 observations on Risbeck soils, 9 had no remaining topsoil. This precluded estimation of a response function. Only 4 observations were made on Endicott soils, compared to 99 on Walla Walla.

Impact: These results provide empirical evidence that soil erosion leads to potential yield declines of winter wheat, that the response varies by soil series and by land use capability class, and that the yield response in most cases is consistent with the morphology of the soil series that we have considered. Additional data, collected in a more systematic fashion, better information on other factors such as past management and climate, and additional systematic modeling will be needed to reach more definitive conclusions.

SUMMARY

The soil-landscapes of the Palouse are complex because of the complex topography, because macro- and micro-climate has strongly influenced soil development, and because buried paleosols occupy part or all of the rooting zone in at least 30 percent of the upland soils. The Risbeck and Endicott soils in the Walla Walla soil association have duripan fragments and duripans within the rooting zone, and the Naff and Garfield soils in the Palouse-Thatuna-Naff soil assocation have strong argillic horizons at shallow depth. These and other similar soils in the Palouse will be more severely affected by continued erosion than will the very deep, uniform Walla Walla and Palouse soils, because of reduction in effective rooting depth, loss of water and nutrient storage capacity, and increased rainfall runoff.

Our USLE water erosion estimates are approximate; nevertheless, they are based on measured hill shapes and soil distributions. The projections of soil loss over a 50-yr period allow us to directly gauge the magnitude of the loss. Our estimates of water erosion differ by almost a factor of ten (8.7 t/ha-yr to 74.6 t/ha-yr) between soils depending on slope position, tillage practice, precipitation zone, and aspect. Tillage erosion on hilltops, estimated for a single deep plowing, is of a similar magnitude (29 t/ha-yr vs. 11.2 to 36.8 t/ha-yr) to the annual water erosion from the same upper hill segment, and this segment is where paleosol horizons are generally nearest the surface. At the rates of water and tillage erosion that we project for conventional tillage over a 50-yr period, all of the topsoil will be removed from the Naff, Garfield, and Risbeck soils, exposing paleosol B horizons at the surface. One-third to two-thirds of the topsoil will be removed from the Walla Walla, Palouse, and Thatuna soils in this 50-yr period.

Based on the projected erosion rates, and on our analysis of the relationship between topsoil depth and wheat yield for selected soils, crop yields will be reduced on soils in both the Walla Walla and Palouse-Thatuna-Naff associations and may be reduced by up to 25 percent on the severely eroded sites of the Thatuna series (Fig. 4) over 50 years. The projected declines in yield, of course, ignore any concurrent yield increases due to improved technology over this time. In the presence of technical progress, the impacts of erosion still represent reductions in yield growth (Papendick et al., 1985; Young et al., 1985). In percentage loss of wheat yield, the Thatuna soil is most severely affected because it has large predicted soil losses, and because of the steep slope of its response function (Table 1, Eq. (1), Fig. 4). The percentage reduction in wheat yield for a given topsoil loss is least on the Naff soil because its wheat yields are less than those on Palouse and Thatuna soils at all topsoil depths, and because the response function for the Naff soil has a relatively flat slope. The terminal wheat yield (yield at zero topsoil) is predicted from our response function to be 2.4 t/ha and 1.8 t/ha for Naff soil on class III and IV sites, respectively. These yields are 54 percent and 47 percent of the yields predicted for class III and IV Palouse soil with 60 cm of topsoil. The influence of the paleosol subsoils and of the loss of topsoil on crop productivity is demonstrated clearly by these relationships.

REFERENCES

1. Donaldson, N. C. 1980. Soil survey of Whitman County, Washington. USDA-SCS and Washington State Univ. Agric. Research Ctr. U. S. Government Printing Office, Washington, D.C.

2. Foley, L. L. 1982. Quaternary chronology of the Palouse loess near Washtucna, eastern Washington. M. S. Thesis. Western Washington Univ., Bellingham.

3. Fosberg, M. A., M. Bramble-Broadahl, A. L. Falen, D. Walker, and R. L. Mahler. 1983. Soil erosion effects on winter wheat yield in northern Idaho. Agron. Abstr., p. 197. 75th Ann. Mtg., Am. Soc. Agron., Madison, Wisconsin.

4. Garber, Lowell W. 1965. Relationship of soils to earthflows in the Palouse. J. Soil. Water Conserv. 20(1):21-23.

5. Gentry, H. R. 1974. Geomorphology of some selected soil-landscapes in Whitman County, Washington. M. S. Thesis. Washington State Univ., Pullman.

6. Hoag, D. L. 1984. An evaluation of USDA commodity program incentives for erodible land retirement. Ph.D. dissertation. Washington State University, Pullman.

7. Hoag, D. L. and D. L. Young. 1983. Yield topsoil depth response functions: Linear versus Mitscherlich-Spillman. STEEP Agric. Econ. Working Paper 82-2. Dept. Agric. Econ., Washington State Univ., Pullman.

8. Frazier, B., D. K. McCool, and D. L. Young. 1984. Estimating the
    physical and economic impacts of downslope deposition from cropland
    erosion. Paper presented at USDA-ERS Off-Site Benefit Estimation
    Workshop, Walla Walla College, College Place, WA, April 18, 1984.

9. James, L., J. Erpenbeck, D. Bassett and J. Middleton. 1982.
    Irrigation requirements for Washington -- estimates and methodology.
    Agr. Research Bulletin XB 0925, Washington State Univ. Pullman.

10. Kaiser, Verle G. 1961. Historical land use and erosion in the Palouse
    - A reappraisal. Northwest Sci. 35(4):139-153.

11. Kaiser, Verle G., Warren A. Starr, and S. Burkett Johnson. 1951.
    Types of topography as related to land use in Whitman County,
    Washington. Northwest Sci. 25(2):69-75.

12. Kardos, L. T., P. I. Vlasoff, and S. N. Twiss. 1941. Factors
    contributing to landslides in the Palouse region. Soil Sci. Soc. Am.
    Proc. 8:437-440.

13. Langdale, G. W., and W. D. Schrader. 1982. Soil erosion effects on
    soil productivity of cultivated cropland. p. 41-51. In B. L. Schmidt,
    K. R. Allmaras, J. V. Mannering, and R. I. Papendick (eds.)
    Determinants of soil loss tolerance. ASA Spec. Pub. 45. Am. Soc.
    Agron., Madison, Wisconsin.

14. Lewis, Peirce. 1960. Linear topography in the southwestern Palouse,
    Washington - Oregon. Ann. Assoc. Am. Geog. 50(2):98-111.

15. McCool, D. K., and G. O. George. 1983. A second-generation adaptation
    of the Universal Soil Loss Equation for Pacific Northwest drylands.
    Paper No. 83-2066. Am. Soc. Agric. Eng., St. Joseph, Michigan.

16. Papendick, R. I., D. L. Young, D. K. McCool, and H. A. Krauss. 1985.
    Regional effects of soil erosion on crop productivity -- Pacific
    Northwest. In R. F. Follett and B. A. Stewart (eds.), Soil Erosion and
    Crop Productivity. ASA-CSSA-SSSA, Madison, Wisconsin (in press).

17. Pawson, W. W., O. L. Brough, Jr., J. P. Swanson, and G. M. Horner,
    1961. Economics of cropping systems and soil conservation in the
    Palouse. Agric. Exp. Station of Idaho, Oregon, and Washington, and
    Agric. Res. Serv. USDA Bull. 2. 82 pp.

18. Power, J. F., and J. O. Legg. 1978. Effect of crop residue on the
    soil chemical environment and nutrient availability. p. 85-100. In W.
    R. Oschwald (ed.) Crop residue management systems. ASA Spec. Pub. 31.
    Am. Soc. Agron., Madison, Wisconsin.

19. Schrader, W. D. 1980. Effect of erosion and other physical processes
    on productivity of U. S. croplands and rangelands. Relationships to
    recent technological developments. Prepared for Office of Technology
    Assessment, United States Congress, Washington, D.C.

20. Soil Survey Staff. 1975. Soil Taxonomy. A basic system of soil
    classification for making and interpreting soil surveys. Agric. Handb.
    No. 436. USDA. U. S. Government Printing Office, Washington, D.C.

21. Taylor, D. B. 1982. Evaluating the long run impacts of soil erosion
    on crop yields and net farm income in the Palouse annual cropping
    region of the Pacific Northwest. Ph.D. dissertation. Washington State
    University, Pullman.

22. Triplett, G. B., Jr., and J. V. Mannering. 1978. Crop residue management in crop rotation and multiple cropping systems. p. 187-206. In W. R. Oschwald (ed.) Crop residue management systems. ASA Spec. Pub. 31. Am. Soc. Agron., Madison, Wisconsin.

23. U. S. Department of Agriculture. 1978. Palouse Cooperative River Basin Study. Soil Conservation Service, Forest Service, and Economics, Statistics, and Cooperative Service. U. S. Government Printing Office, Washington, D. C. 182 pp.

24. Washington Crop and Livestock Reporting Service. (Annual issues, 1977-82). Washington Agricultural Statistics. Washington Department of Agriculture. Seattle, Washington.

25. Wetter, F. 1977. The influence of topsoil depth on yields. USDA-SCS Tech. Note AGRON-10, and unpublished data underlying report. Soil Conservation Service, Colfax, Wash.

26. Winters, Eric, and Roy W. Simonson. 1951. The subsoil. Adv. Agron. 3:1-92.

27. Young, D. L., D. B. Taylor, and R. I. Papendick. 1985. Separating erosion and technology impacts on winter wheat yields in the Palouse: A statistical approach. Paper presented at National Symposium on Erosion and Soil Productivity, Am. Soc. Agric. Eng. New Orleans, Louisiana, December 10-11, 1984. (in press).

CORN YIELD PREDICTION FOR A CLAYPAN SOIL USING A PRODUCTIVITY INDEX

C. J. Gantzer   T. R. McCarty
                                 Member ASAE

Study of relationships between soil properties and a soil's capacity for producing plants, or soil productivity, is the focus of a number of current research projects. An excellent review of much of the recent published work can be found in the article by the National Soil Erosion-Soil Productivity Research Planning Committee (1981). These projects have grown out of a need to improve the quantitative relationships between plant growth and soil properties which may be affected by soil erosion. In response to this need, various approaches have been developing, which attempt to numerically relate a soil's properties to its productivity. Numerous simulation models exist in a wide range of detail, ranging from simple to complex which relate to the topic of erosion and productivity.

Currently, the Erosion-Productivity Impact Calculator (EPIC) (Williams et al. 1982) and the Nitrogen-Tillage-Residue-Management (NTRM) Model (Schaffer et al. 1982), two state-of-the-art models, show promise of developing detailed relationships between quantities related to the erosion-productivity process. Although both models are operational, and have been producing reasonable results, further validation of these models is currently necessary. In the North Central region, for example, a five year Regional Research Project, (NC-174 1983) is currently undertaking such work. When such research further validates these complex models, they may provide good estimates of the effect of erosion on productivity. However, both models are large and complex and require a complete knowledge of soil properties, which will simply be too costly for routine application.

A less complex approach for estimating the effects of erosion has recently been developed by Neill (1979). The method called the Soil Productivity Index (PI), requires less complete knowledge of the exact soil properties, than either EPIC or NTRM. The reduced complexity may involve some loss in prediction of complex interactions, however the simplicity is extremely desirable for quick field determinations. Recently, Pierce et al. (1984) have found coefficients of determination for regression of corn yield on PI ranging from 0.23 for all soils in four midwestern counties, to 0.70 for the same set of soils excluding frequently flooded or depressional soils, using average soil properties reported in soil surveys.

The objective of our study was on-site evaluation of the Productivity Index on a set of artificially eroded plots located on a central Missouri claypan soil. Unlike historical scalping experiments, the plots used in this study were fertilized at high levels reducing the significance of differential fertility on crop yield.

DESCRIPTION OF THE SOIL PRODUCTIVITY INDEX

The Soil Productivity Index is a method used to relate root growth to soil properties within a profile. An outline of the concept is shown in Fig. 1. The approach is based on the assumption that soil properties are major factors constraining crop growth and ultimately crop yield. The suitability of soil conditions for plant growth is in fact the summation of

The authors are: C. J. GANTZER, Assistant Professor, Department of Agronomy and T. R. McCARTY, Assistant Professor, Department of Agricultural Engineering, University of Missouri, Columbia, MO 65211.

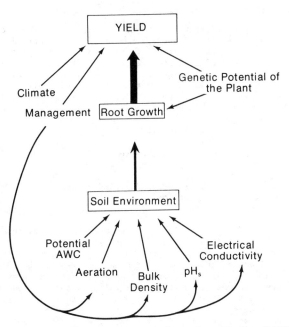

Fig. 1 Concept of the Soil Productivity Index, after Kiniry (1983).

the suitability of each layer or horizon. Realistically soil horizons vary
in importance. In the extreme case, horizons deep enough, have essentially
no influence on crop growth. Horizons slightly closer to the surface,
situated near the lower boundary of the rooting depth, begin to have a small
influence on biological processes related to plant growth. However, the
layers closer than about 50 cm to the surface often exert the major influence
on processes related to plant growth and development. The model assumes that
yield is related to total root growth, which in turn is related to soil
conditions. Other variables such as climate, management and the genetic
plant potential are known to affect plant growth, and thus have been included
in Fig. 1, however at present only the soil environment characterized by the
potential available water capacity (PAWC), bulk density (BD) and salt pH (pHs
i.e. pH in a 1:1 mixture of soil with 0.01 M $CaCl_2$) has been used as input
for the model. Each of these properties has been related to suitability or
sufficiency for growth, ranging from values of 0 representing no growth, to
1.0 representing growth in an ideal medium. Sufficiencies included in this
study, are estimates compiled from existing research, and should not be
interpreted as fixed. Rather sufficiency values should be viewed as estimates which can be improved when additional research indicates improvement is
possible. The equation for PI developed by Neill (1979) is:

$$PI = \sum_{i=1}^{n} (A_i \times B_i \times C_i \times RI_i)$$

Eq. (1)

where PI = Soil Productivity Index;
  A_i = sufficiency of potential available water holding capacity for the
       ith layer;
  B_i = sufficiency of bulk density of the ith soil layer;
  C_i = sufficiency of pHs;

  RI_i = weighting factor for the ith soil layer;
  n = number of soil layers.

171

Estimation of the Root Distribution in Ideal Soils

Estimation of the root distribution found in ideal conditions was originally developed from water depletion studies by Horn (1971). Horn described the profile of water use as the fraction of available water depleted versus depth. The upper limit of available water was defined as the volumetric water content at a field determined field capacity and the lower limit was defined as the volumetric water content at the -15 kPa soil water potential. Horn's prediction equation for the fraction of available water depleted versus depth from a recharged soil is:

$$L_D = 0.152 \log (R + (R^2 + 6.45)^{1/2}) -$$
$$0.152 \log (D + (D^2 + 6.45)^{1/2})$$

Eq. (2)

where L_D = fraction of available water depleted at depth D;
  D = depth within the profile;
  R = total rooting depth.

Horn assumed that the relative frequency of root mass at depth D was equal to L_D, the fraction of available water depleted at that depth. Thus the integral of Eq. (2) between any two depths indicates the fraction of the total root mass contained between those two depths. In reality the distribution of root mass may not necessarily be exactly equivalent to water extraction patterns, however L_D does represent a weighting factor related in some way to root activity at a specified depth. In practical terms, L_D estimates the relative importance of a given layer for the plant. Both the form of L_D and the rooting depth will depend on both crop and soil conditions. Using previous work in Missouri as a guide (Kiniry et al. 1983), we chose to use Eq. (2) directly with an assumed rooting depth of 100 cm.

Estimation of Soil Sufficiency for Root Growth

Response curves of sufficiency for root growth relative to PAWC, BD, and pHs used in this study were developed by Neill (1979). These relationships are based on studies which quantitatively relate root growth to a given soil property.

Sufficiency of Potential Available Water Storage Capacity: The response curve for the sufficiency of PAWC was developed by Neill (1979). The response curve is found in Fig 2. Potential available water capacity is the difference between the volumetric water content of undisturbed soil cores equilibrated to a -33 kPA potential and the volumetric water content of cores equilibrated to a potential of -1500 kPA. In the latter case, the cores were prepared from sieved soil (2 mm sieve) and packed to an equivalent bulk density.

Sufficiency of Bulk Density: The response curve for the sufficiency of BD is found in Fig. 2. The works of Blanchar et al. (1978), Tackett and Pearson (1964) and Taylor and Gardner (1963) were used in developing this relationship. Although work by Pierce et al. (1983) has attempted to correct differences in root resistance due to variation in soil texture, the approach has not been pursued in this study.

Sufficiency of pHs: The response curve for the sufficiency of pHs is found in Fig. 2. This relationship was developed from the work of Adams and Lund (1966), Blanchar et al. (1978), and Fisher (1969).

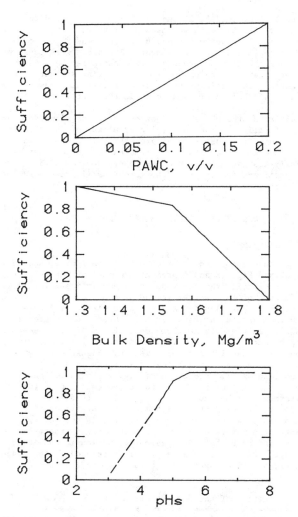

Fig. 2 Sufficiency Relationships for the Productivity Index.

DESCRIPTION OF THE FIELD PLOTS

To evaluate the long term effects of soil erosion on crop yield, field plots
were established in 1982 on a Mexico silt loam soil. The field plot site is
on the University of Missouri's South Farm, about 3.5 km SE of campus. For
ease in reference the field plots are called the ERASE plots. ERASE is an
acronym for Erosion Recovery And System Evaluation. The design consists of
four depths of topsoil in a randomized complete block design replicated four
times. An artificially eroded site was selected for several reasons. First,
the plots could be blocked across slope, reducing variability in water supply
due to topographic position. Second, since the plots would be close
together, less variation in soil and weather would be expected compared to
larger scales of study. Third, the plots would also simulate conditions that
exist after terrace and waterway construction.

Depths of topsoil of 0.0, 12.5, 25 and 37.5 cm were selected for study. A preliminary survey of soil depth was made prior to construction of the plots. Location of the interface between A and B horizons was found to be 25 ± 3 cm making the 25 cm depth the check treatment. The plots were constructed in the summer of 1982. Drainage channels were constructed between the plots in order to prevent water leaving one plot from entering another. In order to minimize compaction, the drainage channels were used as roadways for the elevating scraper and bulldozer used to build the plots.

Actual construction of the plots was done by using the elevating scraper to remove 12.5 cm of soil from randomly selected plots for the 12.5 cm treatments. Measurements from the original ground level were made in order to determine when 12.5 cm of soil had been removed. This soil material was then added to randomly assigned plots in order to produce the 37.5 cm treatment plots. All topsoil was removed from the zero topsoil treatment plots and stockpiled off site.

DESCRIPTION OF THE MEXICO SOIL SERIES

General Characteristics

Table 1 presents the family and subgroup classification for the Mexico soil series. Table 2 and Figs. 3 and 4 present profile information for the soil. The surface 25 cm of soil from check plots is nearly ideal in all respects. An important feature of this series is the pronounced claypan located between the 28-64 cm depths. The claypan is associated with rapid decreases in PAWC and pHs, and with moderate increases in BD. These changes greatly reduce the sufficiencies for plant growth in that zone. Below 64 cm in depth the PAWC and the pHs both increase while BD remains somewhat limiting, thus providing an improved but less than ideal growing medium. Figure 4 presents values for predicted rooting fractions for all four treatments in addition to values expected for an ideal soil. Inspection of Fig. 4 shows all four curves to be significantly to the left of the ideal curve indicating that the PI's for the four depth treatments of Mexico soil are less than that for an ideal soil. In the case of the 37.5 cm depth soil treatment, large reductions begin to occur after a depth of 40 cm. In large part this is due to low pHs values. Below this depth, the pHs values differ little between treatments. Curves from Fig. 4 also indicate that the greatest reduction in quality of soil, occurs above depths of 40cm. This is primarily related to the shape of the weighting factor, but also suggests that soils above this depth are the most valuable.

Table 1. Classification of the Mexico Series
==

Location	Family	Subgroup
South Farm, UMC	Fine, montmorillonitic, mesic	Typic Ochraqualf

==

Table 2. A Representative Mexico Series Profile Description From Section 36,
T48N, R12W, Boone County, MO.

Soil Profile Horizon	Depth	Description
	cm	
Ap	0-15	Dark grayish brown (10YR 4/2) silt loam with weak fine granular structure; pH 6.4.
A_2	15-28	Grayish brown (10YR 5/2) silt loam with weak fine granular structure; pH 6.4.
B_{21}	28-36	Grayish brown (10YR 5/2) silty clay; many fine distinct red (2.5YR 5/8) mottles; moderate medium subangular blocky structure; pH 4.5.
B_{22}	36-64	Brown to dark brown (10YR 4/3) silty clay loam; many medium prominent strong brown (7.5YR 5/8) and yellowish brown (10YR 5/8) mottles; weak coarse subangular blocky to massive structure; pH 4.9.
B_3	64-107	Light brownish gray (2.5YR 6/2) silty clay loam; many medium distinct yellowish brown (10YR 5/6) mottles; massive structure; pH 5.5.
C	107-304+	Light gray (10YR 7/1) silty clay loam; many medium distinct yellowish brown (10YR 5/8) mottles; massive structure; pH 5.7.

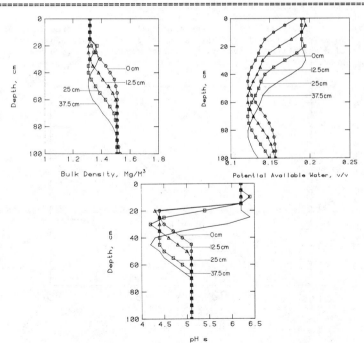

Fig. 3 Estimated Bulk Density, Potential Available Water and Salt pH From 0 to 100 cm for the ERASE Plots, Columbia, MO.

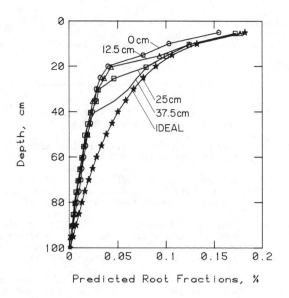

Fig. 4. Comparison of Predicted Rooting Fractions vs Depth for ERASE Plot
Treatments and an Ideal Soil.

DESCRIPTION OF EVAPOTRANSPIRATION AND PRECIPITATION

It is known that weather is one of the principal variables affecting plant
growth. To help understand what part weather played in this experiment
precipitation and potential evapotranspiration measurements were recorded.
Figure 5 presents traces for potential evapotranspiration and rainfall.

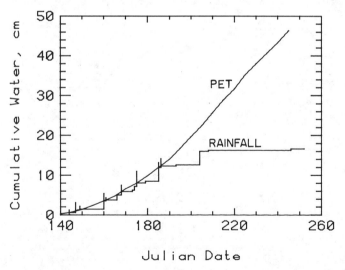

Fig. 5 The Relationship of Potential Evapotranspiration and Rainfall in 1984
for the ERASE Plots, Columbia, MO.

Early portions of the traces from Julian day 140-180, the early part of the growing season, show that weather conditions were favorable for plant growth with precipitation and evaporative demand having equal values during this period. However, from Julian day 185 on through the growing season, conditions were dry. Only one significant rainfall event of about 2 cm occurred during this period, creating extreme water stressed conditions.

Depth of Rooting

One of the underlying assumptions of the Soil Productivity Index is that the root growth is related to the level of sufficiency for the soil. To investigate this relationship measurements of the maximum depth of soil influenced by water extractions by roots with time was measured for each treatment. Depths were estimated using the methods described by McGowan (1973). Table 3 shows that extractions were most rapid for the 37.5 cm topsoil depth treatment. For other treatments time for water extraction to occur at a given depth was progressively delayed as the amount of topsoil was decreased. Regression analysis for data in Table 3 using the depths at which water content was measured within the profile and depth of topsoil as independent variables explained 88% of the variance of that data. The significance of this finding is that reduction in depths of topsoil appear to slow root growth thus increasing the potential for plant water stress.

Table 3. Mean Julian Date for Root Growth to Selected Depths Within the Profile. Data Collected From the ERASE plots, Columbia, MO 1984.

Depth of Topsoil	Depth of Rooting					
	38 cm	53 cm	69 cm	84 cm	99 cm	114 cm
cm	Julian Date					
0.0	189	199	204	218	224	225
12.5	190	198	200	205	221	224
25.0	185	196	199	210	219	224
37.5	180	193	199	209	218	223

Soil Water Depletion

Although the Soil Productivity Index as used in this study includes sufficiencies for BD, pHs and PAWC, the sufficiency for PAWC for the Mexico soil profile is the variable with the greatest total profile reduction across treatments. To investigate how measured experimental data compares with relationships as predicted by the PAWC response curves, soil water depletions for selected depths as well as for the total profile to 144 cm were calculated. Data are presented in Figs. 6 and 7. Essentially no difference in soil water depletion patterns can be observed for treatments with topsoil greater than 12.5 cm in depth. Significantly less water was found in the 0.0 topsoil treatment as compared with others. It should be mentioned that these differences were not found for water depletion patterns found in depths above 50 cm. Figure 8 presents average depletion measured over the total profile. Results are similar to those found from individual depths. These results suggest that the ability of corn roots to deplete water is not linearly related to the depth of topsoil in the Mexico soil. The significance of this result will be discussed in conjunction with both yield and PI values in the following section.

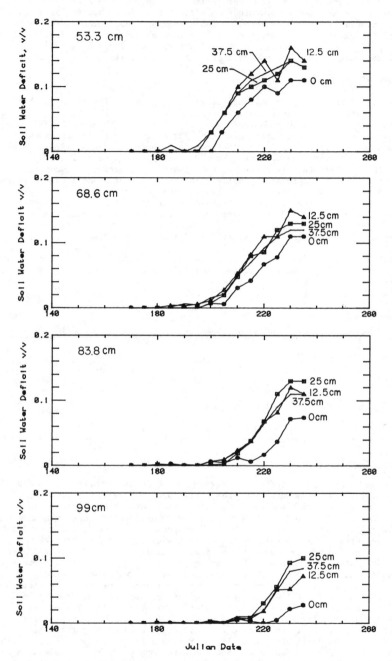

Fig. 6 Soil Water Deficit vs Time at Four Depths for Each Topsoil Treatment on the ERASE Plots, Columbia, MO.

178

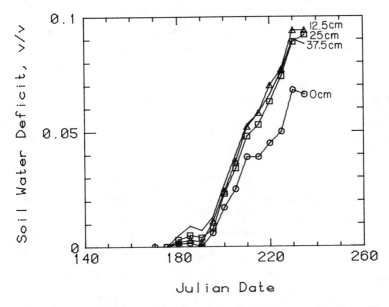

Fig. 7 Soil Water Deficit vs Time for the Whole Profile on the ERASE Plots,
Columbia, MO.

Yield and PI Relationships

Analysis of corn yield data for 1984 is included in Table 4. No significant
replicate effect was observed. Highly significant linear and quadratic
treatment effects are present. Although the yield increases with increasing
depth of topsoil, for practical purposes the yields from the 12.5, 25.0, and
37.5 cm treatments are the same. To evaluate the goodness of fit between
observed yields and PI, linear regression was used and is reported in Table
5. Inspection of the residual values shows a significant lack of fit for the
linear model which causes an overprediction of yield for the 0.0 topsoil and
37.5 topsoil treatment and an underprediction for the intermediate
treatments. This finding strongly suggests that a quadratic component
should be added to the linear model. The results from a quadratic model are
presented in Table 6. This model removes the systematic trend in the
residuals, and significantly reduces the magnitude of residual values.
Further work is necessary to understand why the quadratic term works or if it
holds for all soils, however the soil water depletion patterns within the
50-90 cm zone appear to be the key. Water extraction from this layer was
significantly reduced for the 0.0 topsoil treatment relative to all other
treatments. The yield from the 0.0 topsoil treatment was also significantly
less than the other treatments suggesting that water depletion as moderated
by plant response to water stress may be primarily responsible for
controlling yield reductions. Apparently the 12.5, 25.0 and 37.5 cm
treatments had relatively sufficient water supply and additional water in the
greater topsoil depths treatments did very little to increase yield. These
results show that use of a linear model to predict soil productivity was
improved by addition of a quadratic component. These results suggest that
the use of the soil productivity indexes currently developed would predict
greater yield reduction and soil erosion than may actually be realized.

Table 4. Analysis of Corn Yields From the ERASE Plots, Columbia, MO 1984.

Source	PR>F	Topsoil Depth	Mean Yield
		—— cm ——	—— kg/ha ——
Rep	0.31 NS	0.0	3637
Treatment	<0.01 **	12.5	5892
Linear	<0.01 **	25.0	6017
Quadratic	0.02 *	37.5	6140
	$R^2=0.78$	Average	5421

Table 5. Predicted and Observed Corn Yield for the ERASE Plots, Columbia, MO
1984, Using the Linear Regression Model:
Yield (kg/ha) = -3186 + 12,195 (PI) + e

Depth of Topsoil	PI	Observed Yield	Predicted Yield	Residual Yield
– cm –	– % –		—— kg/ha ——	
0.0	0.615	3637	4315	-678
12.5	0.679	5892	5095	797
25.0	0.725	6017	5656	361
37.5	0.804	6140	6620	-480

Table 6. Predicted and Observed Corn Yield for the ERASE Plots, Columbia, MO
1984, Using a Polynomial Regression Model:
Yield (kg/ha) = -71,387 + 205,944 (PI) -136,302 (PI^2) + e

Depth of Topsoil	PI	Observed Yield	Predicted Yield	Residual Yield
– cm –	– % –		—— kg/ha ——	
0.0	0.615	3637	3715	-78
12.5	0.679	5892	5608	284
25.0	0.725	6017	6278	-261
37.5	0.804	6140	6084	56

CONCLUSIONS

Results from the on-site evaluation of soil productivity index for a Mexico
claypan soil with 4 depths of topsoils show: (1) The date for root water
extraction to reach a given depth was progressively delayed for treatments
with lesser amounts of topsoil. (2) Significantly less water depletion was
observed with a 0.0 topsoil treatment for depths from about 50-100 cm in the
profile. No differences were found between other soil treatments. (3)
Highly significant linear and quadratic treatment effects for yield are

present. However, the majority of yield reduction was found between the 0.0 and 12.5 cm topsoil treatments. (4) Yield results would suggest that significant improvement in the Soil Productivity Index could be accomplished through incorporation of a quadratic component into the index for Mexico series soils.

REFERENCES

1. Adams, F., and Z. F. Lund. 1966. Effect of chemical activity of soil solution aluminum on cotton root penetration of acid subsoils. Soil Sci. 101:193-198.

2. Blanchar, R. W., C. R. Edmonds, and J. M. Bradford. 1978. Root growth in cores formed from fragipan and B_2 horizons of Hobson soil. Soil Sci. Soc. Am. 42:437-440.

3. Fisher, T. R. 1969. Crop yields in relation to soil pH as modified by liming acid soil. Mo. Agric. Exp. Stn. Res. Bull. 947.

4. Horn, F. W. 1971. The prediction of amounts and depth distribution of water in a well drained soil. M. S. Thesis. University of Missouri.

5. Kiniry, L. N., C. L. Scrivner, and M. E. Keener. 1983. A soil productivity index based upon predicted water depletion and root growth. University of Missouri-Columbia, Coll. of Agr., Agr. Exp. Sta. Res. Bull. 1051.

6. McGowan, M. 1973. Depth of water extraction by roots. p. 435-445. In: Isotope and radiation techniques in soil physics and irrigation studies. The International Atomic Energy Agency, Vienna.

7. National Soil Erosion - Soil Productivity Research Planning Committee. 1981. Soil erosion effects on soil productivity: a research perspective. J. Soil and Water Cons. 36:82-90.

8. Neill, L. L. 1979. An evaluation of soil productivity based on root growth and water depletion. M. S. Thesis. University of Missouri.

9. Pierce, F., W. E. Larson, and R. H. Dowdy. 1984. Evaluating soil productivity in relation to soil erosion. p. 33-69. In: F. R. Rijsberman and M. G. Wolman (Eds). Quantification of the effect of erosion on soil productivity in an international context. Pub. by IFIAS ABC Program at Delft Hydraulics Laboratory, Delft, Netherlands.

10. Schaffer, M. J., S. C. Gupta, J. A. E. Molina, D. R. Linden, and W. E. Larson. 1982. Simulation of nitrogen, tillage, and residue management effects on soil fertility. Proc. 3rd Int. Conf. on State of the Art in Ecol. Modeling, May 24-28, Fort Collins, CO, USA.

11. Tackett, J. L., and R. W. Pearson. 1964. Oxygen requirements of cotton seedling roots for penetration of compacted soil cores. Soil Sci. Soc. Am. Proc. 28:600-605.

12. Taylor, H. M., and H. R. Gardner. 1963. Penetration of cotton seedling tap roots as influenced by bulk density, moisture content, and strength of soil. Soil Sci. 96:153-156.

13. Williams, J., P. Dyck, and A. Jones. 1982. EPIC - a model for assessing the effects of erosion on soil productivity. Proc. 3rd Int. Conf. on State of the Art in Ecol. Modeling, May 24-28, Fort Collins, Co, USA.

RESTORING PRODUCTIVITY TO AN ERODED DARK

BROWN CHERNOZEMIC SOIL UNDER DRYLAND CONDITIONS

J. F. Dormaar*   C. W. Lindwall
                                                  Member ASAE

It was established during a recent soil survey of a 453,000 ha area in southern Alberta that 11% of the area suffered erosion losses (W.W. Pettapiece, Personal communication). Human beings are thus not simply figures in the landscape but shapers of the landscape (Chesworth 1982). Even though physical processes per se that transform soils, such as cultivation, do not necessarily lead to a reshaping of the agricultural landscape, soil erosion by wind and water will.

Erosion occurred on the prairies of Western Canada soon after the land was brought under cultivation. Wind erosion has turned out to be a very destructive form of soil loss. It also adversely affects agricultural crop productivity because of selective removal of plant nutrients and organic matter, and removal of finer soil particles leading to compaction of the soil and poor tilth (Anderson 1966; Pimentel et al. 1976).

Soil productivity is the capacity of soil to produce crops. Topsoil thickness is recognized as an important parameter in determining soil quality and productivity (Carlson et al. 1961; Engelstad and Shrader 1961; Power et al. 1981). Once this topsoil has been removed, however, the remaining soil must be treated to restore its full productivity. The literature on soil erosion usually deals with the mechanics of the erosion process and the practices for control. Very few long-term studies have been carried out attempting to determine the effects of soil erosion on crop production and to restore the productivity of subsoil after topsoil removal (Olson 1977; Anonymous 1982). If fact, Cook (1982) noted that research on the effects of erosion on soil productivity all but dried up from the mid-1950's to the early 1970's.

The objective of the present study was to determine in an area with an annual precipitation of about 400 mm and without the benefit of irrigation and manure 1) the effect of erosional loss of soil on certain soil properties and yield of a cereal crop and 2) the extent to which fertilizer and green manure, suitable for use under rainfed cereal production, positively influenced these soil properties and yield.

MATERIALS AND METHODS

A 5.26-ha field on a Dark Brown Chernozemic (Typic Haploboroll) Lethbridge SiCL was levelled in the autumn of 1957 as part of a land development program for the Agriculture Canada Research Station at Lethbridge, Alberta. The indiscriminate levelling procedure was used, in which no effort was made to stockpile and replace topsoil. Cut and fill areas of up to 46 cm existed in the field. The area was continuously cropped to barley (Campana cultivar) from 1958 to 1964, inclusive. The 7-year averages for backfilled to 30 cm, undisturbed, and areas cut to 46 cm or more were 1.7, 1.5, and 0.5 t/ha, respectively.

In 1965, a new series of six "soil erosion" treatments, in 4 replications, was established. The six soil erosion treatments were 1) 30 cm or more of fill, 2) 8 to 10 cm of fill, 3) undisturbed, 4) 8 to 10 cm cut, 5) 10 to 20

*Senior Research Scientist and Tillage Engineer, Agriculture Canada, Research Station, Lethbridge, Alberta, Canada.

cm cut, and 6) 46 cm or more cut. Four fertilizer treatments, check, 45 kg
N + 22.5 kg P_2O_5, 45 kg N + 45 kg P_2O_5, and 45 kg N + 90 kg
P_2O_5/hectare, were superimposed on the soil treatments. The fertilizer
was broadcast and worked into the soil prior to seeding the crop. A
wheat-fallow (Field 1) and a wheat under-seeded to yellow sweet
clover-fallow (Field 2) rotation were established. Fallows were cultivated
with a wide-blade cultivator while the yellow sweet clover (Field 2) was
disced under when it was in the bud stage prior to blading to complete the
fallow. There were thus a total of 2 fields x 6 treatments x 4 fertilizers
x 4 replicates = 192 plots. Chinook spring wheat was used for the first 6
years but an improved cultivar 'Chester' was used in 1979. The study,
after 7 wheat-fallow cycles, was terminated following the 1979 crop year.

Soil samples for chemical analyses were taken at two depths (0-15 and 15-30
cm), air-dried, crushed, and sieved (2 mm). Only the check and high rate
fertilizer treatments were sampled. Soil moisture was determined to a
depth of 1.5 m on all plots before seeding and again after harvest to
determine water use by the crop.

The following soil characteristics were determined: percent organic matter
by Walkley and Black (1934), carbohydrates by Brink et al. (1960), Kjeldahl
nitrogen by Association of Official Agricultural Chemists (1950), NO_3-N
by Bremner (1965), and $NaHCO_3$-soluble phosphorus by Olsen et al. (1954).
The analysis of the available P of the 1969 samples was inadvertently
omitted. Water-stable aggregates, sampled from the 0 to 15 cm horizon only
in spring 1965 prior to the experiment and in spring 1981 at the end of the
fallow cycle of the 1979 crop, were determined after wetting by capillarity
using the wet-sieving technique (Yoder 1936). Protein levels of the wheat
samples were calculated by multiplying the Kjeldahl nitrogen levels by a
factor of 5.75.

The data were first analyzed statistically for each variable in each of the
seven years to determine the effect of soil treatment and fertility.
Although a log transformation was carried out on the available P data,
since it was evident that as the magnitude of the available P increased so
did the variance, the actual available P values were used for plotting.
Since the fields were not replicated, the data of each field were analyzed
separately. The data were also analyzed over the years by incorporating
years as another split-plot factor (Steel and Torrie 1980).

RESULTS

Water-stable Aggregates

The aggregates were analyzed either by using the sum of all aggregate
fractions or by using the sum of the aggregate fractions > 1 mm diameter.
In spite of careful selection of the various "soil erosion" treatments much
variability existed (Table 1).

Significant effects (P < 0.01) were evident for soil treatments in Field
2 (sweet clover) in both years for the total water-stable aggregates, while
in Field 1 (non sweet clover) the water-stable aggregates were different (P
< 0.05) in 1981 only. Since there was no significant effect in fertility
levels in either Field, the comparison between 1965 and 1981 was made with
n=4 averages for 1965 and n=8 averages for 1981. Seven cycles of
wheat-fallow had a significant negative effect on the water-stable
aggregates (P < 0.01 and P < 0.001 for $\geq$ 1 mm diameter fractions and
total, respectively). Conversely, yellow sweet clover had a significant
positive effect (P < 0.001) on the $\geq$ 1 mm diameter water-stable
aggregates and a somewhat lesser significant negative effect (P < 0.01)
on the total water-stable aggregates.

183

Table 1. Effects of Soil Erosional Treatments on Water-stable Aggregates taken from the 0 to 15 cm Depth (n=4)

Aggregates	> 1 mm						Total					
	1			2			1			2		
Field[a]												
Fertility level[b]	1	1	2	1	1	2	1	1	2	1	1	2
Year 19__	65	81	81	65	81	81	65	81	81	65	81	81

Erosion treatment[c] — % —

1	11.4	8.9	8.2	5.7	18.9	21.9	39.5	30.6	28.6	24.3	28.6	34.3
2	23.9	6.2	8.9	21.9	25.4	20.8	58.7	35.9	36.0	49.6	38.3	36.4
3	13.4	11.1	8.6	13.1	27.2	23.2	40.6	35.0	33.0	42.8	39.1	41.8
4	29.6	11.0	9.7	15.6	26.0	25.7	60.1	37.6	37.7	45.2	44.6	42.3
5	26.8	10.7	6.8	24.4	31.4	26.3	61.9	44.4	39.0	64.4	50.8	50.5
6	13.0	3.4	4.5	8.2	22.1	20.9	51.6	22.2	23.5	41.5	33.0	35.6
Av	19.7	8.6	7.8	14.8	25.2	23.1	52.1	34.3	33.0	44.6	39.1	40.2

[a]Field: 1) Wheat-fallow; 2) Wheat/yellow sweet clover-fallow
[b]Fertility level: 1) check; 2) 45 kg N + 90 kg P_2O_5/ha
[c]Erosion treatment: 1) 30 + cm fill; 2) 8-10 cm fill; 3) undisturbed; 4) 8-10 cm cut; 5) 10-20 cm cut; 6) 46 + cm cut

Soil Chemical Characteristics

For the sake of clarity only the results of the 30+ cm fill, undisturbed, and 46+ cm cut soil treatments have been plotted (Figs. 1 to 5).

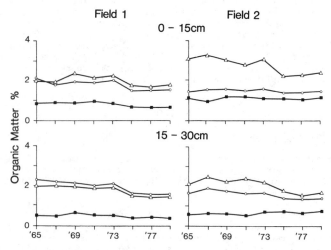

Fig. 1 Organic Matter Changes from 1965 to 1979 Under a Wheat-Fallow (Field 1) and a Wheat/Yellow Sweet Clover-Fallow (Field 2) Regime at Two Different Depths (n=8). (Δ, 30+ cm fill; o, undisturbed; and ■, 46+ cm cut.)

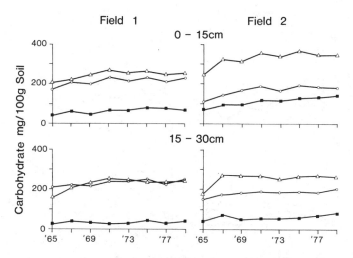

Fig. 2 Carbohydrate Changes from 1965 to 1979 Under a Wheat-Fallow (Field 1) and a Wheat/Yellow Sweet Clover-Fallow (Field 2) Regime at Two Different Depths (n=8). (Δ, 30+ cm fill; o undisturbed; and ■, 46+ cm cut.)

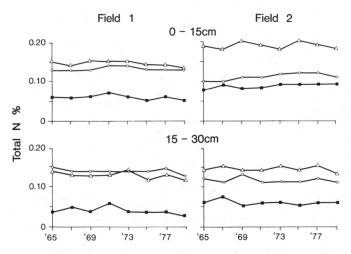

Fig. 3 Total Nitrogen Changes from 1965 to 1979 Under a Wheat-Fallow (Field 1) and a Wheat/Yellow Sweet Clover-Fallow (Field 2) Regime at Two Different Depths (n=8). (Δ, 30+ cm fill; o, undisturbed; and ■, 46+ cm cut.)

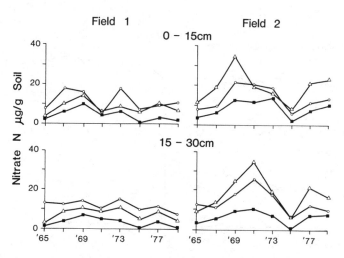

Fig. 4   Nitrate Nitrogen Changes from 1965-1979 Under a Wheat-Fallow (Field 1) and a Wheat/Sweet Clover-Fallow (Field 2) Regime at Two Depths (n=8). (Δ, 30+ cm fill; o, undisturbed; and ■, 46+ cm cut.)

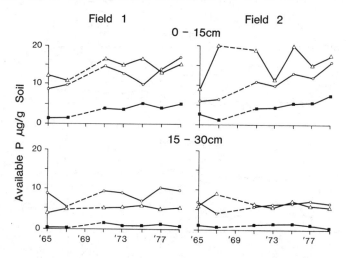

Fig. 5   Available Phosphorus Changes from 1965-79 Under a Wheat-Fallow (Field 1) and a Wheat/Sweet Clover-Fallow (Field 2) Regime at Two Depths (n=8). (Δ, 30+ cm Fill; o, Undisturbed; and ■, 46+ cm Cut.)

The effect of soil treatment on organic matter, carbohydrate, total N, NO_3-N, and available P for both Fields and both depths (0-15 and 15-30 cm) was generally significant with P varying between < 0.1 and < 0.001 except for NO_3-N on Field 2 at the 0-15 depth when for four years there was not a significant treatment effect.

The undisturbed soil treatment generally had, except for NO_3-N, the highest nutrient values, while the 46+ cm cut treatment always had the

lowest values for Fields 1 and 2 for the 0-15 cm depth. Yellow sweet
clover particularly improved the organic matter, carbohydrate, and total N
values at the 0 to 15 cm depth. For the 15-30 cm depth the 46+ cm cut
treatment again had the lowest values of any of the five chemical soil
characteristics determined. The values for the 15-30 cm depth on the
yellow sweet clover field (Field 2) were generally similar to the values
of the 0 to 15 cm depth of Field 1.

There was a significant effect without a soil treatment x fertilizer
interaction with the 45 kg N + 90 kg P_2O_5/ha fertilizer treatment
on the available P levels on Field 1 at the 0-15 cm depth and on Field 2
at both depths (Fig. 6).

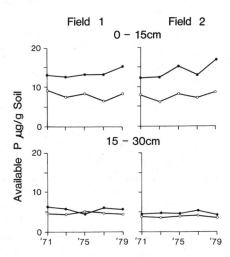

Fig. 6 Available Phosphorus Changes from 1971 to 1979 Under a
Wheat-Fallow (Field 1) and a Wheat/Yellow Sweet Clover-Fallow (Field 2)
Regime at Two Different Depths (n=24). (o, no fertilizer; and ●, 45 kg N
+ 90 kg P_2O_5/ha.)

For organic matter and NO_3-N in both fields and at both depths a
significant (P < 0.001) year x soil treatment interaction was evident.
The response for NO_3-N over time seems to have been affected in 1975 by
the 256 mm precipitation during May, June, and July as compared to a 74
year average of 173 mm over the same period. For the carbohydrate and
total N values, significant effects of soil treatments and year were the
most apparent, but in Field 1, for the 0-15 cm depth the soil treatment
response over years may differ for the soil treatments due to a year x
soil treatment interaction.

Yield and Grain Protein

After 22 years and 14 crops, yields and grain protein on Field 1 continued
to be significantly affected by erosion and fertilizer treatment (Table 2).
Yield variability on Field 2 (sweet clover) due to crop competition and
poorer weed control reduced the statistical significance of erosion
treatment. Determination of yield trends was difficult because of the
high yield variation between years due to large differences in
precipitation during the growing season. The average yields (1967-79)
were the lowest on plots that had 46 cm or more of topsoil removed and
highest on plots that had 8 to 10 cm of topsoil added (Table 3). The
yields from the treatment with 8-10 cm of topsoil removed were nearly
equal to those from the undisturbed soil treatment. The yield per

centimeter of water (precipitation plus stored soil moisture used) for each treatment generally corresponded well with each soil treatment for each field. The water holding capacity did not seem to differ greatly between soil treatments, but water use (plant available water) decreased as the amount of topsoil removed increased. Similarly, the protein of the grain harvested from treatments with topsoil removed was significantly lower than that from treatments that had no topsoil removed or had topsoil added.

Table 2. Analysis of Variance Summary of Erosion and Fertilizer Treatment on Wheat Yields, Yield to Water Ratio, and Grain Protein on Fields with (Field 2) and without (Field 1) Sweet Clover (1967-79)

	df[+]	Wheat yield		Yield/cm H_2O		Protein	
		Field 1	Field 2	Field 1	Field 2	Field 1	Field 2
Erosion	5	**	NS	**	NS	**	*
Fertilizer	3	**	NS	**	NS	**	**
Erosion x Fertilizer	15	**	**	**	*	**	NS
Year	6	**	**	**	**	**	**
Year x Fertilizer	18	NS	NS	NS	NS	NS	NS
Year x Erosion	30	**	**	**	**	**	**
Erosion x Fertilizer x Year	90	NS	NS	NS	NS	NS	NS

*,**Significant effect at $P \leq 0.05$ and $P \leq 0.01$, respectively
[+]Degrees of freedom, NS = Not significant

Table 3. The Effect of Erosion Treatment (Fertilizer Treatments Combined) on Wheat Yield, Yield to Water Ratio and Grain Protein on Fields without (Field 1) and with (Field 2) Sweet Clover (1967-79)

Erosion treatment	Wheat yield		Yield/cm H_2O		Protein	
	Field 1	Field 2	Field 1	Field 2	Field 1	Field 2
(cm)	(kg/ha)		(kg/ha·cm)		(%)	
+30 fill	1900	1782	83.0	85.0	17.02	17.06
+8-10 fill	2040	1704	96.2	80.1	16.62	16.56
check	1847	1601	84.0	90.7	15.87	16.61
8-10 cut	1800	1472	85.1	82.0	15.53	15.76
10-20 cut	1397	1146	60.1	62.6	16.09	16.23
46 or more cut	1023	1164	51.9	61.8	15.32	15.96

There was a significant erosion x fertilizer treatment interaction, with the high rate of fertilizer (45 kg/ha N plus 90 kg/ha P_2O_5) producing the greatest yield response on the most severely 'cut' treatment (Table 4). Although this response also existed on the field with sweet clover (Field 2), only the data from Field 1 are presented here. Fertilizer had little or no effect on the undisturbed soil treatments or the treatments with topsoil added. The high rate of fertilizer had restored yields from the 8-10 cm cut treatment to those of the undisturbed soil treatment. On the soil treatments with more than 10 cm of topsoil removed yields increased with each increment of phosphate fertilizer (data not shown). The water use efficiency was improved with fertilizer on the 'cut' treatments but not on the 'fill' treatments. However, there was a small but consistent improvement in grain protein over all soil treatments, largely attributed to the 45 kg/ha N since there was no increase in protein percentage as phosphate application increased.

Table 4. The Effect of Erosion and Fertilizer Treatment on Average Wheat Yields, Yield to Water Ratio and Grain Protein on Field Without Sweet Clover (1967-79)

Erosion treatment	Wheat yield		Yield/H_2O used		Protein	
	check	45-90	check	45-90	check	45-90
(cm)	(kg/ha)		(kg/ha·cm)		(%)	
+30 fill	1967	1912	85.6	82.8	16.66	17.34
+8-10 fill	2048	2035	97.1	95.6	16.54	16.74
undisturbed	1790	1855	80.7	84.7	15.65	15.90
-8-10 cut	1576	1860	75.2	87.2	15.17	15.51
-10-20 cut	1122	1632	48.0	70.0	15.70	15.79
-46 or more cut	736	1251	37.9	62.9	14.62	15.20

DISCUSSION

The water-stable aggregate level in 1965 was largely the result of seven years of continuous barley. It has been shown elsewhere (Dormaar 1983) that more water-stable aggregates existed under a continuous wheat than under a wheat-fallow regime. The change from continuous barley to wheat-fallow confirms this.

The yellow sweet clover had a decided positive effect on the water-stable aggregate distribution. The $\geq$ 1 mm diameter water-stable aggregates increased while the < 1 mm diameter water-stable aggregates decreased. However, even though the introduction of yellow sweet clover positively improved soil structure probably due to the increased carbohydrate content of the soil, this did not translate into increased yields. The poorer in-crop weed control with the presence of sweet clover and competition for soil moisture reduced wheat yields. Nevertheless, the increase in larger water-stable aggregates would at least aid in the prevention of wind erosion.

The increased precipitation during May, June, and July in 1975 probably leached any NO_3-N present beyond the root zone. Conversely, the increased moisture in the soil increased initially the NO_3-N content of the soil in the first place. The field was sampled on May 2, but because it started to rain, it was resampled on May 14 to properly relate to the wheat/yellow sweet clover-fallow samples taken on May 14. A total of 71 mm of precipitation fell during the interval. There was no change in the organic matter, total N and available P levels. However, the average NO_3-N level changed from 5.1 to 10.4 μg/g soil and the average carbohydrate level changed from 204 to 229 mg/100 g soil. Both changes were significant at the P < 0.01 level.

Added nutrients, particularly phosphate, did increase yield on the wheat-fallow rotation, but the addition of yellow sweet clover confounded the results in terms of response to added fertility even though the clover was beneficial in terms of soil structure. Soil erosion treatment also decreased the quality, i.e., protein content of the wheat, on the wheat-fallow rotation. Duck (1974) concluded, on the basis of data obtained from eroded Chernozemic soils in Hungary, that it was very difficult to relate yield to the nutrient status of the soil. Added organic matter seems to make this relationship even more difficult to perceive.

Soil erosion represented a loss of organic matter and nutrients. The soil left behind became less productive and probably even more erodible because of changes in its physical properties. It is obvious from the data presented that, under low rainfall conditions, it will take years of careful management to rebuild land from which the topsoil has been eroded by wind or water. Topsoil in situ is still the most desirable medium for plant growth. The soil from areas with 'fill' or disturbed topsoil was generally similar to soil in situ in terms of the soil chemical characteristics only without the yellow sweet clover treatment. The 'fill' treatments of this experiment probably included earth stripped from a depth greater than 10 cm and would thus be of lesser quality than that of topsoil in situ. Nevertheless, disturbed topsoil would still be more valuable than no topsoil at all.

Our original thinking in terms of restoring productivity of eroded land under dry-land conditions was to use somewhat more than recommended fertilizer levels for the area and crop selected, and/or green manure. However, for severely eroded land more drastic measures, such as manure, if economically available, or larger doses of fertilizer, may be necessary for dryland. The latter may, of course, retard yield responses during dry growing seasons. Nevertheless, the knowledge obtained with the experiment under discussion will not only be valuable to the present custodians of the land, but also to managers making decisions for areas with special needs such as recovery of land after road alignments, oil well sites, and pipeline corridors.

SUMMARY

In 1957 a field was artificially eroded and then continuously cropped to barley for 7 years. From 1965 to 1979 an experiment was conducted to determine the effects of four fertilizer treatments and green manure (yellow sweet clover) on restoring the productivity to soil that had been 'eroded' to different degrees. There was little evidence that the N, P, or C levels in the soil increased as a result of cropping or fertilizer treatment. Although green manuring with yellow sweet clover improved soil structure, wheat yields were not improved because of crop competition and poorer weed control in this part of the rotation. The addition of 45 kg N plus 90 kg P_2O_5 per hectare in each crop year to soils that had 8-10, 10-20, or >46 cm of topsoil removed resulted in yield increases of 18, 46, and 71% respectively, over the unfertilized check of each treatment; however, the average yields were only 104, 91, and 70% respectively, of the undisturbed, unfertilized (check) treatment. On soil treatments where only 8-10 cm of topsoil were removed, 45 kg N plus 22 kg P_2O_5 per hectare were sufficient to restore the productivity with no benefit from additional phosphate. Precipitation had a greater effect on wheat yields than fertilizer application. The loss of organic matter and associated soil structure characteristics seemed to be critical factors contributing to yield losses associated with soil erosion. More drastic measures such as application of manure, if available, or higher fertilizer applications may result in more rapid restoration of eroded soil.

ACKNOWLEDGMENTS

We wish to acknowledge D.T. Anderson, J.M. Carefoot, U.J. Pittman, G.C. Russell, and P.H. Walker for their participation during various stages of this study. We are grateful for the impeccable field and record keeping support by L.J. Magyar over the total period of the experiment against all odds of weather fluctuations and supervisory personnel changes.

REFERENCES

1. Anderson, D.T. (ed.) 1966. Soil erosion by wind: Cause, damage, control. Agric. Canada Publ. No. 1266/E. 26 p.

2. Anonymous. 1982. Study explores how erosion affects productivity. Farm Light & Power 24(4): A5.

3. Association of Official Agricultural Chemists. 1950. Official methods of analysis. 7th ed. Washington, D.C. 910 p.

4. Bremner, J.M. 1965. Inorganic forms of nitrogen. Pp. 1179-1237 in C.A. Black, ed. methods of soil analysis. Part 2. Chemical and microbiological properties. Agronomy 9. Amer. Soc. Agron. Inc., Madison, Wisc.

5. Brink, R.H., Jr., Dubach, P., and Lynch, D.L. 1960. Measurement of carbohydrates in soil hydrolyzates with anthrone. Soil Sci. 89: 157-166.

6. Carlson, C.W., Grunes, D.L., Alessi, J. and Reichman, G.A. 1961. Corn growth on Gardena surface and subsoil as affected by applications of fertilizer and manure. Soil Sci. Soc. Amer. Proc. 25: 44-47.

7. Chesworth, W. 1982. Late Cenozoic geology and the second oldest profession. Geoscience Canada 9: 54-61.

8. Cook, K. 1982. Soil loss: A question of values. J. Soil Water Conserv. 37: 89-92.

9. Dormaar, J.F. 1983. Chemical properties of soil and water-stable aggregates after 67 yesrs of cropping to spring wheat. Plant Soil. 75: 51-61.

10. Duck, T. 1974. Zusammenhang zwischen der Fruchtbarkeit des Bodens und dem Ausmass der Erosion auf Tschernosjombõden. Transact. 10th ISSS Congress, Moscow. Vol. II: 105-111.

11. Engelstad, O.P. and Shrader, W.D. 1961. The effect of surface soil thickness on corn yields: II. As determined by an experiment using normal surface soil and artificially-exposed subsoil. Soil Sci. Soc. Amer. Proc. 25: 497-499.

12. Olsen, S.R., Cole, C.V., Watanabe, F.S. and Dean, L.A. 1954. Estimation of available phosphorus in soils by extraction with sodium bicarbonate. U.S. Dep. Agric., Circ. No. 939. 19 p.

13. Olson, T.C. 1977. Restoring the productivity of a glacial till soil after topsoil removal. J. Soil Water Conserv. 32: 130-132.

14. Pimentel, D., Terhune, E.C., Dyson-Hudson, R., Rochereau, S., Samis, R., Smith, E.A., Denman, D., Reifschneider, D. and Shepard, M. 1976. Land degradation: Effects on food and energy resources. Science 194: 149-155.

15. Power, J.F., Sandoval, F.M., Ries, R.E. and Merrill, S.D. 1981. Effects of topsoil and subsoil thickness on soil water content and crop production on a disturbed soil. Soil Sci. Soc. Amer. J. 45: 124-129.

16. Steel, R.G.D. and Torrie, J.H. 1980. Principles and procedures of statistics; a biometrical approach. 2nd ed. New York, McGraw-Hill. 633 p.

17. Walkley, A. and Black, I.A. 1934. An examination of the Degtjareff method for determining soil organic matter, and a proposed modification of the chromic acid titration method. Soil Sci. 37: 29-38.

18. Yoder, R.E. 1936. A direct method of aggregate analysis of soil and a study of physical nature of erosion losses. J. Amer. Soc. Agron. 28: 337-351.

EROSION AND PRODUCTIVITY INTERRELATIONS ON A SOIL LANDSCAPE

C. A. Onstad   F. J. Pierce   R. H. Dowdy   W. E. Larson
Member ASAE

Assessment of the productivity of soils as a function of long term soil erosion is actively being pursued by scientists and policy-makers in the United States. The National Soil Erosion-Soil Productivity Research Planning Committee (Williams et al. 1981) documented the problem, identified needed new knowledge, and outlined an approach to solve the problem. As a result, efforts are underway at several locations to develop appropriate technology for the assessment procedure. Two of the most notable are those models being developed by Williams et al. (1984) and Pierce et al. (1983). EPIC (Williams et al. 1984) is a comprehensive deterministic mathematical model for simulating erosion, crop production, and related processes. The procedure by Pierce et al. (1983) is an indexing model utilizing soil variables and their sufficiency for idealized crop production.

Both procedures select representative land areas where assessments are made. Simulated rates of denudation are made based on climatic and soils data and land management techniques. Selected representative inputs for both techniques are considered only as points in the context of soils and topography. An assumption is made that point data can be extrapolated to larger areas. Unfortunately, every point is part of a soil landscape unit and the processes occurring at that point are a function not only of the local variables but also a function of both upslope and downslope variables in the hydrologic continuum. In effect, the basic unit for long-term productivity assessment is the soil landscape rather than a point on a soil mapping unit.

To demonstrate this concept, we selected a soil landscape in southeastern Minnesota and simulated erosion on that unit for 100 years. We compared the productivity of the natural unit to the individual soils within the unit at various points in time, both as independent units and as units of a uniform slope profile.

APPROACH

In cooperation with the Soil Conservation Service, a soil landscape was selected for analysis in Winona County in southeastern Minnesota. The physical description of the landscape is shown in Fig. 1. Land slopes increase from 1% at the crest to a maximum of about 10% at a distance downslope of about 100 m and then gradually decrease to 1.5% at the toe of the slope. Total slope length, about 143 m, was divided into nine reaches for analysis. The soil variable used to estimate productivity were available soil water capacity, bulk density, and pH. These were determined for 30-cm depth increments throughout each of the profiles. Values for these variables are shown in Table 1 for each of the reaches.

*The authors are: C. A. ONSTAD, Agricultural Engineer, ARS-USDA, Morris, MN, and Assoc. Prof., University of Minnesota; F. J. PIERCE, Ass't. Prof., Soil Science Department, Michigan State University, East Lansing, MI; R. H. DOWDY, Soil Scientist, ARS-USDA, and Assoc. Prof.; and W. E. LARSON, Professor and Head of Soil Science Department, University of Minnesota, St. Paul, MN.

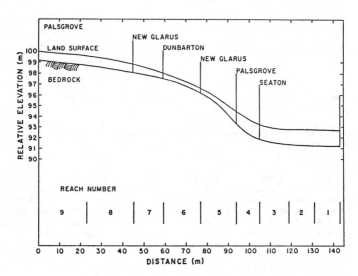

Fig. 1. Soil Landscape Description

Table 1. Characteristics of soil landscape unit by reach

Reach No.	Depth interval	Available water	Bulk density	Clay content	pH	Erodibility
	(cm)	(vol. frac.)	(g/cm^3)	(%)		
1,2	0–30	0.115	1.39	24	6.2	0.37
	30–61	0.110	1.55	29	5.3	
	61–91	0.110	1.49	25	4.9	
	91–122	0.100	1.50	25	4.9	
3	0–30	0.167	1.35	22	5.6	0.37
	30–61	0.150	1.57	28	5.3	
	61–91	0.144	1.55	30	4.8	
	91–122	0.131	1.36	28	4.8	
4	0–30	0.195	1.41	23	6.3	0.32
	30–61	0.105	1.54	28	5.0	
	61–100	0.138	1.63	37	4.7	
5	0–30	0.130	1.51	28	5.8	0.37
	30–68	0.170	1.27	29	5.5	
6	0–26	0.098	1.59	28	6.2	0.37
7	0–30	0.195	1.41	23	6.3	0.37
	30–43	0.105	1.54	28	5.0	
8	0–30	0.195	1.41	23	6.3	0.32
	30–61	0.105	1.54	28	5.0	
	61–73	0.138	1.63	37	4.7	
9	0–30	0.247	1.35	22	5.6	0.32
	30–61	0.143	1.52	30	5.0	
	61–86	0.141	1.59	34	4.8	

194

As Fig. 1 shows, the soils on this landscape are bounded by bedrock at depths of 20 to 165 cm depending on position. The major determinant of each mapping unit is depth to bedrock and depth of surface loess. The soils catena is complex, comprising six mapping units, but typical of the area.

Reach lengths along the landscape range from 23 m at the upper end to 9 m at the lower end. Daily precipitation data for 100 years for this area was developed using a precipitation model developed by Nicks (1974). From these data, other subroutines available in EPIC (Williams et al. 1984) were used to estimate runoff volume, peak flow, total rainfall kinetic energy, and maximum 30-min intensity. These data were used in the erosion-deposition subprogram of CREAMS (Foster et al. 1981). Soil erosion-deposition profiles were constructed using output data from the CREAMS erosion component. The cropping condition assumed in the analysis was continuous corn, cultivated up and downhill. Values for the factors in the erosion component were determined from the storm, soils, topographic, and cropping data for the landscape. The soil erodibility factor, K, was assumed to decrease according to the relation K = (depth remaining/10) x K after the depth to bedrock was less than 10 cm so that the erodibility transition from soil to bedrock was gradual.

RESULTS AND DISCUSSION

Individual Soils

The productivity index (PI) was determined for each soil, as identified on Fig. 1, using site data and data from SOILS-5 (Pierce et al. 1984). Without exception, PI using the SOILS-5 data was higher than that using actual field data. The main reasons for the differences were that available water content was less and bulk densities were higher for soils in this landscape than the SOILS-5 data base.

Information in Table 2 shows differences in PI for two soils when considered in three different ways after various times of simulated erosion. The two example soils are Seaton (Typic Hapludalfs) at the toe of the slope and Newglarus (Typic Hapludalfs), furthest downslope, as shown in Fig. 1. The slope steepnesses were 4.5% and 10% for the Seaton and Newglarus, respectively.

The columns for each soil shown in Table 2 indicate three different methods of analyzing the two soils. The term, "isolated", indicates that PI of the soils for various times was determined without regard to its position on the land-scape. The term, "uniform", means that the soil was analyzed in sequence but assuming that the slope shape was uniform at the average value of slope steepness. "Natural" means that the soils were analyzed in their respective positions on the natural landscape shown in Fig. 1. When isolated, the PI changes very little over the 100-yr period for either soil assuming that the USLE slope length factor (L) is unity and the slope steepness factor corresponds to the slope steepness of the reach on which the soil occurs. The data in Table 2 show that PI decreases only slightly from 0.64 to 0.63 for Seaton and from 0.56 to 0.52 for Newglarus. This represents productivity declines of 1.7% for Seaton and 6.3% for Newglarus, the steeper soil.

For the uniform slope profile, erosion was estimated using a uniform slope steepness of 5.7% which corresponds to the slope calculated from the total relief and slope length. As shown in Table 2, PI decreases for both soils more than under isolated conditions. Additional decreases were due to increased slope length. In this case, PI of the Seaton soil decreased from 0.64 to 0.58, a decline of about 8.5% while PI for Newglarus decreased from 0.56 to 0.49, a decline of about 12%. Most of the additional productivity loss over the isolated case resulted from increased slope lengths that increased both the slope length effect factor and erosivity of runoff in the CREAMS erosion component (Foster et al. 1981).

Table 2. Productivity indices for Seaton and Newglarus soils considered
in three different ways after various times of simulated erosion

	Productivity index					
	Seaton			Newglarus		
Year	Isolated	Uniform transect	Natural transect	Isolated	Uniform transect	Natural transect
0	0.64	0.64	0.64	0.56	0.56	0.56
	100[a]	100	100	100	100	100
10	0.64	0.64	0.66	0.55	0.55	0.53
	100	99	104	99	99	95
25	0.64	0.62	0.69	0.55	0.54	0.49
	99	97	108	99	97	89
50	0.63	0.61	0.73	0.54	0.52	0.37
	99	95	115	97	94	67
75	0.63	0.60	0.74	0.53	0.51	0.17
	98	93	116	95	91	31
100	0.63	0.58	0.74	0.52	0.49	0
	98	91	116	94	88	0

[a]Lower numbers are percents with respect to year 0.

When each soil is analyzed within the natural soil landscape as shown in Fig.
1, the results obtained are shown in the column labeled "natural" in Table 2.
These are more easily interpreted after inspecting Fig. 2 which shows estimated amounts of erosion and deposition on the natural slope at various times.
Data in Fig. 2 show that erosion occurs on the upper 105 m of the transect and
that deposition occurs downslope from that point.   As a result, the Newglarus
erodes and the Seaton receives sediment because of their respective positions

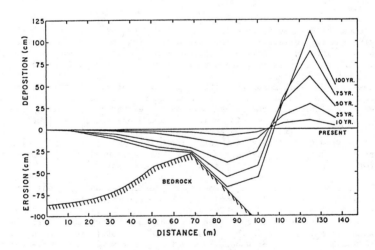

Fig. 2. Description of Erosion and Deposition on Natural Transect
at Various Times

on the slope (Table 2). If the assumption is made that available water content and bulk density of the deposited soil is the same as that of the present top layer, deposition increases PI for the Seaton site. The PI increased from 0.64 to 0.74 or about 16%, while the productivity of the Newglarus decreased from a 0.56 to zero after 100 years because of erosion to bedrock.

Natural Erosion/Deposition Profile

The erosion/deposition profile in Fig. 2 shows the progression of erosion and deposition along the slope at various times. As expected, erosion increased with distance downslope. Scour was limited to the depth of bedrock in the central region of the slope transect. An erosion subprogram was set for bedrock to start affecting soil erodibility at a soil depth of 10 cm. At that point, erodibility was decreased by the ratio of soil depth remaining to 10 cm. Bedrock begins affecting the result after 35 years.

As the erodibility decreased, the unfilled transport capacity of runoff increased, thereby increasing erosion further downslope, which has two effects. First, erosivity of runoff remained high which exposed bedrock at an increasing rate and moved the point of deposition further downslope. The latter effect can be seen from Fig. 2 which shows that the average point of deposition has moved downslope about 5 m over 100 years. This also indicated that previously deposited soil was eroding in this interval and beyond for a distance of about 6 m.

Throughout the erosion analysis, two further assumptions were made in addition to that of the soil erodibility. First, a constant segment slope steepness was assumed as soil was removed or deposited. Erodibility of deposited soil was assumed to be identical to that of the soil where deposition occurred. For PI analysis of this transect, bulk density, available water content, and clay content of deposited soil were assumed to be identical to that of the upper soil layer that received deposition.

Data in Table 3 shows the results of PI analyses for each reach for the years indicated. Overall, the weighted average PI for this landscape decreased to 73% of present PI after 100 years of erosion. The largest decline of 10% occurred between years 25 and 50 when depth to bedrock became a critical factor.

When comparing changes in PI for individual soil mapping units with the overall change in the landscape unit, the PI for the Seaton soil, reaches 1, 2, and 3, increased to an average of 118% of existing PI after 100 years of sediment deposition. The PI for Palsgrove in reach 4 decreased to 33% of current, whereas, the same soil in reaches 8 and 9 decreased to only 89% of the present value. For Newglarus in reach 7, PI decreased to 44% of current level but further downslope in reach 5, PI decreased to zero. The PI in the Dunbarton in reach 6 went to zero within 50 years. As described previously, accelerated erosion increases the rate of decline of PI in reaches 4 and 5. These data illustrate the complex interactions that occur among soil mapping units in a landscape catena when the landscape is considered as the unit of productivity rather than individual soils.

Natural Erosion/Deposition Profile -- No Bedrock Constriction

In Fig. 3, the erosion-deposition distribution of the transect assumed bedrock was not a limiting factor in the erosion and deposition process calculations. Theoretically, the soils would not have the same names as indicated in Fig. 1, but the parameters are assumed to be the same for purposes of calculating PI. Without restricting bedrock, both erosion and deposition increased at various points along the transect as shown in Fig. 3. Maximum erosion of over 90 cm occurred after 100 years in reach 5 while maximum deposition of over 120 cm

Table 3. Results of PI analyses for each reach of the natural transect for the years indicated

Reach	Productivity index Year					
	0	10	25	50	75	100
1	0.47	0.48	0.50	0.52	0.54	0.56
	100[a]	102	106	111	115	118
2	0.47	0.50	0.53	0.57	0.58	0.58
	100	105	112	120	122	122
3	0.64	0.67	0.69	0.73	0.74	0.74
	100	104	108	115	116	116
4	0.54	0.50	0.43	0.27	0.18	0.18
	100	93	79	49	33	33
5	0.56	0.53	0.49	0.37	0.17	0
	100	95	89	67	31	0
6	0.20	0.18	0.12	0	0	0
	100	90	63	0	0	0
7	0.49	0.46	0.43	0.34	0.27	0.22
	100	94	87	69	55	44
8	0.54	0.53	0.52	0.49	0.46	0.43
	100	98	96	91	85	79
9	0.65	0.65	0.65	0.64	0.64	0.64
	100	100	100	99	99	99
Wt. ave.	0.51	0.50	0.49	0.44	0.40	0.37
	100	98	96	86	79	73

[a]Lower numbers are percents with respect to year 0.

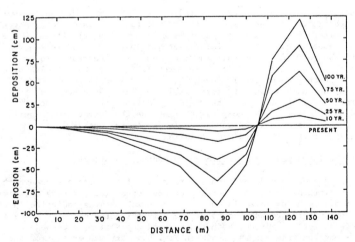

Fig. 3. Description of Erosion and Deposition on Natural Transect without Bedrock Restriction at Various Times

198

occurs in reach 2. These extremes are both larger than those shown in Fig. 2. Because sediment transport capacity and soil erodibility were not affected by the presence of bedrock, the point where deposition began remained at 105 m downslope.

In Table 4, PI is given for each reach of the profile shown in Fig. 1 at various times when the restricting bedrock layer was disregarded. Soil properties for the bottom layer in each reach were assumed to continue to 5000 cm for PI calculation purposes. Comparing PI values at year 0 in Tables 3 and 4 reflect the differences of the bedrock for reaches 5, 6, and 7. The lack of increase in PI of reach 8 is attributed to the high bulk density of the lower soil layer. Bulk density in this case acts as a productivity barrier in the same way as bedrock limits productivity.

Table 4. Results of PI analyses for each reach of natural transect without bedrock restriction for the years indicated

Reach	Productivity index					
	Year					
	0	10	25	50	75	100
1	0.47 100[a]	0.48 102	0.50 106	0.52 111	0.54 115	0.56 118
2	0.47 100	0.50 105	0.53 112	0.57 120	0.58 122	0.58 122
3	0.64 100	0.67 104	0.69 108	0.75 117	0.78 122	0.80 125
4	0.54 100	0.50 93	0.43 79	0.28 51	0.20 37	0.20 37
5	0.72 100	0.73 102	0.77 107	0.81 113	0.81 113	0.81 113
6	0.46 100	0.46 100	0.46 100	0.46 100	0.46 100	0.46 100
7	0.63 100	0.61 97	0.59 93	0.53 84	0.47 75	0.41 65
8	0.54 100	0.53 98	0.52 96	0.49 91	0.46 85	0.43 79
9	0.68 100	0.68 100	0.68 100	0.68 99	0.68 99	0.68 99
Wt. ave.	0.58 100	0.58 100	0.58 100	0.58 99	0.57 97	0.56 96

[a]Lower numbers are percents with respect to year 0.

Overall, the landscape unit retained its productivity throughout the first 25 years of erosion and decreases about 4 percentage points, during the next 75 years. Individually, however, the PI changes are much larger throughout the time period. The PI of reaches 1, 2, and 3 increased to an average of 122% of the present. This increase was the result of sediment being deposited in these reaches. An increase in PI also occurred in reach 5 with time to a value of 113% of the current level. In this case, however, the increase was a result of erosion of the upper layer which is less productive than the lower

199

layer. The lower layer has both a high available water content and a lower bulk density. In reaches 4, 7, 8, and 9, PI decreased to values ranging from 37 to 99% of the initial value of PI. In reach 6, PI does not change with erosion. Again, these data illustrate the importance of considering an entire landscape for projecting soil productivity as opposed to individual soil mapping units. If the soils in a landscape are considered individually without regard for their landscape position, misleading information can be obtained.

SUMMARY

A soil landscape catena was selected in southeastern Minnesota comprising five soil mapping units. One hundred years of rainfall were generated and used as input to estimate erosion and deposition at various points along the soil landscape. Productivity of the various soils and the catena itself was estimated after elapsed times of 10, 25, 50, 75, and 100 years using a productivity index.

The productivity index of isolated soil mapping units decreased with erosion as expected. When the mapping unit was placed in its proper position in the soil landscape, its productivity index changed as a function of its position in addition to its soil physcial characteristics related to erosion and sediment transport. For example, if a soil situated at the toe of a landscape unit receives sediment deposition, it is likely to increase or remain at the same productivity level. If a soil is located midslope, erosion is likely accelerated when compared to the soil considered alone, consequently, the productivity index is likely to decrease at an accelerated rate when compared to the soil considered separately. The analysis illustrates that changes in productivity indexes on soil mapping units can give misleading information unless they are considered in their proper positions on a soil landscape. The data also show that a soil landscape should be given more consideration as the basic unit for determining productivity changes over time as a result of soil erosion.

REFERENCES

1. Foster, G.R., L.S. Lane, J.D. Nowlin, J.M. Laflen and R.A. Young. 1981. Estimating erosion and sediment yield on field-sized areas. TRANS. of the ASAE 24: 1253-1262.

2. Nicks, A.D. 1974. Stochastic generation of the occurrence, pattern, and location of maximum amount of daily rainfall. Proceedings Symposium on Statistical Hydrology, Tucson, AZ, Aug.-Sept. 1971. Misc. Pub. No. 1275, pp. 154-171.

3. Pierce, F.J., R.H. Dowdy, W.E. Larson and W.A.P. Graham. 1984. Soil productivity in the Corn Belt: An assessment of erosion's long-term effects. J. Soil & Water Conserv. 39: 131-136.

4. Pierce, F.J., W.E. Larson, R.H. Dowdy and W.A.P. Graham. 1983. Productivity of soils: assessing long-term changes due to erosion. J. Soil & Water Conserv. 38: 39-44.

5. Williams, J.R., Chairman, National Soil Erosion - Soil Productivity Research Planning Committee, USDA-ARS. 1981. Soil erosion effects on soil productivity: A research perspective. J. Soil & Water Conserv. 36: 82-90.

6. Williams, J.R., C.A. Jones and P.T. Dyke. 1984. A modeling approach to determining the relationship between erosion and soil productivity. TRANS. of the ASAE 27: 129-144.

EROSION'S EFFECT ON PRODUCTIVITY

ALONG NONUNIFORM SLOPES

S. J. Perrens   G. R. Foster   D. B. Beasley[*]
                       Member ASAE   Member ASAE

The Soil and Water Resources Conservation Act of 1977 requires the U.S. Department of Agriculture to appraise the soil and water resources on nonfederal land every five years. These appraisals are used to formulate long range policy for the use and protection of these resources. Consequently, new research has focused on quantifying the relationship of loss of crop productivity to erosion. Research has used measurements from natural and artificial erosion and predictions from productivity models to study loss of productivity caused by erosion (USDA 1981, Meyer et al. 1984). The advantage of studies using naturally occurring erosion is that the research conditions are like those in actual farming situations. A few of these studies were conducted in the 1940's, but the technique was mostly neglected until the 1980's (Meyer et al. 1984). Researchers have generally favored the more closely controlled experiments where erosion is simulated by "scalping" the soil (USDA 1981).

Several models have been recently developed to assess the effect of erosion on crop productivity and to predict yield loss from continued erosion. Larson et al. (1983) developed a simple productivity index (PI) model that relates crop response to the "sufficiency" of available water, bulk density, and pH of the soil. The model assumes optimum soil fertility and no limitations from other physical effects, such as surface sealing, waterlogging, or poor aeration. The lumped parameter model developed by Craft and Cruse (1984) extends the productivity index model to include site and crop specific data like growing season rainfall, soil temperature, and root growth potential. The EPIC (Erosion/Productivity Impact Calculator) model developed by Williams et al. (1984) is a detailed simulation model that describes the effects of water, air, nutrients, and energy on a crop. The impact of erosion on productivity is calculated through the removal of surface soil and its consequent effect on availability of air, water, and nutrients to the crop.

Most studies have assessed erosion's impact on productivity at a "point" on the landscape typified by erosion plots of about 30m^2. For example, the Universal Soil Loss Equation (USLE) estimates average erosion from a uniform slope of given length (Wischmeier and Smith 1978). An underlying assumption

* The authors are: Senior Lecturer, Natural Resources Engineering Department, University of New England, Armidale, New South Wales, Australia, (formerly Visiting Scientist, National Soil Erosion Laboratory and Agricultural Engineering Department); Hydraulic Engineer, USDA and Associate Professor; and Associate Professor, Agricultural Engineering Department, Purdue University, W. Lafayette, Indiana. Contribution from the USDA-Agricultural Research Service, National Soil Erosion Laboratory and the Purdue University Agricultural Engineering Department, W. Lafayette, Indiana, in cooperation with the Purdue Agricultural Experiment Station. Purdue Journal No. 10118.

in the application of the soil loss tolerance concept (Wischmeier and Smith, 1978) is that average soil loss from representative uniform slopes can be used to develop management policies for a field as a whole (Shertz 1983). Although conditions at a point on the landscape are assumed to be representative of a wider area, very few landscapes are uniform over much distance. Nielsen et al. (1973) showed significant variation of soil physical properties within a field-sized area, and Sharma et al. (1983) showed that variability of soil properties increased with distance between sampling points. Also, Meyer et al. (1975) examined a variety of simple shapes of land profiles and showed a wide variation in erosion along a single profile. Similarly, Rogowski et al. (1983) used geostatistical techniques to show the effect of scale and heterogeneity on erosion and productivity estimates. They concluded that erosion estimation on a 1 ha basis was needed for optimum predictive capability for reclaimed surface mined land.

Since neither soil properties or erosion are uniform over the landscape, productivity is likely to vary nonuniformly, which has two important implications. Firstly, since fields are farmed as units, the presence of different degrees of erosion makes selecting an optimal management plan almost impossible. Cultivation practices and the application of fertilizer and herbicides are applied uniformly over a field and can be expected to be excessive at some points and suboptimal at others. Secondly, productivity estimates for farms, counties, and states are based on the assumption that the use of average estimated erosion, cultivation, and land management, together with average fertilizer and herbicide usage, leads to a representative average productivity.

This paper addresses two problems associated with current approaches to assessment of the effect of erosion on productivity; the effect of land profile shape on the variation of erosion along a profile assuming that soil properties do not vary along the profile and the effect of this variation on the local and overall productivity of the profile.

STUDY APPROACH

Two existing mathematical models were combined to study the relationship between erosion as affected by land profile shape and the resulting changes in crop productivity. EROS2 (Foster et al. 1981), the erosion component of the CREAMS model (USDA 1980), was used to estimate erosion or deposition at many locations along several different profile shapes, and EPIC was used to estimate the loss or gain in crop yield caused by erosion or deposition.

The EROS2 Model

CREAMS is a continuous, simulation model containing hydrologic, erosion, nutrient, and pesticide components. Its erosion component EROS2 (Foster et al. 1981) uses characteristic rainfall and runoff rates for individual storms to compute detachment by rainfall and runoff and sediment transport and deposition by runoff. The model treats the landscape as a series of segments over which slope, soils, cover, and management may vary. The steady-state continuity equation for sediment transport is used to route sediment along the profile segments. The output of sediment at the end of a segment is made up of the sediment entering at the top of the segment plus the net erosion or deposition on that segment. Detachment by runoff occurs either at a rate that will just fill the transport capacity of runoff or at the maximum rate that runoff can detach sediment at that point on the landscape. Detachment capacities by rainfall and runoff are described by a modified USLE proposed by Foster et al. (1977):

$$D_i = 4.57 \text{ EI } (\sin \theta + 0.014) K\Phi P \ (\sigma/v) \tag{1}$$

$$D_r = (6.86 \times 10^6)\eta \, \sigma^{4/3} \, (x/22.1)^\eta \, K\Phi P \qquad (2)$$

where: D_i = interrill detachment rate $(g/m^2 \cdot s)$, D_r = rill detachment capacity rate $(g/m^2 \cdot s)$, EI = USLE storm rainfall erosivity (N/h), x = distance (m), θ = slope angle $(^\circ)$, η = slope length exponent, K = USLE soil erodibility $(g \cdot h/N \cdot m^2)$, Φ = USLE cover-management factor, P = USLE contouring factor, v = storm runoff depth (m), and σ = peak runoff rate/unit area (m/s). Our nonstandard units for EI and K are described by Foster et al. (1981).

Yalin's (1963) sediment transport equation was modified (Foster and Meyer 1972, Foster et al. 1981) to estimate sediment transport capacity for particle classes having a range of densities and sizes. If sediment load is greater than transport capacity, deposition is computed according to the equation proposed by Foster and Meyer (1975):

$$D_d = (0.5V_f/q) \, (\, T - G \,) \qquad (3)$$

where: D_d = deposition rate $(g/m^2 \cdot s)$, V_f = particle fall velocity (m/s), q = discharge rate per unit width (m^2/s), T = transport capacity $(g/m \cdot s)$, and G = sediment load $(g/m \, s)$. When deposition occurs all along a segment, the equation for the deposition rate D_l at lower end of the segment is:

$$D_l = [\xi/(1 + \xi)](dT/dx - D_i) \, [1 - (x_u/x)^{1+\xi}] + D_u(x_u/x)^{1+\xi} \qquad (4)$$

where $\xi = 0.5 \, V_f/q$, D_u = deposition rate at the upper end of the segment, and x_u = distance to upper end of segment. Given a value for D_l, G at lower end of the segment is computed from a rearrangement of Eq. (3). When deposition does not occur, the sediment load is estimated from:

$$G_l = (D_u + D_l)\Delta x/2 + D_i\Delta x + G_u \qquad (5)$$

where: G_l = sediment load at lower end of segment $(g/m \cdot s)$, D_u = detachment rate at upper end of segment $(g/m^2 \cdot s)$, D_l = detachment rate at lower end of segment $(g/m^2 \cdot s)$, G_u = rate of inflow of sediment from upslope $(g/m \cdot s)$, and Δx = length of segment. Computations are by particle class and take into account interaction between classes, which range from primary clay to large aggregates. Also, EROS2 computes selective deposition of coarse sediment.

For each runoff producing storm, EROS2 uses storm erosivity (EI - storm energy times maximum 30 minute intensity), depth of runoff (v), and peak runoff rate per unit area (σ) to drive the detachment, deposition, and transport equations. Values for the soil erodibility, sediment properties, slope, cover, and management factors at the time of a storm are also required.

The EPIC Model

The EPIC model (Williams et al. 1984), a collection of submodels, brings together most of the factors that determine how soil erosion affects productivity. The major components of EPIC are:

weather	plant growth
hydrology	soil temperature
erosion	tillage
nutrients	economics

The plant growth submodel operates on a daily time step to simulate water and nutrient uptake and the interception and conversion of energy to above-ground biomass, crop yield, and root growth for most common crops. Plant growth is constrained by water, nutrient, and air temperature stresses.

EPIC describes the soil as a series of layers of varying thickness, each with its own bulk density, hydraulic conductivity, available water capacity, and other characteristics. Cultivation is modeled as a mixing process where the soil layers within the depth of cultivation are mixed to produce a zone of modified properties. Climatic sequences including temperature, wind, precipitation, and solar radiation may be read as input or generated within the model. The hydrology submodel uses daily rainfall to estimate runoff volume using the SCS curve number method and to estimate peak discharge using a modified rational formula method. EPIC estimates erosion with one of three equations: Williams' (1975) modification of the USLE (MUSLE), Onstad and Foster's (1975) modification of the USLE, and the USLE itself (Wischmeier and Smith 1978). Soil depth removed by erosion is subtracted from the top layer of soil assuming that no sorting of sediment occurs and that removal of nutrients is proportional to the depth of eroded soil. As surface soil is eroded, subsoils, which usually have higher bulk density and lower nutrient status, come within the potential root zone of the crop. As a result, water uptake may be restricted by the decreased moisture availability of the subsoil and restricted root growth.

EPIC considers fertilizer input; immobilization and uptake of nitrogen and phosphorous in the soil profile; movement of nitrogen and phosphorous solutes in runoff, within the root zone, and from the root zone; and transport of nitrogen and phosphorous on sediment. Its tilllage submodel simulates row height, surface roughness, and mixing of soil, nutrients, and crop residue by tillage. EPIC allows for management by considering drainage, irrigation, fertilizer and lime application, and pest control measures. Different types of tillage, soil conservation, management, and crops may be analyzed with EPIC.

Linkage between the Models

EPIC uses a daily time step to simulate climate, crop growth, runoff, and erosion to describe the effect of erosion on productivity at a point on the landscape, while EROS2 computes erosion at many locations along a land profile for those days with runoff. The climatic and hydrologic submodels of EPIC were used to generate stochastic sequences of rainfall, runoff, peak runoff, and rainfall erosivity over a 50 year period. The soil erodibility factor was varied in EPIC to calculate the variation of crop yield over a range of erosion rates and cumulative eroded soil depths. EROS2 was run using the climatic and hydrologic data generated by EPIC to compute erosion and deposition rates along the land profiles. Coefficients were adjusted in EPIC and EROS2 so that both models gave the same average soil loss for a particular uniform land profile.

DATA

For this study, a Miami silt loam soil of uniform thickness over the landscape was assumed. Miami soils are deep, well drained, and vary in texture from loam to clay loam. These soils, which occur widely over northern Indiana and Illinois, are predominanatly used for growing corn and soybeans. Properties of the Miami silt loam soil used for this study are given in Table 1, and data given in Table 1 summarize climatic conditions at Iroquois, Illinois and represent the climatic sequences generated for this study. The assumed cropping-managment practice was continuous corn grown with a maximum rooting depth of 900 mm and the field operations listed in Table 1.

Table 1. Some Characteristics of the Assumed Study Site

Climatic summary for Iroquoise, Illinois
    Mean annual rainfall (mm)   912
    Mean annual EI (N/h)   300
    10 year-30 minute rainfall (mm)   41
    10 year-6 hour rainfall (mm)   83
    January average maximum temperature (^{o}C)   2
    January average minimum temperature (^{o}C)   -7
    July average maximum temperature (^{o}C)   30
    July average minimum temperature (^{o}C)   18

Miami soil properties
    Saturated conductivity (mm/h)   9.8
    Porosity (m^3/m^3)   .45
    Surface bulk density (Mg/m^3)   1.45
    pH   5.6
    Erodibility ($g \cdot h/N \cdot m^2$)   37
    SCS runoff curve number   85

Tillage operations
Date	Operation
25 April	Disc
1 May	Field cultivate
10 May	Plant
15 June	Row cultivate
15 October	Harvest
15 November	Moldboard plow

RESULTS AND DISCUSSION

Erosion and Deposition along the Profile

EROS2 was used to estimate erosion along several idealized landscape profiles
of concave, convex, complex, and uniform shape, illustrated in Fig.1, each
having the same average slope of 5 percent and length of 100 m. The
nonuniform profiles varied in steepness from 1 percent at their flattest point
to 11 percent at their steepest point.

Output from EROS2 included rates of erosion or deposition at several locations
along each profile. The average soil loss from a uniform profile (defined as
the equivalent uniform profile) having the same average steepness as the
particular nonlinear profile was used as a base to normalize the erosion data
by expressing them as relative erosion:

$$E_r = -D/A_u \qquad (6)$$

where: E_r = relative erosion (or deposition rate) at a point on a land
profile, D = erosion (or deposition) rate at the point on the land profile,
and A_u = average erosion rate for the equivalent uniform land profile. The
sign convention in Eq. (6) is that negative values indicate erosion and
positive values indicate deposition. The average annual erosion rate for the
uniform profile was 40 t/ha, which agrees with the soil loss estimate from the
USLE for the study conditions. We similarly defined relative soil loss
(sediment yield) Y_r for the entire profile as:

$$Y_r = Y/A_u \qquad (7)$$

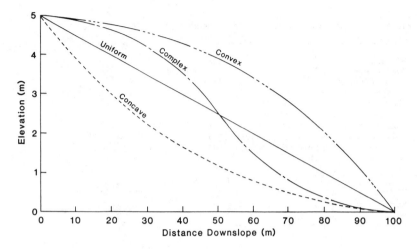

Fig. 1   Slope Shapes Examined (Note Exagerated Vertical Scale)

where: Y = the soil loss (sediment yield) from the land profile. In Eqs. (6) and (7), soil loss from the equivalent uniform profile was used as a base because it is easily estimated with the USLE and therefore provides a useful basis for comparison.

Relative erosion and deposition rates along the land profiles are shown in Fig. 2. The increase in relative erosion along the uniform profile was approximately linear, and at the end of the uniform profile, relative erosion was -1.6, which means that erosion rate at the end of the profile was 1.6 times the soil loss (average erosion rate) from the equivalent uniform profile.

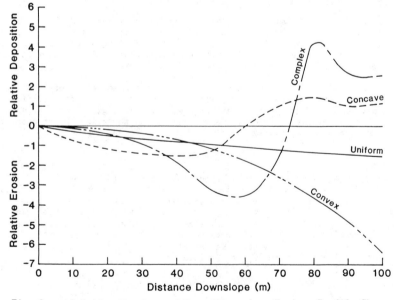

Fig. 2   Relative Erosion and Deposition along Various Profile Shapes

Mild steepness on the upslope section of the convex profile caused relative erosion rates to be lower than that from the equivalent uniform profile for the first 45 m. However, after 50 m downslope, increasing runoff rate and increasing steepness combined to rapidly increase erosion rates. A maximum relative erosion of -6.4 occurred at the end of the convex profile. No deposition occurred on the convex profile and total soil loss from the convex profile was 2.2 times that from the equivalent uniform profile.

The maximum relative erosion for the concave profile was -1.5 at about 25 m from the top of the profile. Therefore, maximum erosion on the concave profile was slightly less than that for the uniform profile. However, net soil loss (sediment yield) from the end of the concave profile was only about 0.16 of the soil loss from the uniform profile because of deposition over the last 47 m of the profile. Maximum relative deposition on the concave profile was 1.6.

The pattern of erosion and deposition was similar on the complex, sigmoid-shaped profile, to that on the concave profile; erosion on the upslope sector and deposition on the downslope sector of the profile. For the complex profile, maximum relative erosion and deposition was -3.7 and 4.7, respectively. Net soil loss from the end of the profile was only 0.27 of the soil loss from the equivalent uniform profile. While the pattern of erosion and deposition along the complex profile and sediment yield from this profile were similar to those for the concave slope, maximum relative erosion and deposition rates for the complex profile were much higher than those for the concave profile. Although relative soil loss from both the complex and concave profiles was low, significant relocation of sediment occurred on these profiles, especially the complex one. Convex profiles had high relative erosion rates and soil losses. Concave and convex profiles were the least and most erodible, respectively. Erosion and deposition patterns on all of the nonuniform profiles were significantly different from that on the equivalent uniform profile.

Loss of Crop Yield with Erosion

The EPIC output of principal interest for this study was the change in crop yield over time for a given erosion rate or deposition rate. Data in the form of crop yield vs. time could not be directly integrated with output from EROS2, and such data also contained strong random effects from the climatic sequence that masked the effect of erosion on crop yield. Therefore, crop yield from an uneroded soil subjected to the same climatic sequence was used to normalize the EPIC results. For each year of simulated crop growth, relative productivity P_r was calculated as:

$$P_r = C_e/C_u \qquad (8)$$

where: C_e = crop yield from the eroded soil and C_u = crop yield from uneroded soil. This definition differs from the Productivity Index (PI) of Larson et al. (1983), which gives a value of 1.0 for the maximum crop yield with an ideal soil. For example, their PI for our Miami soil in its initial condition was 0.77, while our relative productivity P_r was 1.0. Thus change in our P_r values indicates change in productivity from some given point in time.

The variation in productivity loss from year to year was normalized by plotting relative productivity P_r against cumulative depth of soil loss. Figure 3 shows the relationship between P_r and soil loss for our Miami soil between a deposition of 100 mm of soil and a soil loss of 300 mm. With adequate fertilization, EPIC predicted that P_r will decline to about 0.9 after the first 60 mm of topsoil has been removed from an already partially eroded Miami soil. Afterwards, P_r was predicted to decline by only 0.06 percent/mm of soil removed to a value of about 0.85 after 300 mm of soil has been removed.

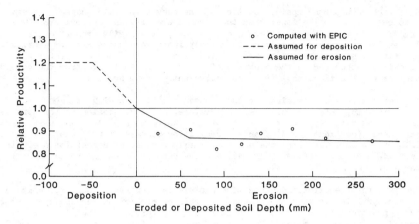

Fig. 3   Short Term Loss or Gain in Crop Productivity with Erosion or Deposition

Because the concave and complex slopes have areas of deposition as well as erosion, the effect of deposition on productivity had to be estimated. Based on limited testing with EPIC and experimental field results of Uhland (1949), Stallings (1950), and Ripley et al. (1961), we assumed that relative productivity P_r would increase to a value of 1.2 when 50 mm of sediment was added with no additional gain in productivity for more than 50 mm of deposition as Fig. 3 shows. Our analysis did not consider the effect of deposition of subsoil material from upslope or the selective deposition of coarse sediment fractions. After our study was completed, J. R. Williams, USDA-Agricultural Research Service, Temple, Texas, made additional computer runs with EPIC, which produced Fig. 4 showing the loss of crop yield for large cumulative soil losses. Note that yield loss was very irregular and exposure of the soil at 800 mm significantly increased productivity.

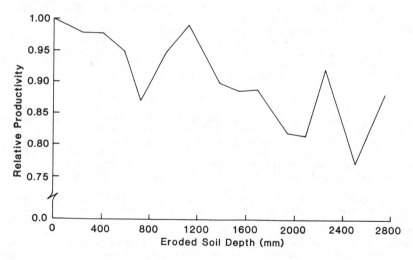

Fig. 4   Long Term Loss of Productivity with Erosion

Loss of Producitivity over Time

The data shown in Fig. 3 were used with the erosion rates in Fig. 2 to estimate the change in productivity along each land profile over 200 years. Relative productivity P_r was integrated along each profile to give the net change in relative productivity for the entire profile over time. The results are given in Table 2 and Fig. 5.

Estimated productivity decline was generally greater on the convex profile than it was on the uniform profile. After about 20 years, the rate of decline in productivity for both the uniform and convex profiles decreased, with the decrease occurring earlier for the convex profile than for the uniform profile. The reason for the reduced rate of productivity decline is that high

Table 2. Relative Productivity by Profile Shape and Time When Productivity Increases with Deposition[a]

Profile	Time (years)				
Shape	10	20	50	100	200
Uniform	1.00	0.90	0.87	0.86	0.83
Convex	0.88	0.87	0.85	0.83	0.78
Concave	0.99	1.02	1.01	1.01	1.00
Complex	1.00	0.99	0.97	0.95	0.92

a   Ratio of net productivity for the profile with erosion and deposition to the net productivity for the profile when no erosion or deposition occurs

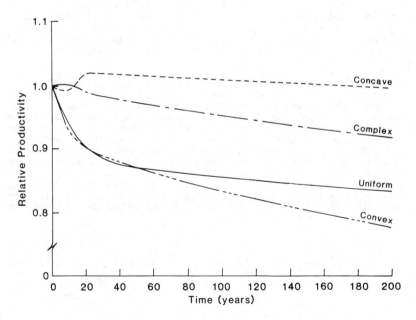

Fig. 5   Net Productivity for Various Shaped Profiles

erosion rates on the end of the profiles rapidly eroded the 60 mm of soil where the relative productivity-soil loss curve in Fig. 3 flattened. After this much soil was eroded at a location, further erosion caused little loss of productivity. Furthermore, the 60 mm of soil was eroded from the lower end of the convex profile before it was from the end of the uniform profile, which accounts for the earlier decrease in the rate of productivity loss for the convex profile.

Even though productivity loss over portions of the concave and complex slopes was as great or much greater, respectively, than the maximum loss on the uniform profile, productivity gains from deposition offset productivity losses caused by erosion during the initial years. The gain in productivity on the depositional areas was so great that net profile productivity was greater than initial productivity for 20 and 200 years for the complex and concave profiles, respectively. Afterwards, the gain in productivity on the depositional area was less than the loss of productivity on the eroding area of the complex profile. The accuracy of these results strongly depend on the accuracy of the assumed relationship for the effect of deposition on productivity and on the neglect of a change in soil properties on the depositional area by deposition of subsoil material eroded from upslope areas. In this case, the relative effect of deposition on productivity was greater than the fraction of area experiencing deposition.

Effect of Productivity-Eroded Depth Function

The effect of profile shape on estimates of productivity loss depends on characteristics of the relative productivity-soil loss curve, Fig. 3, and the soil's starting point on that function. Computations were repeated assuming a new initial soil depth and that Fig. 3 describes the relation of productivity to erosion. The new initial soil condition was set at coordinates (-100, 1.2) in Fig. 3, and the origins of the graph were translated so that the coordinates of this point became (0.0, 1.0). This new relative productivity-soil loss function had the same shape as Fig. 3 but was for a soil with a deeper initial soil profile. With this shift, 50 mm of soil must be eroded before any loss of productivity occurs and deposition causes no increase in productivity.

As the results in Table 3 show, the effect of land profile shape on productivity estimates increased when deposition had no effect on productivity and some soil must be eroded before a loss of productivity occurs. A major difference in the results for the two productivity-soil loss curves is that the concave and complex profiles did not maintain their productivity when deposition was not credited with increasing productivity. This situation may be more typical than where deposition adds to productivity. Generally several soil series occur along a complex profile. Those on the concave part of the profile are already so deep that deposition does not add to their productivity. The ones on the lower part of the convex sector of complex profiles are already shallow and experiencing some loss of productivity from erosion.* This situation further emphasizes the need to consider the variation of soil properties along land profiles.

---

* D. P. Franzmeier. 1984. Personal communication. Agronomy Department, Purdue University, W. Lafayette, IN.

Table 3. Relative Productivity by Profile Shape and Time When Some
          Soil Erodes Before a Loss of Productivity Occurs and When
          Deposition does not Increase Productivity[a]

Profile shape	Time(years)				
	10	20	50	100	200
Uniform	1.00	0.93	0.79	0.73	0.70
Convex	0.91	0.86	0.80	0.75	0.67
Concave	1.00	0.94	0.87	0.86	0.84
Complex	0.95	0.90	0.85	0.83	0.78

a   Ratio of net productivity for the profile with erosion and deposi-
    tion to the net productivity for the profile when no erosion or
    deposition occurs

Use of Average Soil Loss

Representation of a nonuniform profile with a uniform profile of the same
average steepness does not accurately estimate loss of productivity. When the
erosion, deposition, and productivity relationships are linear, average soil
loss or sediment yield for the profile could be used to estimate productivity
loss. However, the relationships are nonlinear and use of average soil loss
or sediment yield can give the differences shown in Table 4. Average soil
loss for the profile over-estimated loss of productivity on uniform and convex
profiles where the degree of difference depended on characteristics of the
relative productivity-soil loss function. However, on the concave and complex
profiles, use of sediment yield over-estimated loss of productivity when
deposition added to productivity and under-estimated loss of productivity when
deposition did not add to productivity.

Table 4. Use of Average Profile Soil Loss to Estimate Relative Productivity
          at 50 Years

Productivity curve	Uniform		Convex		Concave		Complex	
	SY	Non[a]	SY	Non	SY	Non	SY	Non
Deposition adds productivity	0.87	0.87	0.85	0.87	0.95	1.01	0.92	0.97
Deposition adds no productivity	0.75	0.79	0.72	0.80	1.00	0.87	1.00	0.85

a   SY - Productivity loss computed from average soil loss or sediment yield
    for profile
    Non - Productivity loss computed from erosion and deposition rates along
    the profile

IMPLICATIONS

This study was an investigation of mathematical assumptions and interactions
of nonlinear mathematical relationships used to evaluate erosion's impact on
crop productivity. The results show that important mathematical interactions
occur between shape of land profiles and computed erosion, deposition, and
crop productivity along the profiles. For inventory purposes, a clear
distinction must be drawn between net loss of soil from the end of a land
profile and erosion or deposition at a particular point on the landscape.

Average soil loss from a uniform profile is not a good indicator of maximum erosion or loss of productivity on a nonuniform profile. The interaction between the pattern of erosion or deposition on a land profile and nonlinear relationships between erosion or deposition and crop productivity causes a complex pattern of productivity changes in time and space. As a result, average soil loss or sediment yield for a profile do not give good estimates of loss of productivity.

For concave or complex profile shapes where deposition occurs and adds to productivity, little, if any, net loss of productivity for the profile may persist for some time although portions of the profile are being rapidly and extensively degraded by erosion. In view of the potential effect of deposition on net productivity of a concave or complex profile, further field validation and modeling efforts are required to better determine the relationship of productivity to deposition. Also, our analysis considered only nonlinearities associated with profile shape; a more thorough analysis should also consider variation in soil properties along land profiles.

Computed maximum erosion rates along nonuniform profiles are often large. For example, erosion was estimated to lower elevation near the middle of the complex profile by almost two meters, and deposition just 30 m downslope from the point of maximum erosion was estimated to raise elevation by a similar amount. Such changes in elevation represent a major change and adjustment in the landscape that could significantly reduce erosion. If erosion rates are to be projected for the long term, like 500 years, the analysis should consider landscape adjustment.

SUMMARY

Although uniform land profiles, because of their mathematical convenience, are often assumed in analyses of the impact of erosion on crop productivity, most field profiles are nonuniform. Variations in erosion and deposition along nonuniform profiles can be great and nonlinear. These functions combined with nonlinear relations for the effect of erosion or deposition on loss or gain in crop productivity at a point on the landscape produce complex patterns of loss and gain in productivity along nonuniform land profiles.

This study investigated mathematical consequences of these variations, their nonlinearities, and their interactions. The EPIC model was used to compute a random sequence of rainfall and runoff values used as input to the CREAMS model to compute erosion and deposition along uniform, convex, concave, and complex land profiles for a typical Miami silt loam soil in northern Illinois. EPIC was also used to develop a function between loss of productivity and eroded depth for this Miami soil. Computed erosion rates along the profiles were combined with the productivity loss-soil loss function and integrated to compute net loss of productivity for the profiles over 200 years. Indeed, nonlinearity in the mathematical relationships and the very great variation in erosion and deposition rates along concave and complex profiles do cause significant mathematical errors when uniform land profiles are used in erosion/productivity analyses to represent nonuniform land profiles.

Furthermore, computed erosion and deposition rates can be so large at some locations on nonuniform profiles that massive amounts of soil are computed to be relocated over long time periods like 200 years. Such large rates of erosion and deposition would cause major adjustments and changes in landscape profiles to significantly affect erosion. Therefore, future erosion/productivity inventories should consider variation in erosion and deposition in space caused by both landscape profile shape and variation in soil properties. Furthermore, when large erosion and deposition rates are involved, landscape adjustment to erosion and deposition must be considered.

ACKNOWLEDGEMENT

We acknowledge and appreciate the assistance provided by J.R. Williams, F.J. Pierce, and R.M. Cruse during this research. Dr. Williams provided the computer program for EPIC, helped modify the program for our needs, and made additional computer runs after Dr. Perrens left his assignment at W. Lafayette, Indiana. At our request, Dr. Pierce and Dr. Cruse used their models to compute productivity losses as a function of erosion for our conditions.

REFERENCES

1. Craft, E. and R.M. Cruse. 1984. A simple diagnostic model to evaluate soil erosion effects on plant production. In: Proc. of Intl. Confer. on Soil Erosion and Conservation. Soil Conservation. Soc. of Amer., Ankeny, IA. (in press).

2. Foster, G.R., L.J. Lane, J.D. Nowlin, J.M. Laflen and R.A. Young. 1981. Estimating erosion and sediment yield field-sized areas. TRANS. of the ASAE 24:1253-1262.

3. Foster, G.R., D.K. McCool, K.G. Renard and W.C. Moldenhauer. 1981. Conversion of the Universal Soil Loss Equation to SI metric units. J. of Soil and Water Conserv. 36:355-359.

4. Foster, G.R. and L.D. Meyer. 1972. Transport of soil particles by shallow flow. TRANS. of the ASAE 15:99-102.

5. Foster, G.R. and L.D. Meyer. 1975. Mathematical simulation of upland erosion by fundamental erosion mechanics. In: Present and Prospective Technology for Predicting Sediment Yields and Sources. ARS-S-40, USDA-Agric. Research Serv. pp. 190-207.

6. Foster, G.R., L.D. Meyer and C.A. Onstad. 1977. A runoff erosivity factor and variable slope length exponents for soil loss estimates. TRANS. of the ASAE 20:683-687.

7. Larson, W.E., F.J. Pierce and R.H. Dowdy. 1983. The threat of soil erosion to long term crop production. Science 219:458-465.

8. Meyer, L.D., A. Bauer and R.D. Heil. 1984. Experimental approaches for quantifying the effect of soil erosion on productivity. In: Proc. of Natl. Sympos. on Soil Erosion and Crop Productivity. Soil Sci. Soc. of Amer., Madison, WI. (in press).

9. Meyer, L.D., G.R. Foster and M.J.M. Romkens. 1975. Source of soil eroded by water from upland slopes. In: Present and Prospective Technology for Predicting Sediment Yields and Sources. ARS-S-40, USDA-Agric. Research Serv. pp. 177-189.

10. Nielsen, D.R., J.W. Biggar and K.T. Erh. 1973. Spatial variability of field measured soil water properties. Hilgardia 42:215-259.

11. Onstad, C.A. and G.R. Foster. 1975. Erosion modeling on a watershed. TRANS. of the ASAE 18:288-292.

12. Ripley, P.O., W. Kalbfleisch, S.J. Bourget and D.J. Cooper. 1961. Soil erosion by water. Publ. No. 1093. Canadian Depart. of Agric., Ottawa.

13. Rogowski, A.S., R.M. Khanlilrardi and R.J. DeAngelis. 1984. Estimating erosion on a plot, field, and watershed scale. In: Proc. of the Intl. Confer. on Soil Erosion and Conservation. Soil Conserv. Soc. of Amer., Ankeny, IA. (in press).

14. Sharma, M.L., R.J.N. Barau and E.S. DeBoer. 1983. Spatial structure and variability of infiltration parameters. In: Advances in Infiltrat. ASAE Publ. No. 11-83. pp. 113-121.

15. Schertz, D.L. 1983. The basis of soil loss tolerances. J. Soil and Water Conserv. 38:10-14.

16. Stallings, J.H. 1950. Erosion of topsoil reduces productivity. SCS-TP-98, U.S. Dept. of Agric.

17. Uhland, R.E. 1949. Corn yields lowered by erosion. SCS-TP-75, U.S. Dept. of Agric.

18. U.S. Department of Agriculture (USDA). 1980. CREAMS, a field scale model for Chemicals, Runoff, and Erosion from Agricultural Management Systems. Conserv. Research Rept. 26, USDA-Agric. Research Serv. 640 pp.

19. USDA-National Soil Erosion - Soil Productivity Research Planning Committee (USDA). 1981. Soil erosion effects on soil productivity: A research perspective. J. of Soil and Water Conserv. 36:82-90.

20. Williams, J.R. 1975. Sediment yield prediction with the Universal Equation using runoff energy factor. In: Present and Perspective Technology for Predicting Sediment Yields and Sources. ARS-S-40, USDA-Agric. Research Serv. pp. 244-252.

21. Williams, J.R., C.A. Jones and P.T. Dyke. 1984. A modeling approach to determining the relationship between erosion and soil productivity. TRANS. of the ASAE 27:129-144.

22. Wischmeier, W.H. and D.D. Smith. 1978. Predicting rainfall erosion losses - A guide to conservation planning. Agric. Handbook No. 537. USDA-Science and Educ. Admin. 58 pp.

23. Yalin, Y.S. 1963. An expression for bed-load transportation. J. of the Hydr. Div., Proc. of the Amer. Soc. of Civil Engr. 89:221-250.

ASSESSING THE EFFECT OF SOIL EROSION ON PRODUCTIVITY WITH EPIC

J. R. Williams   J. W. Putman   P. T. Dyke

The Erosion-Productivity Impact Calculator (EPIC) model (Williams et al. 1984) was developed to assess the effect of soil erosion on soil productivity. EPIC is composed of physically based components for simulating erosion, plant growth, and related processes and economic components for assessing the cost of erosion, determining optimal management strategies, etc. The physical processes involved are simulated simultaneously and realistically using readily-available inputs. Since erosion can be a relatively slow process, EPIC is capable of simulating hundreds of years if necessary. The model is generally applicable, computationally efficient, and capable of computing the effects of management changes on outputs.

The EPIC model is currently being used to analyze the relationships among erosion, productivity, and fertilizer needs as part of the Soil and Water Resources Conservation Act (RCA) analysis for 1985. EPIC will provide erosion-productivity relationships (E/P) for about 900 benchmark soils and 500,000 crop/tillage/conservation strategies as input to the Center for Agricultural and Rural Development (CARD) model (English et al. 1982). Evaluating all CARD management strategies using EPIC is too expensive and time consuming. Instead, a sample of 15 to 20,000 EPIC simulations will be used to provide the CARD information base. The sample is composed of two EPIC simulations for each eroding soil and major crop in each Major Land Resource Area (MLRA). The E/P developed from these paired simulations will be used to expand the EPIC sample results to the information base required by CARD.

The objective here is to describe a method for developing and applying E/P. To provide a proper foundation, a brief overview of the EPIC model is presented. Details of the EPIC model have been described previously (Williams et al. 1984). Details of the EPIC RCA application are given by Putman et al. (1984).

THE EPIC MODEL

Although EPIC is a fairly comprehensive model, it was developed specifically for application to the erosion-productivity problem. Thus, user convenience was an important consideration in designing the model. The EPIC main program and 68 subroutines contain 3500 FORTRAN statements. Since EPIC operates on a daily time step, computer cost for overnight turnaround are only about $0.03 per year of simulation on an AMDAHL 470 computer. The model can be run on a variety of computers since storage requirements are only 300K.

Hydrology

Surface Runoff: Surface runoff of daily rainfall is predicted using a modification of the SCS curve number method (USDA, Soil Conservation Service 1972). The curve number varies nonlinearly from the 1 (dry) condition at wilting point to the 3 (wet) condition at field capacity and approaches 100 at saturation. EPIC also includes a provision for estimating runoff from frozen soil.

The authors are: Hydraulic Engineer, USDA-ARS, and Agricultural Economists, USDA-ERS, P. O. Box 748, Temple, TX 76503.

Peak runoff rate predictions are based on a modification of the rational formula. The runoff coefficient is calculated as the ratio of runoff volume to rainfall. The rainfall intensity during the watershed time of concentration is estimated for each storm as a function of total rainfall using a stochastic technique.

Percolation: The percolation component of EPIC uses a storage routing technique combined with a crack-flow model to predict flow through each soil layer in the root zone. At saturation the flow rate is the saturated conductivity of the soil. Below saturation the flow rate decreases nonlinearly and approaches zero at field capacity. The routing function also reduces flow if a lower soil layer is saturated.

The crack-flow model allows percolation of infiltrated rainfall even though the soil water content is less than field capacity. When the soil is dry and cracked, infiltrated rainfall can flow through the cracks of a layer without becoming part of the layer's soil water. However, the portion that does become part of a layer's stored water cannot percolate until the storage exceeds field capacity.

Percolation is also affected by soil temperature. If the temperature in a particular layer is 0°C or below, no percolation is allowed from that layer. Water can, however, percolate into the layer if storage is available.

Lateral Subsurface Flow: Lateral subsurface flow is calculated simultaneously with percolation. Lateral flow can occur when the storage in any layer exceeds field capacity after percolation. Like percolation, lateral flow is simulated with a travel time routing function.

Evapotranspiration: The evapotranspiration component of EPIC is Ritchie's ET model (Ritchie 1972). The model computes potential evaporation as a function of solar radiation, air temperature, and albedo. Potential soil evaporation is estimated as a function of potential evaporation and leaf area index. The first stage soil evaporation is equal to the potential soil evaporation. Stage two soil evaporation is predicted with a square root function of time. Plant evaporation is estimated as a linear function of potential evaporation and leaf area index.

Snow Melt: The EPIC snow melt component is similar to that of the CREAMS model (Knisel 1980). If snow is present, it is melted on days when the maximum temperature exceeds 0°C using a linear function of temperature. Melted snow is treated the same as rainfall for estimating runoff, percolation, etc.

Weather

The weather variables necessary for driving the EPIC model are precipitation, air temperature, solar radiation, and wind. If daily precipitation, air temperature and solar radiation data are available, they can be input directly. However, since these data are often scarce, EPIC provides options for simulating temperature and radiation, given daily rainfall, or for simulating rainfall as well as temperature and radiation. If wind erosion is to be estimated, daily wind velocity and direction are simulated.

Precipitation: The EPIC precipitation model developed by Nicks (1974) is a first-order Markov chain model. Given the wet-dry state, the model determines stochastically if precipitation occurs or not. When a precipitation event occurs, the amount is determined by generating from a skewed normal daily precipitation distribution. The amount of daily precipitation is partitioned between rainfall and snowfall using average daily air temperature.

Air Temperature and Solar Radiation: The temperature-radiation model developed by Richardson (1981) was selected for use in EPIC because it simulates temperature and radiation that exhibit proper correlation between one another and rainfall. Details of the multivariate generation model were described by Richardson (1981, 1982a).

<u>Wind</u>: The wind simulation model was developed by Richardson (1982b) for use in simulating wind erosion with EPIC. Average daily wind velocity is generated from a two-parameter gamma distribution. Wind direction expressed as radians from north in a clockwise direction is generated from an empirical distribution specific for each location.

Erosion

<u>Water</u>: The water erosion component of EPIC uses a modification of the USLE (Wischmeier and Smith 1978) developed by Onstad and Foster (1975). The Onstad-Foster equation's energy factor is composed of both rainfall and runoff variables. EPIC supplies estimates of runoff volume, peak runoff rate, and rainfall energy. The soil erodibility factor is estimated as a function of soil texture and organic content. The crop management factor is evaluated with a function of above ground biomass and crop residue. The erosion estimates are adjusted using an exponential function of top soil course fragment content.

<u>Wind</u>: The Manhattan, KS, wind erosion equation (Woodruff and Siddoway 1965) was modified by Cole et al. (1982) for use in the EPIC model. The original equation computes average annual wind erosion as a function of soil erodibility, a climatic factor, soil ridge roughness, field length along the prevailing wind direction, and vegetative cover. The main modification of the model was converting from annual to daily predictions to interface with EPIC.

The ridge roughness is a function of a ridge height and ridge interval. Field length along the prevailing wind direction is calculated by considering the field dimensions and orientation and the wind direction. The vegetative cover equivalent factor is simulated daily as a function of standing live biomass, standing dead residue, and flat crop residue. Daily wind energy is estimated as a nonlinear function of daily wind velocity.

Nutrients

<u>Nitrogen</u>: The amount of NO_3-N in runoff is estimated by considering the top soil layer (10-mm thickness) only. The average concentration for a day can be obtained by integrating an exponential relationship between flow and concentration. Amounts of NO_3-N contained in runoff, lateral flow, and percolation are estimated as the products of the volume of water and the average concentration.

Leaching and lateral subsurface flow in lower layers are treated with the same approach used in the upper layer except surface runoff is not considered. When water is evaporated from the soil, NO_3-N is moved upward into the top soil layer by mass flow.

A loading function developed by McElroy et al. (1976) and modified by Williams and Hann (1978) for application to individual runoff events is used to estimate organic N loss. The loading function estimates the daily organic N runoff loss based on the concentration of organic N in the top soil layer, the sediment yield, and the enrichment ratio. A two-parameter logarithmic function of sediment concentration is used to estimate enrichment ratios for each event.

Denitrification, one of the microbial processes, is a function of temperature and water content. Denitrification occurs only when the soil water content exceeds 90 percent of saturation. The denitrification rate is estimated using an exponential function involving temperature, organic carbon, and NO_3-N.

The N mineralization model is a modification of the PAPRAN mineralization model (Seligman and Van Keulen 1981). The model considers two sources of mineralization: fresh organic N associated with crop residue and microbial biomass, and the stable organic N associated with the soil humus pool. The mineralization rate for fresh organic N is governed by C:N and C:P ratios, soil water, temperature, and the stage of residue decomposition. Mineralization from the stable organic N pool is estimated as a function of organic N weight, soil water, and temperature.

Like mineralization, the immobiliztion model is a modification of the PAPRAN model. The daily amount of immobilization is computed by subtracting the amount of N contained in the crop residue from the amount assimilated by the microorganisms. Immobilization may be limited by N or P availability.

Crop use of N is estimated using a supply and demand approach. The daily crop N demand is estimated as the product of biomass growth and optimal N concentration in the plant (function of crop stage). Soil supply of N is assumed to be limited by mass flow of NO_3-N to the roots. Actual N uptake is the minimum of supply and demand.

EPIC estimates fixation by adding N in an attempt to prevent N stress that constrains plant growth. If N is the active constraint, enough N (a maximum of 2 kg/ha•d) is added to the plant to make the N stress factor equal the next most constraining factor if possible.

To estimate the N contribution from rainfall, EPIC uses an average rainfall N concentration for a location for all storms.

Phosphorus: The EPIC approach to estimating soluble P loss in surface runoff is based on the concept of partitioning pesticides in the solution and sediment phases as described by Leonard and Wauchope (Knisel 1980). Because P is mostly associated with the sediment phase, the soluble P runoff is predicted using labile P concentration in the top soil layer, runoff volume, and a partitioning factor. Sediment transport of P is simulated with a loading function as described in organic N transport.

The P mineralization and immobilization models developed by Jones et al. (1984) are similar in structure to the N models. Mineralization from the fresh organic P pool is governed by C:N and C:P ratios, soil water, temperature, and the stage of residue decomposition. Mineralization from the stable organic P pool associated with humus is estimated as a function of organic P weight, labile P concentration, soil water, and temperature. The daily amount of immobilization is computed by subtracting the amount of P contained in the crop residue from the amount assimilated by the microorganisms.

The mineral P model developed by Jones et al. (1984) transfers P among three pools: labile, active mineral, and stable mineral. Flow between the labile and active mineral pools is governed by temperature, soil water, and P sorption coefficient, and the amount of material in each pool. The P sorption coefficient is a function of chemical and physical soil properties. Flow between the active and stable mineral P pools is governed by the concentration of P in each pool and the P sorption coefficient.

Crop use of P is estimated with the supply and demand approach described in the N model. However, the P supply is predicted using an equation based on soil water, plant demand, a labile P factor, and root weight.

Soil Temperature

Daily average soil temperature is simulated at the center of each soil layer for use in nutrient cycling and hydrology. The temperature of the soil surface is estimated using daily maximum and minimum air temperature, solar radiation, and albedo for the day of interest plus the 4 days immediately preceding. Soil temperature is predicted for each layer using a function of bulk density, soil water, surface temperature, mean annual air temperature, and the amplitude of daily mean temperature.

Crop Growth Model

A single model is used in EPIC for simulating all the crops considered (corn, grain sorghum, wheat, barley, oats, sunflowers, soybeans, alfalfa, cotton, peanuts, and grasses). Energy interception is estimated with an equation based on solar radiation and leaf area index (LAI). The potential increase in biomass for a day is the product of intercepted energy and a crop parameter for converting energy to biomass. The LAI is a function of heat units, the maximum LAI for the crop, a parameter that initiates LAI decline, and four stress factors.

The daily fraction of the potential increase in biomass partitioned to yield is estimated as a function of accumulated heat units and the ratio of total biomass to crop yield under favorable growing conditions. Since most of the accumulating biomass is partitioned to yield late in the growing season, late season stresses may reduce yields more than early season stresses. Root growth and sloughing are simulated using a linear function of biomass and heat units.

Actual daily increase in biomass is estimated using the product of the minimum stress factor and the potential biomass. The water stress factor is computed by considering supply and demand (the ratio of plant accessible water to potential plant evaporation). Roots are allowed to compensate for water deficits in certain layers by using more water in layers with adequate supplies. The temperature stress factor is computed with a function dependent upon the daily average temperature, the optimal temperature, and the base temperature for the crop. The N and P stress factors are based on the ratio of accumulated plant N and P to the optimal values. The stress factors vary nonlinearly from 1.0 at optimal N and P levels to 0 when N or P is half the optimal level.

Potential root growth is a function of soil water in a layer. It may be reduced by a stress factor (minimum of soil texture and bulk density, temperature, aeration, and aluminum toxicity).

Tillage

The EPIC tillage component was designed to mix nutrients and crop residue, simulate the change in bulk density, and convert standing residue to flat residue. Other functions of the tillage component include simulating ridge height and surface roughness. After tillage, the bulk density returns to the undisturbed value at a rate dependent upon infiltration, tillage depth, and soil texture.

Plant Environment Control

Drainage: Underground drainage systems are treated as a modification to the natural lateral subsurface flow of the area. Simulation of a drainage system is accomplished by reducing the travel time in a specified soil layer.

Irrigation: The EPIC user has the option to simulate dryland or irrigated agricultural areas. If irrigation is indicated, he must also specify the runoff ratio (volume of water leaving the field/volume applied), a plant water stress level to start irrigation, and whether water is applied by sprinkler or down the furrows. When the user-specified stress level is reached, enough water is applied to bring the root zone up to field capacity plus enough to satisfy the amount lost in runoff.

Fertilization: EPIC provides two options for applying fertilizer. With the first option, the user specifies dates, rates, and depths of application of N and P. The second option is more automated--the only input required is a plant stress parameter. At planting time enough N and P fertilizer is applied to bring the NO_3-N and labile P concentrations up to the concentration level at the start of the simulation. Additional applications will occur if the N stress factor is the active crop growth constraint and if it is less than the user-specified stress level for fertilizer application.

Lime: EPIC simulates the use of lime to neutralize toxic levels of aluminum in the plow layer. Two sources, KCl-extractable aluminum in the plow layer and acidity caused by ammonia-based fertilizers, are considered. When the sum of acidity due to extractable aluminum and fertilizer N exceeds 4 t/ha, the required amount of lime is added and incorporated into the plow layer.

Pesticides: The effects of insects, weeds, and diseases are expressed in the EPIC pest factor. Crop yields are adjusted by multiplying the daily simulated yield by the pest factor (ranges from 0 to 1).

This method, based on a concept introduced by Perrens (1983), transforms EPIC output into an E/P. Two long-term (≈ 100 years) EPIC simulation runs are required to apply the method to a particular soil within a MLRA. The two runs are designed to envelop the range of conservation strategies that could be applied to the land. The first run represents perfect conservation by preventing erosion (the water erosion control practice factor (P) and the wind erosion climatic factor (WC) are set to zero). Maximum erosion rates are simulated in the second run by assuming no conservation practices (P=1) and assigning the appropriate value to WC. Except for erosion, the two runs are identical (weather, initial conditions, crop rotation, etc.). Annual crop yields from the two runs are used to compute an erosion-productivity index (EPI).

$$EPI_i = \frac{YLD_{e,i}}{YLD_{u,i}} \qquad (1)$$

where YLD is the crop yield for year i, and subscripts e and u refer to the simulations with erosion and without erosion. The E/P is obtained by relating the EPI to accumulated erosion. If top soil is eroded and the sub-soil is less favorable for root growth, EPI decreases rapidly from its initial value of 1.0 There may be considerable variation in EPI from year to year because of weather and soil water content (Figure 1). This is especially true when erosion rates are high. Dry years usually reduce yields on eroded soils more than on uneroded soils because of differences in soil water capacity. Thus, EPI is generally low for dry years. Conversely, EPI may be high for years with favorable rainfall even after considerable erosion.

Because of this extreme variability in EPI from year to year, it is difficult to develop a reliable technique for obtaining E/P for sites throughout the U.S. A better approach is to develop a relationship between accumulated EPI and time. This technique smooths the EPI data and provides a curve with a characteristic shape that can be fit easily with a simple two-parameter exponential function.

The accumulated EPI data can be transformed to fit within a 0 to 1 scale by dividing the accumulated amount by time in years. This transformation gives the average EPI value for any period. When related to time, the average EPI produces a curve that usually departs slowly from its initial value of 1. After a few years when EPI has decreased, the average EPI curve may move downward more rapidly than during the first few years. Finally, the average EPI curve tends to level off after many years (50-100) because each additional year has little effect on the average. The behavior of the average EPI curve can be described quite well using the equation

$$\frac{\sum_{i=1}^{T} EPI_i}{T} = 1. - \frac{T}{T + b_1 \exp(-b_2 T)} \qquad (2)$$

where T is time from the start of the simulation and b_1 and b_2 are shape parameters. To estimate EPI for any year, Eq. 2 is multiplied by T and differentiated to give

$$EPI = 1. - \frac{2T (T + b_1 \exp(-b_2 T)) - T^2 (1. - b_1 b_2 \exp(-b_2 T))}{(T + b_1 \exp(-b_2 T))^2} \qquad (3)$$

The values of b_1 and b_2 are determined by a simultaneous solution of Eq. 2 for T equal the period of simulation and for T equal 1/2 the period. This solution guarantees a fit of the mid and end points of the accumulated EPI data.

The desired E/P can be obtained by subsituting an accumulated erosion equivalent, E, for T in Eq. 3.

$$EPI = 1. - \frac{2 E (E + b_1 \exp(-b_2 E)) - E^2 (1. - b_1 b_2 \exp(-b_2 E))}{(E + b_1 \exp(-b_2 E))^2} \qquad (4)$$

Assuming that erosion occurs as a linear function of time provides for the transition from time to accumulated erosion.

$$E = \frac{(T)(Y)}{Y_e} \qquad (5)$$

where Y is the average annual erosion rate (wind plus water) for a particular conservation strategy and Y_e is the rate for the zero conservation strategy assumed in the EPIC simulation. Thus, EPI can be estimated for any conservation strategy from the E/P (Eq. 4) if the average annual erosion rate is known.

APPLYING THE E/P

To apply the E/P it is necessary to estimate both wind and water erosion for the management strategies considered. It is essential that these estimates compare closely with actual EPIC simulation results. Thus, the Onstad-Foster (1975) and the Manhattan, KS (Woodruff and Siddoway 1965, Cole et al. 1982) equations are used to estimate average annual water and wind erosion. A ratio approach is used in making both estimates.

Water Erosion

For water erosion the ratio is formed by considering a 10-year frequency rain storm on the EPIC simulation site and on the site where erosion is to be estimated. The equation is

$$YH_j = YH_n \frac{0.646\ EI_j + 0.45\ (Q_j)\ (q_{pj})^{0.333}\ (K_j)\ (CE_j)\ (P_j)\ (LS_j)}{(0.646\ EI_n + 0.45\ (Q_n)\ (q_{pn})^{0.333}\ (K_n)\ (CE_n)\ (P_n)\ (LS_n)} \qquad (6)$$

where YH is the average annual water erosion rate in t/ha, EI is the rainfall energy factor in metric units, Q is the runoff volume in mm, q_p is the peak runoff rate in mm/h, K is the soil erodibility factor, CE is the crop management factor, P is the erosion control practice factor, LS is the slope length and steepness factor, and subscripts j and n refer to the estimation site and to the EPIC simulation site, respectively. The rainfall energy factor is estimated at both sites using the EPIC (Williams et al. 1984) equation

$$EI = R_6 (12.1 + 8.9 (\log r_p - 0.434)) (r_{.5}) / 1000 \qquad (7)$$

where R_6 is the 10-year frequency 6-h rainfall amount in mm, r_p is the peak rainfall rate in mm/h, and $r_{.5}$ is the maximum 0.5 h rainfall intensity in mm/h. The peak rainfall rate and the maximum 0.5 h rate can be estimated as previously described (Williams 1984) using the equation

$$r_p = -2\ R_6 \log (1 - \alpha_{.5}) \qquad (8)$$

$$r_{.5} = 2\ \alpha\ R_6 \qquad (9)$$

221

where α is the ratio of rainfall amount during the watershed time of concentration to the 6-h amount and $\alpha_{.5}$ is the ratio of 0.5-h rainfall to 6-h rainfall. The value of $\alpha_{.5}$ can be obtained directly

$$\alpha_{.5} = \frac{R_{.5}}{R_6} \tag{10}$$

where $R_{.5}$ is the 10-year frequency rainfall amount in mm during 0.5 h. To determine α the 10-year frequency rainfall amount during the watershed time of concentration must be estimated. This is done by developing a relationship between time and rainfall amounts from TP-40 (Hershfield 1961).

$$R_t = R_6 \left(\frac{t}{6}\right)^{\beta} \tag{11}$$

where t is time in h and β is a shape parameter. The value of β is obtained from the equation

$$\beta = -\log\left(\frac{R_{.5}}{R_6}\right) / 1.079 \tag{12}$$

EPIC computes the peak runoff rate using the modified rational equation

$$q_p = \frac{(\alpha)\,(Q)\,(A)}{360\,t_c} \tag{13}$$

where A is the watershed area in ha and t_c is the time of concentration in h. The runoff volume is estimated from the SCS curve number (USDA, Soil Conservation Service 1972) equation

$$Q = \frac{(T_6 - 0.2\,s)^2}{R_6 + 0.8\,s} \tag{14}$$

where s is a retention parameter. The value of s is obtained from the SCS equation

$$s = 254\left(\frac{100}{CN} - 1\right) \tag{15}$$

where CN is the antecedent moisture condition 2 curve number taken from the SCS Hydrology Handbook.

The soil erodibility factor, K, is computed using the EPIC equation

$$K = (0.2 + 0.3\exp(-0.0256\,SAN\,(1 - \frac{SIL}{100})))\left(\frac{SIL}{CLA + SIL}\right)^{0.3}$$

$$(1 - \frac{0.25\,C}{C + \exp(3.72 - 2.95\,C)}) \tag{16}$$

where SAN, SIL, CLA, and C are the sand, silt, clay, and organic carbon content of the soil in %.

Since there is no way to obtain an estimation site average CE factor that would be comparable to the long-term simulated average CE factor, both are taken from Handbook 537 (Wischmeier and Smith 1978). Guidelines in Handbook 537 are also used in assigning P and in calculating LS for the two sites.

Wind Erosion

Since the Manhattan, KS wind erosion equation is designed to predict average annual wind erosion, the ratio approach is more direct than that used in water erosion. The ratio equation used to predict average annual wind erosion for the estimation site is

$$YW_j = YW_n \left(\frac{WE_j}{WE_n} \right) \tag{17}$$

where YW_n is the average annual wind erosion simulated on a daily basis by EPIC, YW_j is the EPIC comparable average annual wind erosion for the estimation site, and WE is the average annual wind erosion calculated as described by Woodruff and Siddoway (1965) for the two sites. Although YW and WE should be similar, there may be considerable difference because daily simulation provides much more detailed information on residue, growing biomass, ridge interval and height, and wind direction.

Finally, the total erosion (Y) needed for the estimation site in Eq. 5 is computed as the sum of YH and YW.

Example Problem

To demonstrate the application of the E/P technique an example problem is presented. A hypothetical test site was assumed to be near Lafayette, IN, and to contain Miami silt loam soil. The slope length and steepness were assumed to be 100 m and 5%, respectively. Continuous corn with an annual fertilizer rate of 100 kg/ha N and 20 kg/ha P was the assumed management strategy. Two EPIC simulations of 100 years each (one with maximum and one with zero erosion) were performed to obtain data for calculating the EPI values. Figure 1 shows the annual EPI values (crop yield with erosion/crop yield zero erosion) plotted with the ● symbol. The predicted EPI values plotted in Figure 1 with the * symbol were obtained from a simultaneous solution of Eq. 3 and proper substitution of Eq. 5 into Eq. 4.

The E/P appears to be a reasonable representation of what could occur during 100 years of cultivation without conservation on a Miami soil. Productivity drops rapidly during the early years as the favorable top soil is eroded. After the top soil (≈ 130 mm is eroded, the texture changes gradually from 55% silt, 19% clay to 45% silt, 30% clay, the available water capacity decreases from 0.18 to 0.16, bulk density increases from 1.45 to 1.6, and organic C decreases from 1.02% to 0.5%. These less favorable conditions exist to a depth of 640 mm. Beyond 640 mm the soil is unfavorable for crop production. The available water capacity is ≈ 0.75, bulk density is 1.8, and organic C is $\approx 0.2\%$. As shown by the E/P production begins to level off as the accumulated erosion approaches 6000 t/ha (≈ 360 mm of erosion). The tillage mixing effect smooths the transition between soil layers and prevents direct comparison of the E/P and the soil profile. If soil layers were removed instantaneously, the E/P would reflect soil property differences more distinctly.

SUMMARY AND CONCLUSIONS

A method for use in determining and applying the E/P was developed. EPIC simulated crop yields and erosion rates are the variables involved in the E/P. Two long-term EPIC simulations are used to calculate EPI values (yields with erosion/yields with no erosion) for a given soil in a particular MLRA. A two-parameter exponential function is used to relate average EPI to time. The function is differentiated and the independent variable is transformed from time to accumulated erosion to derive the E/P.

The E/P will be used by the CARD model to complete the 1985 RCA analysis. Besides providing a convenient form for CARD calculations, the E/P also saves a tremendous amount of computing time. Once the E/P is developed for all soils and MLRA's, any management strategy can be evaluated quickly if the average annual erosion rate is known. Short-cut methods for estimating average annual water and wind erosion were developed for use in applying the E/P. The short-cut methods simply adjust EPIC simulated average annual yields with ratios. The ratios are formed by dividing predicted erosion rates for the site to be estimated by those for the EPIC simulation site. For water erosion, the predictions are based on a 10-year frequency, 6-h rain storm. Wind erosion predictions, based on the Manhattan, KS equation, give average annual erosion rates directly.

The technique developed here facilitates the development and application of a reliable E/P. The E/P provides a means for determining the cost of erosion and for evaluating various conservation strategies.

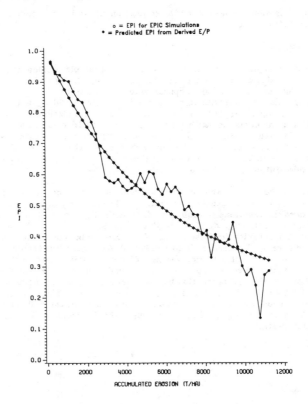

Fig. 1. Erosion-productivity Relationship (E/P) for Miami Soil Near Lafayette, IN

224

REFERENCES

1. Cole, G.W., L. Lyles, and L.G. Hagen 1982. A simulation model of daily wind erosion soil loss. 1982 ASAE Winter Meeting, Paper No. 82-2575.

2. English, B.C., K.F. Alt, and E.O. Heady. 1982. A documentation of the Resources Conservation Act's assessment model of regional agricultural production, land and water use, and soil loss. Center for Agric. and Rural Development Report 107T.

3. Jones, C.A., C.V. Cole, and A.N. Sharpley 1984. A simplified soil phosphorus model, I. Documentation. Submitted to Soil Sci. Soc. Am. J.

4. Hershfield, D.M. 1961. Rainfall frequency atlas of the United States for durations from 30 minutes to 24 hours and return periods from 1 to 100 years. U.S. Dept. of Commerce, Tech. Paper No. 40. 115 pp.

5. Knisel, W.G. 1980. CREAMS, A field scale model for chemicals, runoff, and erosion from agricultural management systems. USDA Conserv. Res. Report No. 26. 643 pp.

6. McElroy, A.D., S.Y. Chiu, J.W. Neben, A. Aleti, and F.W. Bennett. 1976. Loading functions for assessment of water pollution from nonpoint sources. Environ. Protection Tech. Series, U.S.E.P.A., EPA-600/2-76-151. 445 pp.

7. Nicks, A.D. 1974. Stochastic generation of the occurrence, pattern, and location of maximum amount of daily rainfall. pp. 154-171. In Proc. Symp. Statistical Hydrology, Tucson, Arizona, August-September 1971. Misc. Publ. No. 1275.

8. Onstad, C.A. and G.R. Foster. 1975. Erosion modeling on a watershed. Trans. ASAE 18(2):288-292.

9. Perrens, S.J. Evaluation of non-linearity of crop productivity along non-uniform land slope. Unpublished report, USDA-ARS and Agric. Eng. Dept., Purdue Univ.

10. Putman, J., P. Dyke, and G. Wistrand. 1984. Erosion-productivity index simulator (EPIS). USDA, ERS Unpub. report.

11. Richardson, C.W. 1981. Stochastic simulation of daily precipitation, temperature, and solar radiation. Water Resources Res. 17(1):182-190.

12. Richardson, C.W. 1982a. Dependence structure of daily temperature and solar radiation. Trans. ASAE 25(3):735-739.

13. Richardson, C.W. 1982b. A wind simulation model for wind erosion estimation. 1982 ASAE Winter Meeting, Paper No. 82-2576.

14. Ritchie, J.T. 1972. A model for predicting evaporation from a row crop with incomplete cover. Water Resources Res. 8(5):1204-1213.

15. Seligman, N.G. and H. van Keulen. 1981. PAPRAN: A simulation model of annual pasture production limited by rainfall and nitrogen. pp. 192-221. In M. J. Frissel and J. A. van Veen (eds.) Simulation of Nitrogen Behaviour of Soil-Plant Systems. Proc. of a Workshop, Wageningen, January 28-February 1, 1980.

16. USDA, Soil Conservation Service. 1972. National Engineering Handbook. Hydrology Section 4, Chapters 4-10.

17. Williams, J.R. and R.W. Hann. 1978. Optimal operation of large agricultural watersheds with water quality constraints. Texas Water Resources Institute, Texas A&M Univ., Tech. Rep. No. 96. 152 pp.

18. Williams, J.R., P.T. Dyke, and C.A. Jones. 1983. EPIC--A model for assessing the effects of erosion on soil productivity. pp. 553-572. In W. K. Laurenroth, G. V. Skogerboe, and M. Flug (eds.) Analysis of Ecological Systems: State-of-the-Art in Ecological Modelling.

19. Williams, J.R., C.A. Jones, and P.T. Dyke. 1984. A modeling approach to determining the relationship between erosion and soil productivity. Trans. ASAE 27(1):129-144.

20. Wischmeier, W.H. and D.D. Smith. 1978. Predicting rainfall erosion losses, a guide to conservation planning. USDA Agr. Handbook No. 537. 58 pp.

21. Woodruff, N.P. and F.H. Siddoway. 1965. A wind erosion equation. Soil Sci. Soc. Am. Proc. 29(5):602-608.

PRIVATE AND PUBLIC VALUE OF CONTROLLING

SOIL EROSION WITH CONSERVATION TILLAGE

Anthony A. Prato

According to the Conservation Tillage Information Center, conservation tillage is a practice which leaves at least 30% residue cover on the soil surface after planting. This practice has significant potential for controlling soil erosion. Achievement of this potential depends on widespread adoption and successful application of conservation tillage by farmers. Farmers have an incentive to switch from conventional to conservation tillage when it is profitable. When adoption is unprofitable to the farmer, the incentive can be increased by federal programs that reduce private costs and risks and/or increase private returns. Federal assistance is justified when the net social value of conservation tillage is positive; that is, when private plus public benefits exceed private plus public costs.

The purpose of this paper is to evaluate the net private and public value of reducing soil erosion with conservation tillage for annual wheat production in the Palouse area of southeastern Washington. Major emphasis is on determining the sensitivity of net private value to variation in commodity price, cost of production and yield, and the extent to which federal assistance is justified.

OVERVIEW

The net private value of conservation tillage is defined as the change in net farm income that farmers realize by converting from conventional to conservation tillage. Conservation tillage can affect net farm income by altering yields and costs of production. Yield can be affected in two ways. Initially, yield may be lower with conservation tillage than with conventional tillage because the farmer must learn to apply a new technology. During this learning process, the farmer may realize lower yields and higher-than-expected production costs. In the long term, however, conservation tillage reduces soil erosion thereby maintaining topsoil depth, soil productivity and yield.

While long-term production costs are expected to be lower for conservation tillage than for conventional tillage, initial costs can be higher if total fixed costs increase, as a result of a change in machinery complement, by more than total variable costs decrease, as a result of lower labor and fuel costs. Crosson (1981) estimated that production costs would be 5% to 10% lower with conservation tillage compared to conventional tillage because the reduction in labor, fuel and machinery costs exceed the increase in herbicide costs. Changes in commodity prices and crop yields also affect net farm income. Long-term increases in crop yields result from improvements in chemicals, seeds, equipment, soil amendments and cropping practices, commonly referred to as technological change.

The author is: Anthony A. Prato, Economist, West National Technical Center, Soil Conservation Service, Portland, Oregon.

ANNUALIZED NET PRIVATE VALUE

Annualized net private value (ANPV) of conservation tillage is:

$$\text{ANPV} = \sum_{t=1}^{T} [(1+r)^{-t} \ (P_t((1-a)Y_{mt}-Y_{nt})+C_t)] f(r,T) \tag{1}$$

where:
P_t = real wheat price in year t (cents/kg),
a = yield penalty for conservation tillage relative to conventional tillage,
Y_t = wheat yield in year t for conservation (m) tillage and conventional (n) tillage (kg/ha),
C_t = difference in real production costs between conservation and conventional tillage in year t ($/ha),
T = evaluation period in years,
r = real discount rate,
f = amortization factor which depends on r and T.

According to Young and Taylor (1983), wheat yield in the Palouse can be expressed as an exponential function of topsoil depth and technological change:

$$Y_t = [83.45 - 47.01\exp(-0.09864 \ D_t)]\exp(bt) \tag{2}$$

where D_t is topsoil in year t. In the absence of technological change, yield decreases at an increasing rate as topsoil depth is eroded; term in parentheses. The term exp(bt) accounts for the positive effect of technological change on yield; yield grows at a constant proportional rate of b% per year. The joint effect of other determinants of yield, such as organic-matter content (see Burt 1981), rooting-zone depth, precipitation and management practices, is contained in the constant term. This assumes, however, that these other effects are independent of time, which is an oversimplification. The parameters of this equation were estimated with Y in bu/acre and D in inches, using non-linear regression and observations for a 5-year period (Walker 1983). This same equation is used to calculate yields for conservation and conventional tillage.

Topsoil depth is a linear function of time:

$$D_t = d - st \tag{3}$$

where:
d = initial topsoil depth in cm,
s = erosion rate in cm per year,
t = time (1,2,...,T).

The net private value of conservation tillage was determined for the following wheat prices, cost of production differentials, yield penalties and other parameters of Eqs. (1), (2) and (3):

P = 7.35 cents ($2), 14.7 cents ($4) and 22.1 cents ($6) per kg (bu),
a = 0%, 2% and 4% yield penalty,
d = 30.8 cm (12") and 51.3 cm (20") of topsoil,
s = 5.5 metric tons/ha/year (15 tons/acre/year) erosion rate for conservation tillage,

```
C = $0, $0.40 ($1), $0.81 ($2) and $1.62 ($4) per hectare (acre)
    per year lower production cost for conservation tillage,
b = 0.01 (1%/year growth in yield),
T = 50-year evaluation period,
r = 4% real discount rate.
```

The values of P, a, d, s and C are consistent with those selected by Walker (1983). He used: P between $0.81 ($2) and $3.24 ($8) per hectare (acre); a between 1 and 4%; d of 30.8 cm (12") and 53.8 cm (21"); s same as here; and C between $0 and $2.83 ($7) per hectare (acre). ANPV was evaluated for all 72 combinations of the parameters P, a, d and C. Wheat price (P) and the production-cost differential (C) were assumed to remain constant in real terms throughout the evaluation period. An evaluation period of 50 years was selected to allow for the long-term effects of soil erosion on yield. Since a 50-year evaluation period exceeds the planning horizon used by most farmers, the results of this analysis pertain to long-term conservation planning.

RESULTS

Private Value

The sensitivity results for ANPV show that:

1. ANPV is negative in 17 of the 36 cases where initial topsoil depth is 51.3 cm (20").

2. ANPV is negative in all cases where the yield penalty is 4% and in 8 of 12 cases where the yield penalty is 2% and initial topsoil depth is 51.3 cm (20").

3. ANPV is positive in all cases where initial topsoil depth is 30.8 cm (12").

4. ANPV is very sensitive to changes in the yield penalty and relatively insensitive to changes in wheat price or the cost differential between conservation and conventional tillage.

Table 1 gives the average percentage change in ANPV associated with a 1% change in each parameter holding all other parameters constant, i.e., the elasticity of ANPV with respect to each parameter. A 1% increase in yield resulting from a reduction in the yield penalty (a) causes ANPV to increase 273% when topsoil depth is 51.3 cm (20") and 141% when topsoil depth is 30.8 cm (12"). When the cost differential increases by 1%, making conservation tillage less expensive than conventional tillage, ANPV increases 1.8% for the 51.3 cm (20") topsoil depth and 0.4% for the 30.8 cm (12") topsoil depth. For a 1% increase in wheat price, ANPV decreases 2.5% when topsoil depth is 51.3 cm (20") but increases by 0.67% when topsoil depth is 30.8 cm (12").

Table 1. Sensitivity of ANPV to Initial Topsoil Depth, Wheat Price, Cost and Yield
===

Initial topsoil depth	Average percentage change in ANPV from a 1% increase in:		
(cm)	Wheat price	Cost	Yield
30.8	0.67	0.4	141
51.3	-2.5	1.8	273

===

Public Value

Controlling soil erosion has public value because it maintains long-term productivity of cropland and reduces the offsite damages of cropland erosion. The value of maintaining long-term productivity is not included in this analysis. Offsite damages, which include sedimentation and the accumulation of nutrients, pesticides, and salts, in rivers and lakes can be significant. In a study of eleven Illinois watersheds, offsite sediment damages were estimated to be 9% to 16% of net farm income (Guntermann et al 1975). The regional public cost of offsite erosion damages has not been extensively evaluated. However, a recent SCS analysis gives the following national costs for damages caused by sediment erosion on cropland (USDA 1984):

Category	Annual cost (10^6 \$)
Lakes and reservoirs	170
Navigation	160
Flood damages	320
Recreational fishing	50
Total	700

Total sediment damages of $700 \cdot 10^6$ were divided by the annual U.S. cropland erosion of $2.75 \cdot 10^9$ metric tons ($3.03 \cdot 10^9$ tons) (USDA 1984) to obtain an annual public cost of $0.21 per metric ton ($0.23 per ton) of erosion for the nation. Applying this national figure to the Palouse, where erosion can be reduced by 4.8 metric tons per hectare (13 tons per acre) per year with conservation tillage, gives an average public benefit of $1.21 per hectare ($3 per acre) per year for conservation tillage.

Conversion to conservation tillage entails an additional public cost when technical and/or financial assistance is provided. The annual cost of SCS technical assistance has been estimated at $0.056 per metric ton ($0.062 per ton) of erosion control for targeted areas. The Palouse is a targeted area. This is equivalent to about $0.32 per hectare ($0.80 per acre) per year for an erosion reduction of 4.8 metric tons per hectare (13 tons per acre) per year. The administrative costs incurred by FmHA and ASCS for providing financial assistance to farmers was not included in this analysis. Subtracting the cost of SCS technical assistance from the public value of sediment reduction gives an estimated annual net public value of $0.89 per hectare ($2.20 per acre) for converting to conservation tillage in the Palouse.

Social Value

Net social value of erosion reduction is the sum of net private value and net public value as defined above. The estimate of net social value derived here may be low because it ignores the public value of improving water quality and maintaining long-term cropland productivity which result from lower rates of soil erosion. When the net private value of conservation tillage is negative, farmers are unlikely to adopt it. However, when net public value is positive and exceeds the private loss, net social value is positive. In such cases, federal financial assistance in an amount up to the private loss is justified.

Table 2 gives the annualized net private and social values for conservation tillage in the Palouse for each yield penalty and initial topsoil depth, averaged over all three wheat prices and four cost differentials analyzed. Both average net private and social values are significantly greater when initial topsoil depth is 30.8 cm (12") rather than 51.3 cm (20") and when the yield penalty is 4% and initial topsoil depth is 51.3 cm (20").

Table 2. Average Annual Net Private and Social Value by Yield Penalty and
          Initial Topsoil Depth
==

Initial topsoil depth	Yield penalty					
	0%		2%		4%	
(cm)	ANPV	ANSV	ANPV	ANSV	ANPV	ANSV
	($/ha)					
51.3	3.24	4.13	0.25	1.14	-2.75	-1.86
30.8	6.29	7.18	3.61	4.50	0.93	1.82

==

    ANPV = annualized net private value
    ANSV = annualized net social value (ANPV + $0.89)

Annualized net private value is negative in 17 of the 36 cases for an
initial topsoil depth of 51.3 cm (20"). In 7 of these 17 cases, net public
value exceeds ANPV, so social welfare can be increased by subsidizing
conservation tillage. This does not imply that such subsidies should be
made. As Crosson and Stout (1983) point out, public expenditure on erosion
reduction should be evaluated in a broader context, namely the avoidance of
long-term increases in agricultural production costs. Such an evaluation
would compare the efficiency of alternative policies for achieving this
objective. Federal assistance is not justified in cases where net social
value is negative.

In this analysis, ANPV is positive in all cases where initial topsoil depth
is 30.8 cm (12") indicating that conservation tillage is economically
feasible for this initial soil depth. While economic feasibility is a
prerequisite for adoption by farmers, it does not guarantee it. Other
factors influence a farmer's decision to adopt conservation tillage,
including attitudes towards risk and financial feasibility.

                          POLICY IMPLICATIONS

Although conservation tillage is an effective way of reducing soil erosion,
this analysis shows that it is unprofitable for farmers to adopt this
practice when topsoil depth is deep and the yield loss exceeds 2%.
Profitability increases with reductions in the yield loss and decreases in
topsoil depth. Since long-term profitability of conservation tillage is
very sensitive to the yield penalty, technical assistance programs designed
to help farmers maintain crop yields with conservation tillage should
accelerate adoption.

Short-term risk and financial constraints faced by farmers can discourage
the adoption of conservation tillage even when it is economically
profitable. Under these conditions, adoption can be stimulated by financial
assistance programs such as cost sharing.

In conclusion, this analysis demonstrates the importance of considering
social value relative to private value when evaluating federal assistance
for erosion control. It also indicates that changes in wheat yield are a
more important determinant of farmers' willingness to adopt conservation
tillage in the Palouse than changes in commodity prices or production costs.

                          REFERENCES

1. Burt, Oscar R. 1981. Farm Level Economics of Soil Conservation in the
Palouse Area of the Northwest. Am. J. Agr. Econ. 63:83-92.

2. Crosson, Pierre R. and Anthony A. Stout. 1983. Productivity Effects of Cropland Erosion in the United States. Research paper from Resources for the Future, Inc., The Johns Hopkins University Press, Baltimore, Maryland.

3. Crosson, P. 1981. Conservation Tillage and Conventional Tillage: A Comparative Assessment. Soil Conservation Society of America, Ankeny, Iowa.

4. Guntermann, Karl L., Ming T. Lee and Earl R. Swanson. 1975. The Off-site Sediment Damage Function in Selected Illinois Watersheds. J. Soil and Water Cons. 30:219-224.

5. United States Department of Agriculture, Soil Conservation Service. 1984. Offsite Impacts of Agriculture. Unpublished paper, Washington, D.C.

6. United States Department of Agriculture, Soil Conservation Service. 1984. Preliminary Data, 1982 National Resources Inventory, Executive Summary. Washington, D.C.

7. Walker, David J. 1983. A Damage Function to Evaluate Erosion Control Economics. Am. J. Agr. Econ. 64:690-698.

8. Young, Douglas L. and Daniel B. Taylor. 1983. A User's Guide to Projecting Long Run Soil Erosion Impacts. Agricultural Economics Department Staff Paper A.E. 83-10, Washington State University, Pullman, Washington.

ECONOMIC IMPLICATIONS OF SOIL CHARACTERISTICS AND PRODUCTIVITY

IN THE SOUTHERN PIEDMONT, WITH COMPARISONS TO THE PACIFIC NORTHWEST

Lee A. Christensen   David E. McElyea

Pressures on the agricultural resource base associated with fence row to fence row planting, coupled with concerns about environmental quality, have again raised the issue of the adverse impacts of soil erosion on sustained agricultural production. Renewed emphasis and money are being directed toward the identification and implementation of policies designed to reduce soil erosion and to insure the continued productivity of the cropland base. Two essential information needs for addressing this problem are the specification of the physical relationships between soil erosion and productivity, and the linkages of these relationships to economical practices for the reduction of soil erosion.

Soil erosion is typically measured in terms of inches or tons of soil removed from a particular field by wind or water. The impacts or damages associated with this erosion are typically measured as either effects on crop yields or as water quality degradation off the farm. While there is an assumed adverse effect of diminishing the topsoil base on yields, this relationship is inadequately documented to reflect the tremendous variability in soils across the United States. Limited studies have been made to relate crop yields to topsoil depth (Langdale 1979, Langdale 1982, Hoag and Young 1983). More are needed to expand the information base necessary to address soil erosion problems on a nationwide basis. The development and application of the EPIC (Erosion-Productivity Impact Calculator) model is an example of a comprehensive effort to do so. EPIC, however, assumes no soil loss/productivity functions, but rather generates them from the system of relationships within the model (Williams et al. 1983). Soil erosion/productivity functions are needed for major soils and regions of the country to aid in comprehensive analyses of the micro-economic effects of soil erosion on crop yields. These relationships are not the same on all soils within a physiographic region and certainly there are differences between physiographic regions. While some general assumptions are usually made about the form of the soil depth/productivity relationships, there is a need for more location specific analysis. This need for site specific analysis was succintly noted by Theodore Shultz (1982), the Nobel economist.

    Soil erosion is location specific. It's technical and economic
    attributes vary widely both within and between locations. For
    the purpose at hand, the unit of land on which it occurs is a
    farm and the decision entity is the farmer. This being the case,
    a nationally administered soil conservation program that is
    politically designed to provide funds and services to all parts
    of agriculture, is bound to be a model of inefficiency.

Soil erosion and the associated changes in productivity reflect the interaction of complex physical processes. Changes are first measured by soil physical and chemical relationships, and their subsequent impacts on crop yields. But the impact is eventually reflected in the costs to farmers and consumers. The development of policies for reducing erosion

The authors are: LEE A. CHRISTENSEN, Agricultural Economist, USDA-ERS, and Adjunct Professor, and DAVID E. MCELYEA, Research Associate, Department of Agricultural Economics, University of Georgia, Athens, Georgia 30602.

and associated productivity losses need an adequate description of
erosion-productivity interactions and their relationship to the economic
conditions facing farmers. This paper presents a comprehensive
evaluation procedure which incorporates both the physical erosion
processes and economic factors. We will use data on the relationship
between topsoil characteristics and soybean yields on Cecil soils in
Georgia to derive and argue the existence of a sigmoid or "S" shaped
functional relationship between yield and soil depth. The function
derived from Georgia soils will then be compared and contrasted with the
generally assumed function which is a continuously decreasing curvilinear
relationship (Walker 1982, Hoag and Young 1983). Some data taken from
the curvilinear soil depth/yield relationships for loess soils in eastern
Washington will be used for comparison purposes. Regional differences in
the profitability of soil conservation will be identified. This analysis
will then identify how differences in the form of soil depth/yield
relationships influence the effectiveness of government policies to
encourage adoption of soil conservation practices.

PROCEDURE

A model was developed to estimate the value to the farmer of the top
layers of soil subject to erosion (Eq. 1). This model considers the soil
a capital good for use in crop production, and soil erosion represents a
depreciation or a decline in value of this capital good. Thus, the cost
of erosion can be defined as the depreciation of the soil resource. If
soil losses occur at relatively small increments per year, the value to
the farmer of productivity lost due to erosion can be estimated as the
discounted value of the decline in crop yields.

Many factors influence the expected yield from a given acre, including
soil type, depth of topsoil, weather, fertilizer applications, pesticide
use, and other crop cultural practices. Soil scientists have developed
yield functions relating yields to soil types, soil depth, and other
characteristics. We applied the generalized model, which uses a
yield/soil depth function for a given crop, soil type and geographical
location, to estimate the value of soil. In this model, the value of
soil varies inversely with the discount rate and varies positively with
the value of the crop, the rate of yield growth due to technology, the
length of the planning horizon, and the change in yield.

$$V_S = \sum_{t=1}^{n} \frac{P\Delta Y (1 + k)^t}{(1 + r)^t} \tag{1}$$

where

V_S = The present value to the farmer of the yield associated
with a specified layer of soil

$\Delta Y = Y_1 - Y_2$

$Y_1 = f(D_1)$ = yield at topsoil depth D_1

$Y_2 = f(D_2)$ = yield at topsoil depth D_2

D_1 = current topsoil depth

$D_2 = D_1 - .007\ L$

L = soil erosion in ton/acre, where .007 is the assumed depth
of one ton of soil spread over an acre

P = price of output over the planning horizon

234

n = years in farmer's planning horizon

r = farmer's real discount rate

k = the proportional rate of yield growth due to technology for next n years

Yield-Topsoil Depth Relationships

The critical factor influencing the yield component of the model is the slope of the yield function, which varies with soil depth in all nonlinear yield-topsoil depth functions. Differences in the shape of the yield-topsoil function have important implications for economic interpretation and the formulation of soil conservation policies. In the following discussion, a functional form derived from Georgia data will be presented and compared and contrasted with results from a similar study in the state of Washington.

Palouse Soils: Hoag and Young (1983) estimated a yield-topsoil response function for wheat on the soils in the Palouse area of Whitman County Washington. The soils in the study area are classified as Argixerolls which include the Thatuna and Naff series and Haploxerolls which include the Palouse series. These soils are in the mesic region and have a silt loam texture in all horizons. The Argixerolls have a distinctly greater clay content than the Haploxerolls. The surface horizons are 24 to 36 inches (61-91 cm) thick and overlay subsoils of similar texture. Since the subsoils are of similar sand, silt and clay compositions as the topsoil, the mechanical composition of the topsoil remains nearly constant as the soil erodes and the subsoil becomes mixed with the topsoil.

Hoag and Young (1983) stated that the requirements of a proper theoretical model to represent yield topsoil response function should (1) display nonnegative marginal returns to topsoil throughout, (2) allow a nonzero intercept, (3) have diminishing marginal returns to topsoil, and (4) have some maximum level of attainable yields.

The functional form used by Hoag and Young (1983) to describe yield-topsoil response, which they labeled a Mitscherlich-Spillman (M-S) function, is:

$$Y = A + B (1 - R^{Topsoil\ depth}) \tag{2}$$

where

Y = winter wheat yield

A = intercept term or yield at zero topsoil

B = maximum yield increment from topsoil

R = a constant ratio unique to the relationship being described; always between 0 and 1.

This functional form, developed by E. A. Mitscherlich in the nineteenth century, was shown to apply to yield-topsoil relationships by Spillman and Lang (1924) and Stewart (1932). The general form of this function, which we refer to as the single factor Mitscherlich-Spillman function, is shown graphically in Fig. 1.

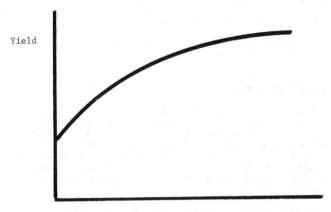

Fig. 1:   General Functional Relationship Between Yield and Topsoil Depth,
Single Factor Mitscherlich-Spillman Function

Hoag and Young's (1983) empirical investigation found that the fit to
their data of the M-S function was superior to the fit of a linear
function.   The M-S function relates yield to a single factor, topsoil
depth, which has a fixed proportion of sand, silt, and clay over the
relevant depth.   In the Palouse case, the M-S function is concave to the
horizontal axis, with increasing slope and yield loss as the topsoil
depth decreases as a result of erosion.

Cecil Soils: The relationship of yield and soil depth was investigated
for soybeans on a major Georgia soil, Cecil sandy loam.   We developed a
function from 1982 and 1983 data obtained from scientists at the USDA's
Southern Piedmont Conservation Research Center, Watkinsville, Georgia
(White et al. 1983 and 1984).   These data came from 40 farm fields with
conventionally tilled soybeans, each with slightly, moderately, and
severely eroded areas.   Slope and field size were not critical factors
for selection purposes.   Management practices, fertilization, and choice
of cultivars were determined by the grower.

The Cecil soil series is a member of the clayey, kaolintic, thermic
family of Typic Hapludults.   These soils have sandy clay loam to clay
subsoil horizons underlying a sandy loam surface horizon.   The depth to
the clayey subsoil or Bt horizon in slightly eroded sites averages about
12 inches (30 cm) including about 8 inches (20 cm) of the Ap, or topsoil
horizon.   The clayey Bt horizon is moderately dense and somewhat
restrictive to root proliferation and drainage.   As the topsoil erodes,
the clayey subsoil is mixed into the topsoil by cultivation, resulting in
increasing clay content of the Ap horizon.

Extensive statistical analysis (ordinary least square analyses and other
econometric tests) of these data gives evidence of a sigmoid or "S" shape
function.   A Mitscherlich-Spillman function can be sigmoid or "S" shaped
when the variable in question contains increasing proportions of a
limiting factor.   The limiting factor is that characteristic of topsoil
that is not sufficient to achieve maximum yield.   In this example, the
limiting factor is the sand and silt content of rooting zone.

The general form of this sigmoid function is presented in Fig. 2. This function, called a varying proportion M-S function, is:

$$Y = A + B (1-R^{f(\text{Topsoil depth})}) \qquad (3)$$

where

      Y = crop yield

      A = an intercept term

      B = the maximum yield increment from topsoil

      R = a constant ratio unique to the relationship being discussed; always between 0 and 1.

      f = the limiting factor, which is an increasing function of topsoil depth

Physical evidence of the increase of the limiting factor with erosion in Georgia Cecil soils is the change in the mechanical composition of the topsoil. For example, clay content varies from 5 percent for slightly eroded soil 8–12 inches (20–30 cm) deep to approximately 50 percent for severely eroded topsoil 1.5–6 inches (4–15 cm) deep. As noted before, the varying clay content can be explained by the mixing of the clay subsoils with the shallow Cecil topsoils through repeated plowing. As erosion occurs, the proportion of clay increases due to this mixing process. Therefore there are decreasing proportions of the nonclay components, sand and silt, over the topsoil range which could result in an "S" shaped Mitscherlich-Spillman yield-topsoil depth function for the Cecil soils. This analysis gives support to the assumption that for Cecil soils the yield-topsoil function is sigmoid or "S" shaped.

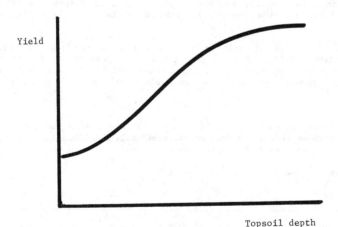

Fig. 2. Shape of Functional Relationship Between Yield and Topsoil Depth, Varying Proportion Mitscherlich-Spillman Function

APPLICATION OF THE MODEL

The economic model was applied using the yield functions we estimated for Cecil soils and the functions for Palouse soils presented by Hoag and Young (1983). This application demonstrates the important influence of the slope of the yield/topsoil depth function on estimating the value of soil and subsequent policy implications.

The soybean yield function for Georgia Cecil soils estimated from our data by a linear transformation regression is.

$$Y_s = 9.4 + 29.3 \ (1 - e^{-7.28(NCC - .5) \ X/12}) \qquad (4)$$
$$(27.5)^* \ (10.7)^*$$

$$R^2 = .446 \quad * = \text{t-value significant at the .0001 level}$$

where

Y_s = soybean yield in bushels

NCC = nonclay content of topsoil, and varies directly with soil depth

X = topsoil depth in inches

12 = depth in inches of rooting zone for soybeans

The limiting factor for soybean yields is assumed to be the sand and silt proportion of the primary rooting zone. This 12 inch (30 cm) rooting zone for soybeans typically extends through the entire Ap horizon and part of Bt horizon. The value of the sand and silt content (SSC) is estimated using measured values of the NCC for the Ap horizon and assumes the nonclay content of the Bt is .5. Thus the average SSC for the rooting zone can be computed to be (NCC - .5) X/12 + .5. For analytical purposes, (SSC - .5) or (NCC - .5) X/12, is used in the regression. The value of R, the constant term in equation 3, was estimated using a nonlinear regression of a 1983 subset of the data. The NCC typically varies from .95 to .50 as topsoil depth goes from uneroded to severely eroded. In this example, uneroded topsoil depth is assumed to be 10 inches (25 cm) and the topsoil is assumed to be severely eroded at 5 inches (12.5 cm).

The value of a ton of soil at different soil depths was estimated assuming soybean prices of $7.00 per bushel, a 50-year planning horizon, an 8 percent discount rate, and a 1 percent annual yield increase due to technology. Results are presented in Table 1 and shown graphically in Fig. 3 and Fig. 4.

Table 1. Estimated Relationship Between Topsoil Depth, Clay Content, Soybean Yield, and Present Value of Soil, Cecil Soils

Topsoil depth (inches)	5.5	6.5	7.5	8.5	10.0
Clay content	.5	.35	.25	.15	.05
Soybean yield (bushels)	9.4	22.5	29.3	33.9	36.8
Value of soil (V_S) (dollars/ton)	0	.97	.94	.67	.25

The wheat yield function for the Palouse soils is a single factor M-S function developed by Hoag and Young (1983). The function, based on a linear transformation regression analysis of 4 years of data, is:

$$Y_w = 38.9 + 40.5 \ (1 - e^{-.105X}) \qquad\qquad (5)$$
$$(8.46)*$$

$$R^2 = .452 \quad * = \text{t-value significant at the .05 level}$$

where

Y_w = wheat yield in bushels/acre

X = topsoil depth in inches

The topsoil depth was assumed to be a proxy for the limiting factor to wheat growth, which in the Palouse soils is probably the organic content of the topsoil. The value of a ton of soil at different soil depths was estimated assuming wheat prices of $3.00 per bushel, a 50-year planning horizon, an 8 percent discount rate, and a 1 percent annual yield increase due to technology. Results are presented in Table 2 and shown graphically in Fig. 3 and 4.

Table 2. Estimated Relationship Between Topsoil Depth, Wheat Yield, and Present Value of Soil, Palouse Area Soils

Topsoil depth (inches)	0	5	10	20	30	40
Wheat yield (bushels)	38.9	55.4	65.2	74.4	77.7	78.8
Value of topsoil (V_S) (dollars/ton)	1.18	.70	.42	.14	.05	.017

INTERPRETATION OF THE RESULTS

Both the shape and slope of yield-topsoil functions have important economic interpretations. For the single factor M-S function on Palouse area soils, the present value of income loss due to erosion on deeper soils may be so low that conservation benefits are not worth additional control costs. However, yield damages, measured by present value of lost income, increase as topsoil depth decreases (Fig. 3 and 4). These damages will reach a maximum at zero topsoil depth.

For the "S" shaped increasing proportion M-S yield-topsoil function on Cecil soils, the yield damage is very small for slightly eroded areas. It then increases over a range of decreasing topsoil depth and reaches a maximum at the inflection point A (Fig. 3). For soil depths less than at the inflection point, the yield damage decreases until it is close to zero for the severely eroded soils (Fig. 4). Hence, farmers with severely or slightly eroded soil will have less incentive to conserve the soil than those with moderately eroded topsoils.

The economic feasibility of a particular soil conservation practice is greatly influenced by the shape of the yield damage function. If the single factor M-S function exhibited by Palouse area soils is applicable, and a soil conservation practice is used which costs C_1 dollars per ton of erosion control, it would be profitable for the farmer to adopt the practice only if the value of the soil saved is greater than the

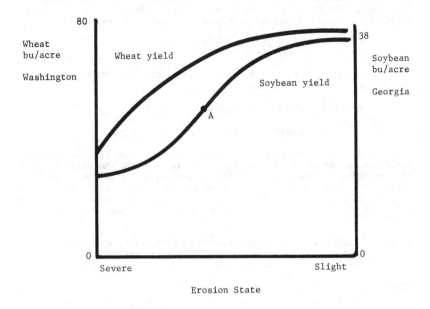

Figure 3 - Yield-Erosion State Response Functions

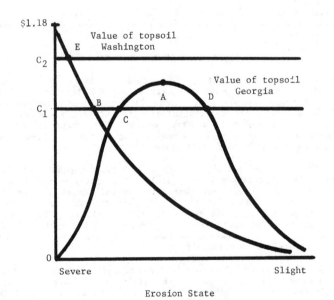

Figure 4. The Value of Topsoil Under Different Soil Conditions
and Erosion States

conservation costs. This occurs at the level of erosion represented by point B or worse, as shown in Fig. 4. In contrast, farmers with soils exhibiting characteristics of the "S" shaped function, as on Cecil soils, will find it profitable to employ the conservation practice with cost C_1 for erosion conditions between points C and D. If the practice costs C_2 per ton of erosion control, the farmer with the sigmoid M-S function (e.g. Cecil soils) will find it unprofitable to employ the practice at any topsoil depth, while it may be profitable for a farmer with a single factor M-S function (e.g. Palouse area soils) at erosion state E.

IMPLICATIONS

Because of the variation in soil types and climatic conditions within the crop producing areas of the United States, productivity and erosion state relationships of different soils and crops between and within regions can be very different. As Crosson and Stout (1982) note, "We need empirically estimated curves relating erosion, or soil depth to yields on all the major soils in all the major crop-producing regions." This analysis shows how different the relationship can be and reinforces the need for research generating erosion-productivity data for different soils and crop combinations. While this analysis compares soils with a wide geographic separation, the same type of differences are possible within the same area.

Our analysis shows the need for new and more sophisticated methods of empirically estimating yield-erosion state response functions. Topsoil depth is not necessarily the best variable for estimating these relationships. For example, for shallow topsoils with less productive subsoils, such as the Cecil soil, the composition of the plant rooting zone can be a superior explanatory variable. On deep homogeneous soils, such as Palouse, topsoil depth may be an acceptable proxy for those soil attributes which determine yields.

This analysis focuses primarily on the benefit side of the conservation issue. By using present value methods we have estimated values of topsoil which may be lost through erosion. These values represent the private benefits of soil conservation to farmers. These benefits need to be compared with the costs of various soil conservation practices to estimate the net benefits of soil conservation to farmers. As demonstrated, a conservation practice economically feasible for one region or soil is not automatically transferable to another area or soil.

Effective, efficient, and equitable soil conservation policy requires that the different economic effects of soil erosion and the incentives for soil conservation reflect the variations between the many soil types, erosion states, and crops which exist both within and between regions of the United States. Farm, regional, and national soil erosion analysis, using either farm models or macro models such as EPIC, need reliable information on topsoil-productivity relationships for many soils. Such information, combined with costs of alternative conservation practices will aid in the formulation of conservation policy which recognizes both the significant variation in soil conditions and practice costs throughout the United States.

REFERENCES

1. Crosson, Pierre R., and Anthony T. Stout. 1982. Productivity effects of cropland erosion in the United States, Resources for the Future, Washington, D.C. 103 p.

2. Hoag, Dana L., and Douglas L. Young. 1983. "Yield-topsoil depth response functions: linear versus Mitscherlich-Spillman." STEEP Agricultural Economics Working Paper, 82-2, Dept. of Agricultural Economics, Washington State University.

3. Langdale, G. W., J. E. Box, Jr., R. A. Leonard, A. P. Burnett, and W. C. Fleming. 1979. "Corn yield reduction on eroded southern Piedmont soils." Journal of Soil and Water Conservation 34(5). pp. 226-228.

4. Langdale, G. W., and W. D. Shrader. 1982. Soil erosion effects on soil productivity of cultivated cropland. pp. 41-51. In B. L. Schmidt, R. R. Allmaras, J. V. Mannering, and R. I. Papendick (eds.). Determinants of Soil Loss Tolerance. Amer. Soc. of Agron. Spec. Publ. No. 45. Madison, Wis. 153 p.

5. Schultz, Theodore W. 1982. "The dynamics of soil erosion in the United States: a critical view." Agricultural economics paper presented at the Conference on Soil Conservation, Agricultural Council of America, Washington, D.C.

6. Spillman, W. J., and Emil Lang. 1924. The Law of Diminishing Returns. New York, World Book Co.

7. Soil Conservation Service, National Resource Inventory of 1977. 1981. Unpublished U.S.D.A., RCA Appraisal, Parts 1 and 2, Washington, D.C.

8. Stewart, R. 1932. "The Mitscherlich, Wiessman and Neubauer methods of determining the nutrient content of soils." Imperial Bureau of Soil Science, Technical Communication No. 25. London, England: His Majesty's Stationery Office.

9. Walker, David J. 1982. "A damage function to evaluate erosion control economics." American Journal of Agricultural Economics, 4:690-698.

10 White, A. W., Jr., R. R. Bruce, A. W. Thomas, G. W. Langdale, and H. F. Perkins. 1983. "The effects of soil erosion on soybean production in the southern Piedmont of Georgia in 1982." U.S.D.A., Southern Piedmont Conservation Research Center, Agricultural Research Service, Erosion-Productivity Investigations, 1982, Research Report No. IRC060183, Watkinsville, Ga.

11. White, A. W., Jr., R. R. Bruce, A. W. Thomas, G. W. Langdale, and H. F. Perkins. 1984. "Effects of soil erosion on soybean yields and characteristics of Cecil-Pacolet soils." U.S.D.A., Southern Piedmont Conservation Research Center, Agricultural Research Service, Research Report No. 1RC060184, Watkinsville, Ga.

12. White, A. W., Jr., R. R. Bruce, A. W. Thomas, G. W. Langdale, and H. F. Perkins. 1984. "Characterizing productivity of eroded soils in the southern Piedmont." Paper presented at National Symposium on Erosion and Soil Productivity, New Orleans, La.

13. Williams, J. R., K. G. Renard, and P. T. Dyke. 1983. EPIC, a new method for assessing erosion's effect on soil productivity. Journal of Soil and Water Conservation 38(5): 381-83.

SOIL PRODUCTIVITY AND VULNERABILITY INDICES
FOR EROSION CONTROL PROGRAMS

G. A. Larson   F. J. Pierce   L. J. Winkelman

The Minnesota legislature first appropriated funds in 1977 to the Soil and Water Conservation Board for providing financial assistance to landowners as a means of cost-sharing the installation of erosion control or water quality protection measures. The enabling legislation (Minnesota Statutes 1977) directed the Board to allocate the funds to those "areas within the state where erosion, sedimentation and related water quality problems appear most in need of control methods." Those critical erosion areas were determined by ranking counties on the basis of estimated average annual erosion rates according to the most current USDA data.

Since the purpose of this targeting effort with respect to soil erosion was ostensibly to reduce losses in agricultural productivity, the productivity index (PI) research of Pierce et al. (1983), which suggested that soils experiencing high rates of erosion may not necessarily be facing large losses of agricultural productivity, was viewed with interest. Subsequent work by Pierce et al. (1984a) in assessing soil productivity and erosion effects in the corn belt by using applications of a PI model included several southeast Minnesota counties. These counties are viewed by the Soil and Water Conservation Board and other agencies as a critical (water) erosion area.

Our objectives here are to (a) discuss the ranking of Houston, Olmsted, and Winona counties in southeast Minnesota when based on gross erosion rates alone versus their use in concert with an index of productivity (PI) and a soil vulnerability (V) concept; (b) examine the usefulness of incorporating a landscape vulnerability factor and other criteria into a prioritization scheme; and (c) discuss the relationship of planning horizons, and other issues to soil conservation program efforts.

SOIL EROSION AND PRODUCTIVITY: AN OVERVIEW

"Soil productivity is the capacity of a soil for producing a specified plant or sequence of plants under a physically defined set of management practices. A "productive" soil is generally regarded as one that will give good crop yield in relation to inputs of materials and labor when used for a combination of principal crops such as corn, soybeans, or wheat" (Larson et al. 1982).

The authors are: Gregory A. Larson, Program Specialist, Soil and Water Conservation Board, Minnesota Department of Agriculture, St. Paul, Minnesota; Francis J. Pierce, Assistant Professor, Department of Crop and Soil Science, Michigan State University, East Lansing, Michigan; and Larry J. Winkelman, Senior Systems Analyst, USDA, Agricultural Research Service, St. Paul, Minnesota.

Soil productivity inputs can be placed into two categories: replaceable and nonreplaceable. Fertilizers and lime are examples of replaceable inputs. Usually, after a productive soil is cropped for a period of time without any external inputs, the yield of the crop starts to decline because of a reduced nutrient supply or a low pH. If the nutrients are replaced and lime is added and the soil receives reasonable management, the soil may continue to produce crops at a high level for an indefinite period.

Limitations of plant rooting depth or the decline of available water holding capacity are examples of nonreplaceable inputs. If some of the soil profile is removed through erosion, the desirable depth of soil may be reduced. Unless soil material beneath the rooting zone is as favorable as that on the surface, the total depth of rooting and water storage capacity will be reduced and yields will be limited in spite of additions of fertilizer and lime (Larson et al. 1983).

The concept discussed in the previous two paragraphs can be illustrated as shown in Fig. 1. (Pierce et al. 1983). Figure 1A represents the soils with deep favorable characteristics to a depth of 5 feet or more. Figure 1B represents soils with favorable surface horizons but unfavorable subsurface horizons, often because of fine or coarse texture, or low pH. Figure 1C represents soils with favorable surface horizons and consolidated or coarse fragment (rock or gravel) subsurface horizons.

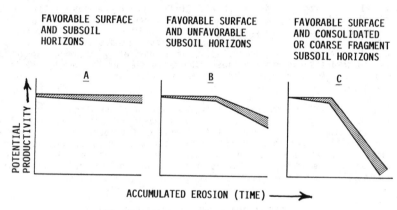

Fig. 1 Concept of Eroding Productivity

Soils of each type indicated above are cultivated in southeast Minnesota. Figure 1 illustrates the limitation of erosion rate as an indicator of productivity loss. Soils with A characteristics could conceivably erode at significantly higher rates than soils with B or C characteristics and experience less loss of productivity. Erosion control programs directed at those areas experiencing the highest rates of erosion may be overprotecting some deep soils and underprotecting some shallow ones.

PRODUCTIVITY INDEX MODEL

To quantify the concepts presented in Fig. 1, Pierce et al. (1983) made modifications to a model developed by Kiniry and Associates (1983). Based upon the factors of available water capacity, bulk density, and pH, the Kiniry model indexes the soil according to its suitability as an environment for plant roots. The factors are weighted by an idealized rooting distribution in 100 cm. of soil.

The productivity index (PI) model used is as follows:

$$PI = \sum_{i=1}^{r} (A_i \cdot C_i \cdot D_i \cdot WF_i) \tag{1}$$

where A_i is the sufficiency of available water capacity, C_i is the sufficiency of bulk density, D_i is the sufficiency of pH, WF_i is a weighting factor representing an idealized rooting distribution, and r is the number of horizons in the rooting depth. PI ranges from 0.0 to 1.0.

The approach makes use of easily obtainable inputs. It assumes a high degree of management, assesses only the change in nonreplaceable inputs as affected by erosion (Larson et al. 1983), and assesses long-term productive potential without consideration of annual fluctuations in yield caused by, for example, climate and plant differences. No estimation is made for the effects of gullying or loss of plant population due to erosion.

Data needed to calculate PI and the changes in productivity due to erosion over time are obtained from the Soils-5 (USDA 1982a) and the National Resources Inventory (NRI). For this discussion, we used the 1977 NRI data (USDA 1982b). Although it was designed for state level interpretations, the 1977 NRI data, with certain qualifications, proved acceptable for this county level analysis.

STUDY AREA

The topography of the study area is characterized by sloping to hilly uplands dissected by large and small tributaries of the Mississippi River. Soils are moderately deep and deep medium-textured Udalfs formed in loess over bedrock or glacial till. Steep, stony, and rocky soils are common. An average annual precipitation of 750 to 900 mm occurs, with two-thirds or more falling during the growing season (USDA 1981). The dominance of row crops is indicated by Table 1. The extent of row and close grown crops combined with the sloping topography and loess soils suggest the erosion potential of the area.

Table 1. Distribution of Row and Close-Grown[a] Crops among Total Cropland

County	Total Cropland	Row and Close-Grown Crops	Percent of Total Cropland
	(ha)	(ha)	
Houston	56,700	36,855	65
Olmsted	103,680	79,785	77
Winona	69,255	36,855	53

[a]Crops usually drilled or broadcast, such as oats, wheat or barley

RESULTS AND DISCUSSION

The method of analysis utilized by Pierce et al. (1984a), (1984c) was applied to data from Houston, Olmsted, and Winona counties. Initial PI, the percentage change in PI, and erosion rate, all weighted by area in slope class, as well as the cropland area in hectares and percent by slope class are presented in Table 2 for each county.

Table 2. Cropland[a], Percent Cropland by Slope Class, Weighted Average Erosion Rate, Initial PI, and Change in PI by Slope Class for each County in the Study Area

County	Slope	Area	Cropland by Slope Class	Estimated Erosion	Initial PI	Change in PI (%) 25	50	100
	(%)	(ha)	(%)	(t/ha·y)			(y)	
Houston	0-2	0						
	2-6	22,680	61.5	13.6		0	1	1
	6-12	11,340	30.8	12.9		2	4	8
	12-20	2,835	7.7	45.2		3	3	3
	20-45	0						
	>45	0						
	Total	36,855	100.0	19.7	0.86	1.0	1.9	3.2
Olmsted	0-2	17,010	21.3	5.2		0	0	1
	2-6	42,930	53.8	13.5		1	2	5
	6-12	14,175	17.8	46.8		3	6	12
	12-20	5,670	7.1	14.2		0	0	1
	20-45	0						
	>45	0						
	Total	79,785	100.0	20.3	0.86	1.2	2.2	4.8
Winona	0-2	0						
	2-6	11,340	30.8	16.2		1	2	3
	6-12	17,010	46.2	18.6		1	2	4
	12-20	5,670	15.3	147.7		51	51	51
	20-45	2,835	7.7	143.7		38	100	100
	>45	0						
	Total	36,855	100.0	40.1	0.82	11.6	17.1	18.3

[a]Includes row and close grown crops

The rate of change in productivity due to erosion depends upon the presence of soil profile characteristics favorable for rooting. This was illustrated in Fig. 1. The rate of change in PI as soil is eroded is a way of representing the soil's vulnerability to long-term productivity losses. Originally defined as the rate of change in PI with 100 cm of soil eroded (Larson et al. 1983), soil vulnerability (V) is somewhat arbitrary. A working definition of V at 50 cm of soil eroded was proposed by Pierce et al. (1984a) for soils in the Corn Belt because a number of shallow soils (< 100 cm thick) occur in the region. Values for V in the Corn Belt range from −1.2 to +1.0.

With the exception of the 12 to 20 percent slope class in Houston County, the weighted average erosion rates appear to correlate with changes in PI. This difference is reflected primarily by soil vulnerability, with a deep relatively invulnerable soil (V=-0.03) occurring on this slope class. Figure 2 displays the distribution of row and close grown crops according to V-values.

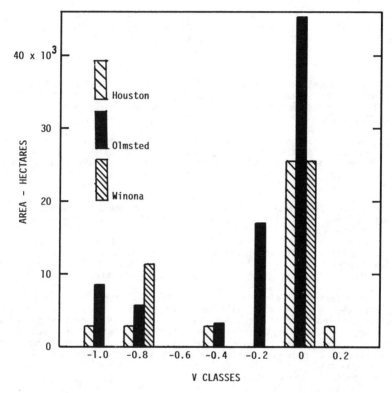

Fig. 2 Distribution of Row and Close-Grown Crops by V Classes

Nearly 44 percent of the cropland in Olmsted County has a V class less than 0.0, indicating that over 35,000 hectares are vulnerable to productivity loss (Fig. 2). Weighted average values for each county (Table 3) were negative, indicating some potential for reducing PI. The difference in vulnerable hectares of cropland (44 percent versus 24 percent) between Olmsted and Houston, respectively, is reflected on Table 3 V values.

Table 3. Weighted Average Values for RKLS, C, P, V, and PI and Projected Reductions in PI for each County in the Study Area

County	RKLS	C	P	V	PI	Potential Reduction R	Adjusted Potential Reduction R'	R"	Change in PI
	(t/ha·y)					(%)	(%)	(%)	(%)
Houston	138.2	0.21	0.68	-0.23	0.86	16.0	28.4	4.1	3.2
Olmsted	86.8	0.26	0.90	-0.30	0.86	21.4	23.3	5.5	4.8
Winona	274.6	0.20	0.73	-0.29	0.82	20.4	74.7	10.9	18.3

While some changes in PI were large (8 to 100 percent after 100 years of erosion) in the higher slope classes, the cropland area was small (Table 2). The weighted average reduction in PI was thus dominated by the lower slope classes, where reductions in PI were low (1 to 5 percent).

In general, soil erosion rates increase with increasing slope, and within a given county, productivity losses increase with increasing slope. However, there is no clear relationship between erosion rate and productivity losses because of the differences in vulnerability among soils in each of the counties.

Winona County data must be interpreted with particular care due to the unusually high rates of erosion occuring on the 12 to 20 and 20 to 45 percent slope classes. Since V is related to erosion rate, it is likely that the -0.29 V value is lower than would normally be expected for Winona County. This is suggested by comparing data in Fig. 2 and Table 2. Of the 11,000 hectares with V values of less than 0.0, 8,500 hectares are represented by the 12 to 20 and 20 to 45 percent slope classes.

The distribution of cropland by vulnerability, V (Table 3, Fig. 2) suggests the potential for reducing soil and productivity in a given county. Consideration could also be given to what might be termed a potential reduction, R, defined as the percentage PI reduction that would result if 50 cm of soil were eroded uniformly from cropland. This relates directly to the V concept but provides an estimate of the potential percentage reduction in soil productivity in a given land region. In this analysis, R exceeds 20 percent in Olmsted and Winona County.

Caution is urged when interpreting soil vulnerability because the soils susceptability to erosion processes is not considered. An adjusted potential reduction (R') can be calculated by combining V with a measure of the potential for erosion, such as the RKLS product from the universal soil loss equation (USLE) (Wischmeier and Smith 1978). The RKLS product represents the soil loss that would occur if the landscape were tilled continuously and kept fallow. R' is defined as:

$$R' = -(RKLS \cdot V \cdot a \cdot t)/PI_0 \qquad (2)$$

where RKLS is the product of the R, K, and LS factors of the USLE, V is the soil vulnerability, a is depth per ton of soil per acre, t is time in years, and PI is defined by Eq.(1). Values for R' (Table 3) indicate that the potential for productivity reduction over the next 100 years is greatest in

Winona County. If the C and P factors of the USLE are applied to the previous equation, the result is:

$$R'' = -(RKLS \cdot V \cdot a \cdot t \cdot C \cdot P)/PI_0 \qquad (3)$$

where R" is the predicted reduction in PI. Comparing the difference between R" and R' values on Table 3 suggests that conservation practices have been more effective in Winona than Houston or Olmsted in protecting the soil resource.

The use of USLE factors limits R' and R" to water erosion areas. Further development of these concepts is needed before they can be used for assessing potential wind erosion damage to soils and associated land areas.

The data provided on Table 3 demonstrates the utility of V and PI when used in combination with estimates of erosion potential, such as the USLE. Table 4 summarizes the rankings of the counties using the techniques just described. Agencies faced with determining critical areas for erosion control, projecting long term changes in soil productivity resulting from erosion, or analyzing the effectiveness of conservation practices could find these concepts to be useful (Pierce et al. 1984a, 1984c).

Table 4. Ranking[a] of Houston, Olmsted, and Winona County on the Basis of USLE Factors, Erosion Rate, Applications of a Productivity Index (PI) Concept, and Row and Close Grown Crops on Six to Twenty Percent Slopes

County	RKLS	C	P	Estimated Erosion	V	Initial PI	Potential Reduction R
Houston	2	2	3		3		3
Olmsted	3	1	1	2	1	2	1
Winona	1	3	2	1	2	1	2

County	Adjusted Potential Reduction R'	R"	Change in PI	Row and Close Grown Crops on 6 to 20% Slopes (ha)	(b)	(rank)
Houston	2	3	3	14,175	38.5	2
Olmsted	3	2	2	19,845	24.9	3
Winona	1	1	1	22,680	61.5	1

[a]Most potentially severe situation = 1
[b]Percentage of total row and close grown crops

Differences between counties would likely be more striking if an analysis similar to Table 4 were conducted for several land resource areas or a state. The ranking, by itself, will not insure equitable erosion control allocations. Other criteria such as land treatment cost and the ability of local implementing groups to organize and conduct effective programs must be considered.

OTHER ISSUES

Defining the amount of erosion that can be tolerated is difficult because the future demands on soil resources are unknown and social, ethical, and technical issues are involved (McCormack and Larson 1981). In spite of these difficult and sometimes vague issues, government agencies at all levels establish policies regarding allowable soil loss and land treatment goals. The Minnesota Soil and Water Conservation Board (1982) established a twenty year time frame for completing land treatment goals.

With respect to the estimated soil productivity losses which would occur if 1977 erosion rates continued for 25 years, Table 2 suggests that it is difficult to make a strong case for saving soil on the basis of the productivity lost in a (short) 25 year time frame. Better arguments for maintaining soil productivity in this example could be developed if longer planning horizons were used.

If agencies are to set allowable productivity losses and associated planning horizons, several points need to be considered. Short planning horizons are acceptable only if the allowable productivity loss is low, otherwise the indication is given of being too tolerant of soil erosion. An infinite planning horizon is unacceptable because it is by definition intolerant of erosion. Compounding the difficulty is the problem agencies encounter selling long term funding proposals to legislative bodies.

The productivity index concept is defined in terms of nonreplaceable soil productivity. Therefore, the selection of an appropriate allowable reduction in productivity is critical because soil is a slowly renewable resource. Even a non-vulnerable soil may be damaged if large losses in productivity are permitted.

The Minnesota Soil and Water Conservation Board adopted the currently utilized concept of allowable soil loss, "T", in developing their twenty year plan. Considerable review has been given to the appropriate level of "T" necessary to insure long-term soil productivity and resource protection (ASA 1982), (McCormack and Larson 1981), (Pierce et al. 1984b). A two-tiered "T" concept has been proposed (McCormack and Larson 1981) as a means of addressing the goals of different users; one level of "T" directed at soil productivity concerns, and another level aimed at water quality degradation, crop damage, or other offsite consequences of soil erosion.

Because of their knowledge of local resource and economic conditions and ability to gain cooperation from private landowners, local government officials working in cooperation with state and federal agencies are possibly in the best position to determine appropriate levels of "T" for both soil productivity and offsite concerns. Although the productivity index and associated concepts do not directly address the offsite consequences of soil loss, they have been used in establishing "T" levels that correspond with a soils productivity, vulnerability, allowable reduction in productivity and a planning horizon established by the user (Pierce et al. 1984b). This approach in combination with soil survey information could prove useful to local government officials as a means of identifying critical areas and developing programs to address offsite concerns. The appropriateness of addressing the offsite consequences of soil erosion is suggested by Crosson (1984) who estimates that the cost of offsite damages outweigh the cost of lost soil productivity for selected planning horizons.

Another issue is suggested by Table 2. The sample points in Winona County which generated the 12 to 20 and 20 to 45 percent slope class data consisted of Dubuque soils, a shallow (50-75 cm) Typic Hapludalf consisting of loess and residuum over limestone bedrock. This soil and slope combination falls in the VI e land capability classification. Land in capability classifications V - VIII are not considered suitable for crop production (USDA 1961). To this end, the Minnesota Soil and Water Conservation Board is proposing to deny cost - sharing assistance for erosion or sediment control measures to be installed on such land (Minnesota Soil and Water Conservation Board 1984). The American Farmland Trust (1984) offers a related argument. If these arguments prevail, the problem suggested by the reduction in PI must be addressed by other types of programs. The American Farmland Trust (1984) suggests conversion of these lands to conserving uses such as pasture or wildlife habitat. With respect to the vulnerability of these lands to lost productivity, offsite damage potential created by the volume of soil being eroded, and cost of installing erosion or sediment control measures, conversion programs appear justifiable.

CONCLUSION

The concept of targeting erosion control funds emphasizes giving priority to those areas where erosion damage to soils is greatest. Gross erosion rates have been used as the basis for selecting target areas. However, selecting target areas solely on the basis of erosion rates does not insure that emphasis will be given to those areas where erosion damage is greatest. Given the varying vulnerability of soils to erosion, the sole use of gross erosion rates would overprotect some thick soils and underprotect some thin ones. A promising approach is to select areas by using applications of a soil productivity index and existing data bases such as the USDA Soils - 5 and National Resources Inventory. This type of assessment will allow the identification of land resource areas facing the biggest risk of productivity damage. This approach has utility at both a local and state or federal level, and offers several options to users, including assessment of the effectiveness of soil and water conservation measures. The local need for more specific information can be met by incorporating soil survey data and local knowledge of resource conditions. The approach discussed herein offers a framework for establishing policies and programs to provide long-term protection for our soil and water resources, including the determination of appropriate planning horizons.

REFERENCES

1. American Farmland Trust. 1984. Soil conservation in America - what do we have to lose? Washington, D.C. 133 p.

2. American Society of Agronomy. 1982. Determinants of soil loss tolerance. Spec. Publ. 45. Madison, Wisc. 153 p.

3. Crosson, Pierre. 1984. New perspectives on soil conservation policy. J. Soil and Water Conserv. 39(4): 222-225.

4. Kiniry, L. N., C. L. Scrivner, and M. E. Keener. 1983. A soil productivity index based upon predicted water depletion and root growth. University of Missouri - Columbia, College of Agriculture, Agricultural Experiment Station Research Bulletin 1051, 26p.

5. Larson, W. E., F. J. Pierce, R. H. Dowdy, and W. A. P. Graham. 1982. Soil erosion and productivity. In Proc. of Iowa State University Farm Agricultural Resource Management Conference on Conservation Tillage. p. 2-10.

6. Larson, W. E., F. J. Pierce, and R. H. Dowdy. 1983. The threat of soil erosion to long-term crop production. Science. Vol. 219. p. 458-465.

7. McCormack, D. E. and W. E. Larson. 1981. A values dilemma: standards for soil quality tomorrow. In Economics, Ethics, Ecology: Roots of Productive Conservation. Soil Cons. Soc. America. p. 392-406.

8. Minnesota Soil and Water Conservation Board. 1982. Minnesota's soil and water conservation program - a process of gaining ground. St. Paul, MN. 56 p.

9. Minnesota Soil and Water Conservation Board. 1984. Soil and water conservation board cost-share program rules, second edition. (Draft). St. Paul, MN. 20 p.

10. Minnesota Statutes. 1977. Chapter 304. Section 40.035.

11. Pierce, F. J., W. E. Larson, R. H. Dowdy, and W. A. P. Graham. 1983. Productivity of soils: assessing long-term changes due to erosion. J. Soil and Water Conserv. 38(1): 39-44.

12. Pierce, F. J., R. H. Dowdy, W. E. Larson, and W. A. P. Graham. 1984 a. Soil productivity in the corn belt: an assessment of erosion's long-term effects. J. Soil and Water Conserv. 39(2): 131-136.

13. Pierce, F. J., W. E. Larson, and R. H. Dowdy. 1984b. Soil loss tolerance: maintenance of long-term soil productivity. J. Soil and Water Conserv. 39(2): 136-138.

14. Pierce, F. J., W. E. Larson, and R. H. Dowdy. 1984c. Evaluating soil productivity in relation to soil erosion. In Quantification of the Effect of Erosion on Soil Productivity in an International Context. Delft Hydraulics Laboratory, the Netherlands. p. 53-69.

15. USDA, Soil Conservation Service. 1961. Land - capability classification. USDA Agric. Handbook 210, 21 p.

16. USDA, Soil Conservation Service. 1981. Land resource regions and major land resource areas of the United States. USDA Agric. Handbook 296, p. 77.

17. USDA, Soil Conservation Service. 1982a. Soil interpretation record, SOI - SCS - 5.

18. USDA, Soil Conservation Service. 1982b. Basic statistics - 1977 national resources inventory. USDA Stat. Bulletin 686, 267 p.

19. Wischmeier, W. H. and D. D. Smith. 1978. Predicting rainfall erosion losses - a guide to conservation planning. USDA Agric. Handbook 537, 58 p.

NATIONAL COSTS OF EROSION EFFECTS

ON PRODUCTIVITY

Pierre Crosson

Soil erosion may increase crop production costs in several ways: (1) costs of additional fertilizer and other measures farmers take to compensate for effects of erosion on soil nutrients and other soil properties; (2) costs of measures farmers take, such as terracing, to control erosion to prevent yield loss; (3) loss of crop yield which occurs despite compensatory and preventive measures farmers take; (4) costs of losses incurred by deposition of eroded soil on seedlings, by the cutting action of wind blown soil, and by other "ephemeral" consequences of erosion.

In this paper I discuss what currently is known about these various costs, looking both backward in time and at the present. I also speculate about the future behavior of these costs under various assumptions about future erosion. In the concluding section I discuss some of the implications of the analysis for soil conservation policy.

Only sheet and rill erosion from cropland is considered. Gullying and ephemeral erosion damages also can increase crop production costs, but we have no measures of this. For soil erosion policy the lack is not as serious as it might appear because both kinds of damage are obvious to the eye. If they seriously begin to increase costs farmers will know it and take corrective measures if the cost of the loss is greater than the cost of the measures.

Wind erosion also may increase costs, both by reducing soil productivity and by imposing "ephemeral" costs. However, the data for wind erosion generally are less reliable than those for sheet and rill erosion, and there are no comprehensive estimates of the effects of wind erosion on soil productivity.

Off-farm costs of erosion such as sediment-induced losses of reservoir capacity, dredging to keep channels clear, and so on are not considered. These costs are of major importance, and almost surely are substantially greater than costs resulting from on-farm productivity loss.* A comprehensive estimate of erosion damages and discussion of soil conservation policy would have to include off-farm costs. The focus of this symposium, however, is on effects of erosion on soil productivity, so this paper is restricted accordingly.

---

*For an estimate of off-farm erosion costs see Clark (forthcoming). For a comparison of these costs with those of on-farm productivity loss, see Crosson (1984).

The author is: PIERRE CROSSON, Senior Fellow, Resources for the Future, Washington, D.C.

EROSION COSTS SINCE 1950

The focus is on the period since 1950. The supply of data and other information for estimating production costs of erosion in this period is sparse but adequate to support some informed speculation.

Costs of Compensation

Depending on circumstances, farmers attempt to compensate for erosion effects on soil productivity by doing things such as putting on more fertilizer to replace nutrients, more lime to maintain favorable pH, and changing tillage to restore bulk density or improve soil water retention and infiltration. They may also have to expend more energy in plowing where erosion reduces soil tilth. All of these compensating measures add to production costs and so must be counted as costs of erosion.

Larson et al. (1983) estimated the cost of erosion-induced nutrient loss in 1977 at about $1 billion. They began with estimates of sheet and rill erosion on cropland from the 1977 National Resources Inventory (NRI), used estimates of the amounts of N, P and K in the soil body, applied an enrichment ratio to estimate the amount of each nutrient in eroded soil, then applied "availability" ratios to estimate the amounts of the nutrients in eroded soil actually available annually to support plant growth. These estimates then were multiplied by fertilizer prices to estimate the value of the loss of each nutrient and the results summed to get the total value of the loss. Prices per metric ton were $440 for nitrogen, $500 for phosphorus and $300 for potassium. Valued at prices of the early 1980s the total annual cost of lost nutrients would be closer to $500 million than the $1 billion estimated by Larson et al.* Their estimates made no allowance for restoration of soil nutrients through rainfall or natural soil processes.

These estimates of the cost of erosion-induced nutrient loss clearly are highly sensitive to changes in fertilizer prices. However, the estmates are subject to great uncertainty for other reasons as well. There are major difficulties in estimating the amounts of nutrients actually lost. Five sorts of data are required: (1) the amount of each nutrient in the soil body; (2) the nutrient enrichment ratio (soil carried away generally is richer in nutrients than the soil body because nutrients are concentrated in the surface soil); (3) the percent of the nutrient in the soil which is available to support plant growth; (4) the amount of soil nutrient replenishment resulting from natural processes; (5) the extent to which soil counted as eroded in one place augments nutrient supply in places of deposition.

No completely reliable estimates of any of these data are available, but the last two are particularly problematical. How much natural nutrient replenishment occurs annually on soils in various erosion stages, and what does the total add up to on a national basis? No one seems to know. The size of the problem (and of the net nutrient loss) would be reduced considerably if it could be assumed that T values measure the amount of soil that can be lost before nutrient loss exceeds natural nutrient replenishment. The definition of T--the maximum annual soil loss per acre consistent with economical production into the indefinite future--could be interpreted to mean the amount of erosion at which nutrient loss equals natural nutrient replenishment. But so far as I know no soil scientist has ever explicitly interpreted T in this way. And on deep soils with favorable subsoils T is consistent with use of fertilizer to replace lost nutrients since on these soils this practice can be economical over long periods of time.

---

*Fertilizer prices in the early 1980s were only about half those assumed by Larson et al. (USDA, 1984).

Larson et al. used total sheet and rill erosion from cropland, not that in excess of T, to estimate nutrient loss. The amount in excess of T was about 75 percent of the total.

The effect of soil deposition on nutrient supply also seems to be little understood. It is well known that most of the soil counted as eroded is not permanently deposited in water bodies. Some of that which is not ends up in ditches or other non-farmable places, but much of it is deposited where it still is at least potentially available for agricultural production. Indeed, Larson et al. (1983) assert that in the mid-west most soil eroded from culti- vated land is deposited on other cultivated land.

The fact of deposition and the little known about it greatly complicates the estimation of erosion-induced nutrient losses. As an example, consider a Major Land Resource Area (MLRA) included in a study of erosion-induced losses of productivity done by a group of soil scientists at the University of Minnesota (Pierce et al. 1984). The MLRA (103), located in southern Minnesota and northern Iowa, contains 5.1 million hectares of cropland which erodes at an average annual rate of 10.5 t/ha, according to the 1977 NRI. Almost half this land erodes at 11.2 t/ha or more. The topography of MLRA 103 is common in areas of the north central region with glacial derived soils. It is characterized by "small relief, no major surface outlet, and containment of run-off water and transported sediment in depressional areas... In this landscape very little or no sediment may leave the cultivated area" (Larson et al. 1983, p. 459). If all soil counted as eroded in such a landscape were deposited in places from which there were no erosion, and if the nutrient supply (and other soil productivity character- istics) in the places of deposition already was sufficient, then the nutrients lost from the eroded places would be a net loss from the entire region even though no soil actually left the region (leaving aside the disputed issue of natural nutrient replenishment in the eroded places). However, this does not appear to be what happens in MLRA 103, or any of the other 14 MLRAs in the Cornbelt studied by Pierce et al. (1984). Sixteen percent of the eroded soil in MLRA 103 came off 0-2 percent slopes and 44 percent came off slopes of 2-6 percent. Since little soil leaves the MLRA, most of the soil counted as eroded on slopes of 6 percent or less must have been simply moved around on those slopes. The remaining 40 percent of the soil counted as eroded came off slopes of 6 percent or more, and much of it must have been deposited on slopes of less than 6 percent. That is to say, much of the more gently sloping land must have been both sending and receiving soil, hence both sending and receiving nutrients. There may still have been a net loss of nutrients because some receiving sites already were nutrient rich, but the loss surely was less, probably substantially less, than if all sites in the MLRA were either exclusively senders or exclusively receivers of eroded soil. Accordingly, estimates of the cost of nutrient loss which assume that all nutrients carried by eroded soil are lost would be overstated, probably by a significant amount.

Costs of Prevention

The costs of terracing, strip cropping, contour farming, establishment and maintenance of grassed waterways and windbreaks, and of anything else farmers do to prevent erosion-induced losses of productivity must be counted as costs of erosion. Thanks to the work of the USDA's George Pavelis (1983) we have estimates of gross and net stocks of capital invested in erosion control works. Net stocks are depreciated gross stocks. Gross stocks are cumulated annual investments in the works less retirements.

Between 1935 and 1980 about $39 billion was invested in on-farm conservation measures (in 1977 dollars). Gross stocks (in 1977 dollars) increased from 1940 to 1965, reaching a peak of $28 billion. They declined steadily after that, and in 1980 were $16 billion. Net stocks followed a similar course, but peaked earlier, rising to $16 billion in 1955 and then declining to $10 billion in 1980 (Pavelis, 1983).

One could use the capital stock estimates in various ways to estimate annual costs of erosion prevention measures. The most meaningful way is to take the annual return to the capital represented by gross stocks invested in the measures. Assuming a real return to capital of 5 percent and applying it to the Pavelis data, the estimated annual cost in 1980 was $800 million (1977 dollars). Some unknown but relatively small amount must be added to reflect annual costs of maintaining terraces and other conservation works.

These estimates are too high, however, probably substantially so. Although the investment studied by Pavelis ostensibly was for soil conservation, much of it in fact was not related to erosion control. The 1977 NRI showed that one-half of the nation's terraced cropland had slopes of 3 percent or less and on two-thirds slopes were 4 percent or less (American Farmland Trust, 1984, p. 40). Seventy-five percent of the terraced land was in the Great Plains states. Of that, 37 percent was land which in bare fallow would erode at less than 22.4 t/ha per year, according to the RKLS factors in the Universal Soil Loss Equation. On another 32 percent of the terraced land in these states the RKLS factors indicated erosion of 22.4-44.8 t/ha per year if the land were in bare fallow (AFT, 1984, p. 41). When cropped in continuous corn, soybeans or wheat, the crop cover provided would reduce erosion by 65 to 70 percent compared to the bare fallow condition (i.e., the C factor in the USLE for these crops is .30 to .35). Consequently, on 37 percent of the terraced land in the Plains states erosion would be less than 7.8 t/ha per year, if the land were in one of the three crops mentioned, even in the absence of terraces or any other soil conservation practice. On another 32 percent of the terraced land, erosion would be 7.8 to 15.6 t/ha per year, if in one of the three crops.

Why should a preponderance of the nation's terraces be on gently sloping land with low potential for sheet and rill erosion? On long slopes gullying may be a problem even on gently sloping land. By shortening slope length, terraces could reduce this threat. However, terraces also conserve water by reducing runoff and this likely explains why three-quarters of the terraced land is in the semiarid Plains (AFT, 1984, p. 41).

Investments in establishment and improvement of permanent vegetative cover are an important component of Pavelis' estimates of stocks of erosion control capital. In a review of the USDA's Agricultural Conservation Program (ACP) the Agricultural Stabilization and Conservation Service (ASCS), the agency responsible for funding the program, found that in over half the cases checked for use of vegetative cover erosion was not a serious problem. In a separate study of the ACP the General Accounting Office (GAO) came to the same conclusion (1983). The ASCS and GAO studies were of practices in which the costs were shared between the federal government and the farmer. Where farmers bear the full costs of the practices they may be more directly related to erosion control. However, Pavelis' data show that over time about one-half of the total investment in soil conservation practices has been under cost-share programs.

Costs of Yield Loss

Despite farmers' efforts to compensate for erosion's effects on productive properties of the soil, or to prevent these effects by controlling erosion, yields still may decline. This is the third kind of cost specified above. We did a study at Resources for the Future (RFF) which provides insights to these costs over the last several decades. The study is an analysis of the effect of erosion on the growth of yields of corn, soybeans, and wheat between 1950 and 1980. Details of the study are in Crosson and Stout (1983). Least squares analysis was used to compute the annual trend growth of crop

257

yields (in bushels) for each crop in each county in major producing areas.
For corn the counties were in the Cornbelt, parts of Northern Plains, and
western Tennessee; for soybeans the counties were in the Cornbelt and western
Tennessee; and for wheat they were in the Northern Plains and the Palouse
region of Idaho and Washington. For each crop trend yields by county were
regressed against erosion on lands in the crop by county and a couple of
dummy variables designed to capture some of the effects of technological
change on yield growth. The erosion data were taken from the 1977 NRI.

The procedure assumes that intercounty differences in erosion as measured by
the NRI were proportional to cumulative intercounty erosion differences
between 1950 and 1980. That the assumption is precarious goes without
saying. Yet the results obtained accord with expectations in the sense that
for all three crops erosion had a negative effect on the growth of yields.
For wheat the effect was not statistically significant, but it was for corn
and soybeans. For these two crops the effect was small--yield growth was
about 4 percent less from 1950 to 1980 than it would otherwise have been--but
this is consistent with other recent studies of erosion-productivity
relationships (USDA 1981; Pierce et al. 1984).

From the RFF study one can calculate the average annual erosion-induced loss
of corn and soybean yield for each year 1950 to 1980. In the first year,
i.e. 1951, corn yields were 4.8 kg/ha less because of erosion than they would
have been and soybean yields were 1 kg/ha less. In 1952 the per hectare loss
was 9.6 kg for corn and 2 kg for soybeans, and so on through 1980, the losses
cumulating each year by 4.8 kg for corn and 1 kg for soybeans. In 1980 corn
yields were 144 kg less than otherwise because of erosion, and soybean yields
were 30 kg less. Of course, for both crops yields in 1980 were substantially
higher than in 1950 because of the vast technological and managerial
improvements that occurred in that period.

The present value of the losses in 1980 could be calculated by multiplying
each year's loss by the price of the crop that year (converted to 1980
dollars) times the amount of land in each crop, then expanding each year's
value to 1980 by applying some real rate of compound interest, and summing
the annual values so calculated.* For example, the price of corn in
1951 in 1980 dollars (converted by the Consumer price Index) was 20.6 cents
per kg. The per hectare value of the 4.8 kg loss of corn yield in 1951,
therefore, was $.99. Since there were 28.7 million harvested hectares of
corn that year, the total loss was $28 million. Compounded at 5 percent
annually, present value of the loss in 1980 would have been $115 million.**
Repeating these operations for each subsequent year and summing the annual
estimates would give the cumulative present value of the loss as of 1980.
One could do the same thing for soybeans.

I have not performed these calculations, although it could be done with data
in the USDA's annual Agricultural Statistics. But what would one do with
such estimates if one had them? Since they reflect the unrecallable past,
their main function, as for all history, would be educational. They would
provide a rough calculation of the social cost of erosion-induced losses of
crop production from 1950 to 1980. But there is a caveat to this. Except
for a few years in the 1970s, the period from 1950 to 1980 was generally

---

*One would have to be careful about using the actual price observed for each
crop. Had erosion not reduced yields, total output would have been greater
and price, therefore, probably would have been lower, unless government price
support programs prevented this. Using the observed price, therefore, might
overvalue the yield loss. The measured yield losses are quite small so the
price effect, if any, probably also would be small.

**Corn prices, CPI and land in corn from USDA 1972 and 1980.

characterized by overproduction of corn and wheat, if not soybeans. The
federal government adopted a variety of programs to support corn and wheat
prices, with some success. If corn production was excessive should we value
the small erosion-induced loss of corn production at the (supported) market
price? Surely not, although I am not prepared to say what the appropriate
price would be. The general point, however, is important. Erosion-induced
productivity losses impose social costs only if the lost output would serve
some useful social purpose. If the long-term prospect is for chronic crop
surpluses then the social cost of erosion-induced losses (or any other kind
of losses) clearly will be less than if the prospect is for scarcity in crop
markets.

Inferred Effect of Erosion Costs on Total Costs

Despite the inadequate data on the three kinds of erosion costs, it is quite
clear that whatever they were their effect on total production costs in the
years 1950 to 1980 was more than offset by cost reducing advances in technology and management. Indeed, these advances were sufficient to more than
offset the additional costs of gullying and ephemeral erosion damage as well.

The evidence for this conclusion is that the real (inflation adjusted) prices
received by farmers for corn and soybeans declined from the early 1950s to
the late 1970s (Table 1).* These price declines are all the more impressive
because real prices farmers paid for inputs rose 10 percent (see Table 1) and
demand for corn and soybeans increased substantially over the period. The
cost reducing thrust of technological and managerial improvements, therefore,
were more than sufficient to offset the combined cost increasing effects of
rising demand, higher input prices and erosion damages to the soil.

Table 1. Prices Received and Paid by Farmers, 1950-54 and 1975-79

Index of real prices paid by farmers[a] 1967=100	Prices received					
	Nominal		Real			
			Deflated by prices paid		Deflated by the CPI	
	Corn	Soybeans	Corn	Soybeans	Corn	Soybeans
			($/kg)			
1950/54	104	.06	.10	.07	.12	.08	.12
1975/79	114	.09	.23	.04	.11	.05	.12

[a]Prices of inputs purchased for production plus wages, interest, taxes,
and expenditures for family living, deflated by the CPI.
[b]Consumer price index, 1967=100.
Source: USDA 1972 and 1980.

FUTURE EROSION COSTS

The old saying that by-gones are forever by-gones has special relevance to
thinking about the effects of erosion on production costs and what we should
do about them. It is comforting to know that so far these effects have been
more than offset by advances in technology and management, but what about the
future? That is what counts from here on.

---

*Movements of real prices only approximate movements in costs because prices
are also affected by transitory and non-cost factors. The decline in corn
prices, for example, probably overstates the decline in costs of producing
corn because price supports for corn in 1975-79 were weaker than in 1950-54.

Costs of Future Yield Loss

Modeling work done by soil scientists at the university of Minnesota provides
a point of departure (Larson et al. 1983; Pierce et al. 1983; Pierce et al.
1984).* The model produces an index of crop yield and shows how the index
changes over time as erosion changes soil characteristics important to
productivity. Three characteristics are singled out: soil bulk density, pH,
and water holding capacity. Nutrient supply is not specified in the model,
the assumption being that farmers will maintain nutrient adequacy. It also
is assumed that they will maintain adequate bulk density and pH in the top 20
cm of the soil profile. Consequently, the model essentially measures
relative losses in productivity attributable to losses in soil water holding
capacity.

Pierce et al. (1984) applied the model to 39.7 million hectares of cropland
in the Cornbelt on the assumption that erosion rates on that land as measured
by the 1977 NRI would continue for periods of 25, 50, and 100 years. The
results are shown in Table 2. Average yields would decline by 1 percent in

Table 2. Erosion and Its Productivity Effects in the Cornbelt

	I. By Period			
	Decline in PI		Soil removed	
Years of Erosion	Average	Range	Average	Range
	- - - (%) - - -		- - - (cm) - - -	
25	1	1-3	3.3	1.0-7.0
50	2	1-5	6.6	2.0-14.0
100	4	2-8	13.2	4.0-28.0

	II. By Slope Percent				
	Erosion		Decline in PI after 100 years		
Slope Percent	Average	Range	Average	Range	Total land
	- - (t/ha.y) - -		- - - - - - - - (%) - - - - - - - -		
0-2	4.5	2.2-11.2	2	1-4	45.3
2-6	15.7	6.7-26.9	4	2-11	38.1
6-12	44.8	17.9-67.2	9	5-48	13.4
12-20	100.8	33.6-168.0	10	3-100	3.0
20-45	226.2	129.9-602.6	18	0-48	.2

Notes: PI means productivity index.
1977 rates of erosion in each of 15 Cornbelt MLRAs are assumed
to continue for 25, 50, and 100 years.
Total land = 39.7 million cropland hectares.
Average erosion = 17.5 t/ha.y.
Average number years to remove 2 cm soil = 19.6.
Average initial PI = .83.
Source: Pierce et al. (1984).

in 25 years, 2 percent in 50 years and 4 percent in 100 years. Average yield
losses over 100 years would range from 2 percent on land with 0-2 percent

---

*The Erosion Productivity Impact Calculator (EPIC), developed by Jimmy
Williams, Paul Dyke and John Putman at the USDA's facility in Temple, Texas,
also will provide insights into future productivity impacts of erosion.
Usable outputs from EPIC were not available at this writing.

slopes to 18 percent on land with 20-45 percent slopes. Eighty-three percent of the land has slopes of 6 percent or less. On this land the average yield loss in 100 years would be a little less than 3 percent.

These appear to be modest losses. What do they imply for production costs? Consider the next 100 years and make the following assumptions: (1) in an average year corn yields in the Cornbelt now average 7229 kg/ha per year and soybeans average 2345 kg/ha; (2) for both crops yields decline 4 percent in 100 years in equal annual increments, reaching 6940 kg for corn and 2251 kg for soybeans in the 100th year. For corn each year's loss is 2.9 kg/ha and for soybeans it is .94 kg/ha. The losses are cumulative; (3) the real price is $.10/kg for corn and $.257/kg for soybeans; (4) the 39.7 million hectares of land studied by Pierce et al. (1984) is all in corn and soybeans, the proportions between them being the same as in the Cornbelt in the early 1980s; and (5) the rate of discount is 5 percent.

Under these assumptions the first year's per hectare loss of yield is 29 cents for corn and 24 cents for soybeans. The total first year production loss for corn is $6.2 million (29 cents per hectare times 21.5 million hectares in corn). The losses are assumed to be permanent, so the second year loss, undiscounted, is $12.4 million, the third year loss is $18.6 million and so on, reaching $620 million in the one-hundredth year. Discounted at 5 percent, the present value of the corn losses is about $2.5 billion. Calculated in the same way, the present value of the soybean losses over 100 years is about $1.7 billion. For the two crops combined, therefore, the present value of the future 100 year loss on the 39.7 million hectares is a little over $4 billion.

Given the loss in yield projected by the Minnesota model, the estimate of the dollar value of the 100 year loss depends entirely upon the assumptions about corn and soybean prices, the amounts of land in each crop and the discount rate. If one believes prices will average higher than assumed, that more of the 39.7 million hectares will be in corn and less in soybeans, and that the appropriate discount rate is less than 5 percent, then one's estimate of the present value of the loss will be higher than $4 billion plus. Of course if the assumptions are changed in the opposite direction, the present value of the loss would be less.

Future Compensatory Costs

The difficulties of estimating erosion-induced nutrient loss already have been discussed. However, studies done in two Iowa river basins suggest that these costs, and costs of additional fuel needed to till more eroded land, are less than the cost of the lost yield. One of the studies focused on the Southern Iowa Conservancy District, a region of 2.1 million hectares, 1.4 million of which were cropland (USDA, 1980a). About .8 million hectares of the cropland were judged to be eroding in excess of T so the analysis focused on this land. It was assumed that crop rotations and tillage practices currently used would be continued to 2020. The Universal Soil Loss Equation (USLE) was used to calculate annual erosion over that period on the .8 million hectares, and the amount of land moving from slightly eroded to moderately eroded to severely eroded was computed. Studies done at the Iowa State University (ISU) agricultural experiment station were used to estimate the decline in yield consequent upon moving from one erosion phase to the next. ISU studies also were used to estimate the additional fuel needed to till the more eroded soils and the additional fertilizer required to replace lost soil nutrients. Prices for crops (corn and soybeans were the principal ones), fuel and fertilizer were assumed and used to estimate the additional costs imposed by erosion. The results showed that by 2020 the cost of yield loss would be 71 percent of the total, additional fertilizer would be 23 percent and fuel would be 6 percent (USDA 1980a, p. 10). The value of the yield loss that year would be $8.1 million.

The prices for corn and fertilizer assumed in the study were about the same as at present. However, fuel was priced at only $.52 per gallon and soybeans at 18.7 cents per kg (below the current level). If present fuel and soybean prices were used, the cost of additional fuel would be about twice as high as estimated in the study and the value of the yield loss also would be higher. Yield loss still would dominate the total additional cost, but fuel costs would be relatively more important and fertilizer costs relatively less.

The other study (USDA, no date) dealt with the Des Moines River basin, an area of 3.8 million hectares, 2.8 million of them cropland, stretching up through central Iowa from the southeast to the northwest. The methodology and data sources for this study were for the most part the same as in the one just described. And the results were comparable. By 2020 erosion would reduce crop production by $10 million annually, most of it lost corn and soybean output.* Additional fertilizer would cost $1.9 million annually by 2020 and additional fuel $.42 million. The total erosion-induced increase in cost therefore would be $12.32 million, with yield loss accounting for 81 percent of the total, additional fertilizer for 15 percent and extra fuel for 4 percent.

The results of the Iowa studies may not be representative of other regions of the country. As far as they go, however, they indicate that costs of compensating for the effects of erosion on soil productivity are far outweighed by the costs of yield loss.

Future Prevention Costs

Pavelis' data show a marked decline in both gross and net stocks of on-farm soil conservation over the last two to three decades. It is not clear why this occurred, or whether it will continue. In much of the 1970s farmers had incentive to use their land more intensively, and some terraces and other soil conservation capital may have been taken out as a consequence. The period since 1965 also has seen a major expansion of conservation tillage, and some of this may have substituted for traditional conservation practices. To the extent that conservation tillage is adopted to control erosion the cost of doing so is a cost of erosion. However, the 1977 and 1982 NRIs showed that much conservation tilled land is not particularly erodible. Farmers evidently have adopted the technology primarily because it saves fuel and labor.

In any event, a major part, if not most, of the investment in terraces and other forms of soil conservation capital was not designed primarily to prevent erosion, as pointed out earlier. In this respect these investments are similar to those in conservation tillage. The future course of that part of these investments that farmers might undertake to prevent erosion is quite unpredictable. Much depends on future demand, particularly export demand, and on the technologies farmers can choose among in responding to demand. If the technologies are land-using, then the demand for land will rise and the erosion threat increase since the additional land almost surely will be more erodible than land now in production. In this case incentives to invest in erosion control measures will strengthen. If the technologies are land-saving, however, the demand for land will increase less, perhaps substantially so. The erosion threat and incentives to deal with it will be weaker.

---

*This is an overestimate. In the study $6.5 million of the $10 million loss of output is attributable to land going out of crop production because of erosion. No alternative production on that land, e.g., in pasture or woodland, was calculated, although there almost surely would be some.

Conclusions About Future Costs

Continuation of present rates of erosion will tend to increase future crop production costs. The prospective 4 percent yield loss over the next 100 years on the 39.7 million Cornbelt hectares would support this tendency. In other regions where topsoil is thinner and subsoils less favorable than in the Cornbelt the yield loss likely would be greater than 4 percent. So for the nation as a whole the prospective 100 year yield loss may be--probably is--more than 4 percent. But it cannot be substantially more if the 4 percent estimate is reasonably accurate. Corn and soybeans are the most erosive major land-using crops, and the 39.7 million hectares include a major share of the nation's land in those crops. Erosion in the Palouse region may reduce wheat yields, but the Palouse produces a small percentage of the nation's wheat. For the major wheat producing areas as a whole erosion does not appear to pose a serious threat to productivity (Crosson and Stout 1983). On some land cotton is a highly erosive crop, but only some 4-6 million hectares of land are, or likely will be, in cotton. Moreover, much cotton production is on irrigated, low erosion land in west Texas, Arizona, and California.

The two studies of Iowa River basins indicated that costs of compensating for erosion's effects on soil nutrients and other soil characteristics were only one-quarter to one-half the costs of lost yield. Assuming a 5 percent discount rate, I estimated the present value of the 100-year yield loss on the 39.7 million cornbelt hectares at a little over $4 billion. Making generous allowance for yield losses for other crops in other regions, suppose the present value of the prospective national yield loss for all crops is $8 billion. If compensatory costs are one-quarter to one-half the cost of yield loss then the combined present value of the two kinds of cost over the next 100 years would be $10 billion to $12 billion.

We know that costs of preventing erosion are substantially less than Pavelis' capital stock estimates would indicate, but we do not know how much lower. Suppose the annual cost is $600 million, three-fourths that suggested by Pavelis' data. At 5 percent this has a present value of $12 billion. The total for the three kinds of costs therefore has a present value of $22-$24 billion.

Over the five years 1979-1983 cash receipts from crop production in the United States averaged $69 billion. Make the conservative assumption that 80 percent of this reflected costs of production, in which case these costs were $55 billion.* Capitalized at 5 percent the present value of the costs would be $1.1 trillion. Compare this with the estimates of $22-$24 billion as the present value of the three kinds of erosion cost.

The implication of this line of argument is that continuation of present rates of erosion would not likely affect crop production costs significantly. The cost effects of other factors--growth of demand, technological advance, and input prices--will swamp the effects of erosion. Additional demand growth, particularly from abroad, is likely, and despite recent experience, most observers still expect long-term increases in energy prices, if not those of fertilizer. These trends would increase production costs unless technological advance compensates. There is some reason to expect a lag in technology over the next two or three decades (Crosson and Brubaker 1982) in which case production costs could rise. But the main factors would be increasing demand and input prices pressing ahead of technological advance. The contribution of erosion would be negligible.

---

*From 1979 through 1983 farm production expenses averaged 84 percent of gross farm income. This included income from animal production, from government support payments and home-consumed output as well as crop production (USDA 1983).

Beyond the next 20 to 30 years foreign demand for U.S. crop output should begin to decline as developing countries satisfy an increasing share of their food demand from domestic production. And there is every reason to believe that by then scientific research will have developed new, more productive technologies less dependent on fossil fuels than current ones. If this happens unit production costs should stabilize if not decline. But whatever happens to production costs, the effect of erosion will not be very important.

SOME POLICY IMPLICATIONS

Although past, present and future effects of erosion on crop production costs appear small, it does not follow that as a society we should ignore them. The analysis here has focused on major producing regions and the nation as a whole. For some small regions and for some farmers, erosion is high enough to seriously threaten productivity over a period much shorter than the 100 years used generally in this analysis. Those regions and farmers merit attention even if the prospective losses of productivity are not large in a national perspective. Moreover, most farmers' knowledge of erosion-productivity relationships is based primarily on their experience with their own land. If the relationships are non-linear--and there is increasing evidence that on many soils they are--then farmers' experience will be a poor guide to future effects of erosion on yields. With more knowledge of these effects farmers could act in a timely way to avoid uneconomical yield losses or higher costs of compensation. It would not be easy to patent or otherwise establish property rights in the additional knowledge, so private firms lack incentive to invest in the research needed to provide it. If the research is to be done it will have to be publicly financed.

The USDA's Agricultural Research Service already is engaged in such research. The effort merits additional encouragement and funding. I am not suffi- ciently familiar with the research to comment further on it, except to suggest that it ought to pay more attention to the economic dimensions of erosion-productivity relationships. Better knowledge of the physical proper- ties of the relationships is important, indeed essential. But when farmers consider what to do about erosion they need information about its present and prospective costs.

The research would not only serve farmers. The conclusion here that produc- tion cost effects of erosion have been, are, and likely will continue to be small is based on limited evidence: the RFF study of erosion effects on growth of crop yields since World War II; the application of the University of Minnesota productivity index model to the Cornbelt; and two studies in Iowa of the costs of erosion-induced yield losses and of compensatory measures. The evidence is suggestive but too incomplete for firm policy action. For this more research is needed on erosion-productivity relation- ships in areas other than the Cornbelt, but more in-depth analysis in that region also would be desirable.

The past, present and prospective effects of erosion on crop production costs almost surely are smaller than most members of the soil conservation community have long believed. But although small, the costs probably are higher than in the public interest they ought to be. There is a place on the nation's soil conservation agenda for public action to bring them down.

REFERENCES

1. American Farmland Trust. 1984. Soil conservation in America: what do we have to lose. Washington, D.C.

2. Bennett, H. 1939. Soil conservation. McGraw-Hill Publishing Co., New York and London.

3. Clark, II, E. C. 1985. The off-site costs of erosion. Forthcoming in the Jour. of Soil and Water Conservation.

4. Crosson, P. and S. Brubaker. 1982. Resource and environmental effects of U.S. agriculture. Resources for the Future, Washington, D.C.

5. Crosson, P. with A. T. Stout. 1983. Productivity effects of cropland erosion in the United States. Resources for the Future, Washington, D.C.

6. Crosson, P. 1984. New perspectives on soil conservation policy. Jour. Soil and Water Cons. 39:222-225.

7. General Accounting Office. 1983. Agriculture's soil conservation programs miss full potential in the fight against erosion. Comptroller General of the United States, Washington, D.C.

8. Held, B. and M. Clawson. 1965. Soil conservation in perspective. Johns Hopkins Press for Resources for the Future, Baltimore, Md.

9. Larson, W. E., F. J. Pierce, R. H. Dowdy. 1983. The threat of soil erosion to long-term crop production. Science 219 no. 4584:458-465.

10. Pavelis, G. 1983. Farm conservation in the United States, 1935-1980. Jour. Soil and Water Cons., 38:455-458.

11. Pierce, F. J., W. E. Larson, R. H. Dowdy and W. A. P. Graham. 1983. Productivity of soils: assessing long-term changes due to erosion, Jour. of Soil and Water Cons. 38:39-44.

12. Pierce, F. J., R. H. Dowdy, W. E. Larson and W. A. P. Graham., 1984. Productivity of soils in the cornbelt: an assessment of the long-term impact of erosion. Jour. of Soil and Water Cons. 39:131-136.

13. USDA. 1938. Soils and men. Government Printing Office, Washington, D.C.

14. USDA. 1972 and 1980. Agricultural Statistics, Government Printing Office, Washington, D.C.

15. USDA. 1980a. Soil depletion study reference report: Southern Iowa Rivers Basin. Soil Conservation Service and Economics, Statistics and Cooperatives Service, Washington, D.C.

16. USDA, 1981. Soil, water and related resources in the United States: analysis of resource trends. 1980 Appraisal, part II. Washington, D.C.

17. USDA. 1983. Agricultural outlook, Economic Research Service AO-90 (August), Washington, D.C.

18. USDA. 1984. Outlook and situation: inputs. Economic Research Service IOS-3, Washington, D.C.

19. USDA. No date. Soil depletion study reference report: Des Moines River Basin. Soil Conservation Service and Economic Research Service, Washington, D.C.

SOIL EROSION - SOIL PRODUCTIVITY:

A LOOK TO THE FUTURE

L. D. Meyer   F. E. Rhoton   K. G. Renard
Fellow ASAE   Member ASAE

History has shown that disregard for the future effects of soil erosion on productivity has resulted in disastrous consequences for many nations. Great empires fell, millions perished, and land productivity was irrecoverably lost (Bennett, 1939; Lowdermilk, 1948). Could the same fate befall our nation and our world as a whole, or do we now have the technology to overcome any abuses to our soil and related resources? Our future and the future of our descendants are at stake (see Resources for the Future, 1984), so these matters are of crucial importance.

In his thought-provoking book for the Worldwatch Institute, Building a Sustainable Society, Lester Brown (1981) contends that civilization cannot survive the continuing wholesale loss of topsoil, with its associated impact on food production. Other experts agree that soil erosion will intensify future food problems, and some foresee an international food crisis that will make other past resource crises seem minor. The recent famine in eastern Africa, exacerbated by past land abuses and the resultant desertification, grimly illustrates the cruel consequences of disregard for proper soil management. Certainly, consideration of the effect of soil erosion on productivity at this Symposium was not only appropriate, but vital.

This Symposium differed from others because its focus was on the technical aspects of our theme rather than the policy aspects, dominant as the latter often seem. A wealth of information was presented and is published in this proceedings. We need to heed these reports and build on them to assure that our nation and the world as a whole will have a future that is safe, abundant, and healthy for all humanity.

The task of looking toward the future in the area of this subject, as in any area, is quite a challenge. However, to the best of our ability, we explore the current status of knowledge about the effects of soil erosion on productivity, identify those matters that merit increased attention, acknowledge related issues that may affect future technology on this topic, and speculate on how and why our efforts will have an important impact.

CURRENT KNOWLEDGE AND EFFORTS TO QUANTIFY
THE EFFECT OF SOIL EROSION ON PRODUCTIVITY

The effect of soil erosion on productivity has long been recognized as a problem in agricultural production (Nat'l SE/SP Planning Comm., 1981). From the 1930s through the early 1950s, crop yield experiments on land with variable past erosion were an important part of soil conservation research.

The authors are: L. D. MEYER, Agricultural Engineer, F. E. RHOTON, Soil Scientist, USDA Sedimentation Laboratory, Oxford, MS; and K. G. RENARD, Hydraulic Engineer, Southwest Rangeland Watershed Research Center, USDA-ARS, Tucson, AZ.

However, that early research involved crop varieties, fertility practices, tillage operations, and pest control methods that differed from those used today. Furthermore, research techniques that were used made it difficult to extrapolate results to conditions different from those of the studies.

Nevertheless, the results were so conclusive that most erosion research then shifted to measurements of erosion rates for different conditions and to development of erosion-control practices. Only during recent years has research in this area reemerged, primarily because of Public Law 95-192, the Soil and Water Resources Conservation Act of 1977 (RCA). RCA gave special emphasis to the need for better quantifying erosion-induced productivity losses, their economic consequences for modern agriculture, and their short- and long-term impacts on our nation's ability to produce food, fiber, and feed.

RCA specified that USDA make an appraisal of our nation's soil and water resources on private lands every 5 years. For the initial RCA appraisal in 1980, an empirical crop yield - soil loss relationship based on statistical data was used (Hagen and Dyke, 1980). This first attempt to develop a nationally applicable mathematical model sparked great interest in improving the crop yield - soil loss relationship. A workshop of federal agency personnel was held in Washington, D. C. during February 1980, and a research planning committee was appointed soon thereafter. As one of their first efforts, this National Soil Erosion - Soil Productivity Research Planning Committee (1981) reported the status of knowledge and activity concerning the effect of erosion on productivity at the start of this decade. That report summarized past studies, referenced most pertinent literature, and described ongoing and needed research.

To respond to research needed for implementing RCA, the Agricultural Research Service initiated a coordination effort with personnel of the Economic Research Service, Soil Conservation Service, various state agricultural experiment stations, and other interested agencies. It began with a planning workshop at Lafayette, IN in September 1981. Research planning was divided into four thrust areas: (1) mechanics of wind and water erosion (to better understand and describe the causative problem), (2) erosion/productivity experimentation (to experimentally investigate the relationships), (3) erosion/productivity modeling (to develop improved means of expressing the relationship mathematically), and (4) conservation tillage technology (to improve this farming methodology because of its perceived potential to maintain productivity while controlling erosion). Tasks were defined, scientists were identified to work on the tasks individually or as teams, and deadlines were set. Details of this 1981 workshop are contained in a mimeographed report, and a updated progress report was prepared in May 1983[1]. This planning effort was undertaken to foster cohesiveness and completeness of the research while attempting to keep all participants aware of work planned by others and approaches being taken. Many of the reports at this Symposium described research by persons participating in the 1981 workshop.

In March 1983, the American Society of Agronomy (ASA) sponsored the Soil Erosion and Crop Productivity Symposium in Denver, CO. That symposium provided an overview of the relationship between soil erosion, crop production and other relevant issues related to maintaining high-yielding agricultural lands. Speakers presented a historical perspective on erosion research, methods for erosion control, and discussions of soil productivity as well as the issues associated with public policy and economics. Seven papers addressed regional problems associated with erosion and productivity. These presentations will be published by ASA in mid 1985 as the book, Soil

---

[1]Both available from K. G. Kenard, USDA-ARS, Southwest Rangeland Watershed Research Center, 2000 E. Allen Road, Tucson, AZ 85719.

Erosion and Crop Productivity. ASA also held a special session on the effect of erosion on productivity at its 1983 Annual Meeting in Washington, D. C. Many of the reports given at such meetings are published in professional journals such as the Soil Science Society of America Journal, Transactions of the American Society of Agricultural Engineers, and Journal of Soil and Water Conservation.

Conservation tillage technology has been the focus of many past meetings including a recent conference on soil microbiology in Seattle, WA during March 1984 that dealt with microbiological problems encountered in conservation tillage cropping systems.[2]   Another conference, "Conservation Tillage -- Strategies for the Future" was held in Nashville, TN during October 1984 to discuss key issues and implications of this conservation practice.   Many reports about conservation tillage are published in professional journals, including a special issue on this topic in the May-June 1983 Journal of Soil and Water Conservation.

Several regional research committees, made up primarily of scientists at land-grant universities, are pursuing research on the effect of soil erosion on productivity.   In Southern Regional Project S-174, yields of major crops are measured on plots of varying natural or simulated erosion, and extensive climatic, soil water, soil properties, and nutrient status measurements are made at the plot sites.   In the north central region, Project NC-174 includes work on this topic.   A physically based mathematical model will be calibrated and refined to evaluate the effect of erosion on productivity for corn and small grain, using data from experiments on one or more benchmark soils in each state.   Measurements for the model are planned on both eroded and noneroded sites for each soil.

Probably, the most dramatic change in research methodology during the past few decades has been the use of mathematical models.   The techniques of model building have closely paralleled advances in computer hardware.   Modelers can now conceptualize complex systems and emulate prototype situations with algorithms to levels of detail that are almost impossible to measure experimentally.   Thus, data to test a model such as EPIC (Williams, et al., 1984) in its entirety are not presently available.   The tremendous potential of models for comprehensive (in both time and space) evaluations of the effect of soil erosion on productivity has fostered major efforts to parameterize existing models, and in other instances, to develop and validate new models.

PRIORITIES FOR FUTURE RESEARCH

Research on both wind- and water-induced soil erosion effects on productivity needs to be expanded to provide information that will improve our overall understanding of the processes involved and enable us to maintain or increase current soil productivity levels.   In our opinion, research is especially needed on the following topics; therefore we feel these topics should receive future priority.

Fragile Soils

Studies of soils where erosion is likely to create serious productivity problems in a relatively short time deserve special priority.   These soils, appropriately termed fragile, have relatively shallow subsurface features with physical and/or chemical properties that restrict plant rooting depths.

---

[2]Work Planning Conference of Soil Microbiological Issues as Related to Conservation Tillage.   Mimeographed report available from L. E. Elliott, ARS-USDA, 215 Johnson Hall, Washington State University, Pullman, WA 99164.

Thus, lack of adequate soil water storage becomes an increasingly limiting factor as the soil profile depth decreases due to progressive erosion. Examples of limiting features include: fragipans, argillic horizons relatively high in clay (claypans), plinthite, natric and petrocalcic horizons, and impervious parent material or bedrock that occurs at relatively shallow depths below the soil surface. Soils with these characteristics represent a major portion of the cultivated land in most regions of the United States. Some of the effects of these features have been investigated (Frye et al., 1983; Langdale et al., 1979; Perkins and Kaihulla, 1981), but additional data are needed, especially for purposes of documenting the problem and predicting when cultivation of these soils will no longer be economically feasible.

Rates of Soil Formation

Future soil productivity depends on the maintenance of A-horizons and rooting zones that are thick enough to provide most plant growth requirements. Therefore, any comprehensive study relating future declines in productivity with continued soil losses should account for the soil formation factor, as it relates to the rate at which soils regenerate the materials lost to erosion. Estimates of soil formation rates derived from such research would also help in establishing more accurate soil loss tolerance values. For a detailed discussion of this topic, refer to Hall, et al. (1982).

Variability of Soil Water and Productivity

Much more information is needed to describe changes in soil water status with progressive erosion and the consequent effects on production. The lack of available soil water due to inadequate intake rate or storage capacity is often the primary factor limiting production, particularly on moderately to severely eroded soils. Soil water data are needed for a variety of soils with different degrees of past erosion, especially those with restricted rooting depths. The spatial variability for these soils in terms of standard soil water characterization parameters and crop yields should be measured as a function of slope and past erosion. Yields within farm fields may vary appreciably due to differential erosion and deposition associated with differences in landforms and/or previous land use. In such instances, point estimates may lead to incorrect conclusions concerning the integrated effect of these processes on productivity. Additionally, field water balances need to be monitored to determine how the water content of soil profiles occurring on differentially eroded slopes is affected by the various addition and depletion factors of the water balance equation.

Effect of Deposition on Productivity

Detailed studies which measure the effect of both soil erosion and deposition along a slope on yields are rare. Therefore, data are needed which show the net effect of erosion on productivity within a given field or small watershed. Information needed includes: (1) the effect of deposition on yields when it occurs prior to seedling emergence or in the early stages of seedling growth; and (2) the extent to which yield increases that are generally observed on thicker profiles formed by deposition on downslope positions compensate for yield reductions due to erosion upslope. Additionally, similar data are needed for floodplain areas where sediment deposits on a more massive scale.

Evaluation of Experimental Procedures

Some research should be directed toward improvement of laboratory and field experimental procedures. The methods used to estimate depths of past erosion or assign an erosion class to a given research site merit special attention. Results from naturally eroded versus scalped sites and from farm fields versus carefully controlled experimental field plots should be assessed. The advantages and shortcomings of each technique need to be clearly defined. Also, analytical laboratory procedures used for chemical characterization of eroded soil samples should be investigated, particularly those used to determine plant nutrient requirements. Since soil test extraction techniques for fertilizer recommendations were developed using samples from the more fertile, relatively uneroded sites, a determination is needed concerning whether they or other extraction methods are appropriate for use on samples of less productive, eroded soils.

Restoring Productivity of Eroded Soils

Although protection of our highly productive land must be of greatest concern, the requirements for reestablishment or maintenance of productivity on eroded soils should be investigated for at least the major cropland soils subject to erosion throughout the United States. This research would determine if and how crop yield limitations on eroded soils can be overcome, and the costs involved. Special attention should be given to isolating those adverse effects of erosion that can be overcome by increased fertilization rates, alternative land uses, different residue management practices, crop varieties, and pest control methods from those that cannot. We must recognize where damage is permanent, identify the limiting factors, and determine how to deal with the consequences.

Conservation Tillage

The previously mentioned report from the conference on soil microbiology[2] discussed unsolved problems of conservation tillage:

"These include poor plant vigor and growth, residue management problems, soilborne diseases, and plant nutrient management and use efficiency. Most of these problems are not unique to conservation tillage systems; however, we have learned to cope with them to a degree with current tillage systems. When systems are changed, the problems tend to be magnified because we do not understand the underlying principles governing the causes and effects and the changes in the soil environment. We must develop a data base so that soil-plant-biological nutrient relationships can be predicted when tillage and residue management systems are changed."

Additional research needs in conservation tillage are discussed by Ritchie and Follett (1983).

Validation of Models

Models to describe the effect of erosion on productivity such as EPIC have not been tested in their entirety because of the lack of necessary data. Validation data are needed to test such complex models and also to verify specific algorithms that have been tested only regionally. As a more specific illustration, EPIC's generalized plant growth routine, used for a wide variety of crops, involves selection of parameter values which may vary both temporally and spatially. Parameters like the optimal and base temperature for plant growth, the parameter which converts energy to biomass, and the nutrient conversion parameters are likely different for corn grown in Minnesota versus Georgia. Data for these evaluations are not available. Finally, the EPIC model as used in the 1985 RCA assessment has recognized problems handling some conditions encountered in agricultural practices that need to be corrected using findings from research that may or may not have been completed.

General Comments Regarding Future Research

Various topics were omitted from the foregoing list that certainly merit future research; we included only those of the highest priority. Furthermore, the listed items are not discrete research entities; most erosion/productivity studies will likely encompass several of these topics plus other research areas as well. We especially want to stress the importance of fundamental research, to better understand the basic processes involved, as a major component of any research program to control soil erosion and enhance soil productivity.

In regard to future research efforts, the benefits from continued national coordination of erosion/productivity research and the importance of effective transfer of pertinent technology to users deserve special emphasis. Interagency cooperation and interaction among researchers in this field need to be continued. An awareness of other studies and research techniques can improve the productivity and efficiency of individual research studies, and also, major program gaps can be identified and overlaps avoided. Furthermore, individual research efforts can be better coordinated to focus on critical issues, and the overall effort can be viewed from a systems approach rather than as individual studies. Futhermore, technology gained from this research must be efficiently conveyed to those who need it, including farmers, decision makers, and other scientists. The excellence of our research efforts will be diminished should we fail. However, through the successful transfer of needed erosion/productivity technology, these efforts have the potential to be a major factor influencing world-wide policy decisions related to soil conservation and agricultural production.

NONTECHNICAL ISSUES THAT WILL IMPACT ON THE IMPORTANCE OF FUTURE EFFORTS
TO BETTER DEFINE THE EFFECT OF SOIL EROSION ON PRODUCTIVITY

As professionals concerned about the production of food, fiber, and feed and especially about the effect of soil erosion on such production, we are very interested in the future importance of improved technology in this area and prospects for support of research on this topic. Is the effect of erosion on productivity a topic that will soon go away as it did after the 1930s and 40s, or is it here to stay this time? The answer will depend on many factors, few of which we can or will influence significantly. Some of the important "nontechnical" issues and their possible impacts follow.

National and International Factors

We operate in a world where major national and international developments often affect us and our work. Some will have a great impact on crop production demands.

Population Trends: Experts project an annual population growth of about 1% in the United States and other industrial nations and 2 1/2% in developing nations (Calhoun, 1979). By the year 2000, world population will be between 6 and 8 billion persons, and it may exceed 25 billion during the next 100 years. The United Nations Food and Agriculture Organization (FAO) has estimated that worldwide agricultural production needs to increase by 60% between 1980 and the year 2000 (Dudal, 1981). Most of this increase will have to come from land that is already being cultivated, and it will also have to compensate for any decrease in productivity on current cropland due to erosion, salinization, lack of irrigation water, waterlogging, and pollution.

Energy Availability and Cost: The energy situation can affect crop production and erosion control in many ways. High fuel costs discourage intensive cultivation and encourage reduced-tillage methods such as no-till, a soil conserving practice. Energy costs increase costs of many pesticides and fertilizers that are used extensively in crop production. Since most of the soil's nitrogen is in the near-surface part of the profile, topsoil losses by erosion and reductions in nitrogen usage would reduce crop production. In the USA alone, annual soil-nitrogen losses from erosion amount to more than $600,000,000, and the annual total for all plant nutrients is over a billion dollars (Larson et al., 1983). Any increase in production costs leaves less money available for erosion control practices, and shortages of energy might preclude construction of conservation practices that require major earthmoving.

Economic Situation: Our national economic situation has a major impact on the availability of public and private funds for production aids, soil conservation practices, and research. Internationally, the United States has been relying heavily on agricultural exports (about $30,000,000,000 per year) to improve our "balance of payments" and thereby counteract our massive imports of oil and durable goods. High commodity prices encourage cropping of marginal lands that are subject to serious erosion and rapid loss of productivity.

Legislation: Significant legislation has been enacted during recent years that impacts on erosion and its effect on productivity. Section 208 of PL 92-500 was aimed toward reduced nonpoint source pollution, and eroded soil, the greatest pollutant by volume (Robinson, 1971), was a major target. About the same time and since, several states passed erosion, runoff, and sediment control laws aimed at combating land uses that caused serious offsite problems. The 1977 RCA focused on soil as a production resource rather than as a pollutant (USDA, 1980). The effect of erosion on productivity is a major concern of RCA, and the act requires a continuing appraisal of our nation's natural resources every 5 years.

National Priorities: We Americans seem to take the availability of high quality food for granted, and we also seem to have assumed a self-imposed obligation to help feed impoverished nations who are not as fortunate. Yet, we have shown relatively little concern about excessive soil erosion and its effect on productivity. Recently, both agricultural and nonagricultural interests have shown increased concern, with concomitant state and national efforts to better control soil erosion. Future progress will depend on the priorities given to such work, including support for a strong research program in this area.

International Stability: A major cause of revolutions, riots, and other human conflict is the deterioration of the environment from causes such as excessive erosion and deforestation that affect food supplies and other necessities. Such conditions increase demands on productivity by the rest of the world. Certainly, the United States will be one of the nations most expected to help alleviate food shortages and thereby reduce hunger-related tensions throughout the world, as evidenced by the late-1984 consignment of 300,000 tons of U. S. wheat from a national emergency reserve to aid Ethiopia and other African nations.

Agricultural Factors

Within the agricultural community, numerous factors impact on the importance of how erosion affects productivity.

Agricultural Policies: Policies concerning agricultural production controls, conservation incentives, land use zoning, subsidies, and other such options influence crop production and erosion-control efforts. These policies are

272

established in various ways and may change from time to time. Policy alternatives that are aimed toward better conservation of national soil resources are discussed by CAST (1982).

Farmer Attitudes: Concern about the effect of soil erosion on productivity by farm owners and operators seems to range from indifferent to serious, from very short-sighted to many generations in the future, and from ignorance to strong knowledgeable leadership. Unless and until very comprehensive erosion legislation is enacted, the attitudes, abilities, and economic well-being of those persons farming cropland will be dominant factors in the effectiveness of soil conservation efforts.

Crop Production Technology: The large increases in agricultural crop production during the past half century have slowed considerably, and some agriculturalists believe that yields are beginning to plateau (see Heady, 1984) because major breakthroughs are not occurring as rapidly as they once did. Major advances in crop variety improvement and pest control technology still are needed before widespread use will be made of soil-conserving cropping practices such as no-till.

The Price/Cost Squeeze: The greatest dilemma facing many farmers today is how to "make ends meet" and still properly care for their land. When costs for interest, equipment, and supplies are high and prices received for products are low, farmers cannot afford to spend much for conservation practices and pollution controls. Long-term considerations necessarily are overlooked to survive immediate economic crises.

Conversions of Cropland to Nonagricultural Uses: During recent years, approximately a half million hectares of U. S. cropland have been lost annually from agricultural production to other uses such as urban development and highways (Timmons and Curtiss, 1979). This loss is in addition to the thousands of hectares that go out of production each year due to excessive salinity, irrigation-water shortages, and serious past erosion that make cropping them unprofitable.

Alternatives to the Use of Agricultural Land for Crop Production: Some futurists question whether cropland will be necessary for future production. Alternative crop production methods, such as hydroponics, greenhouse farms, space farms, and aquaculture, are touted for crop production. These methods may someday provide a significant supplement to conventional cropland production, but their capacity to largely replace the 167 million hectares of U. S. cropland soils and billions of hectares worldwide is nowhere in the foreseeable future.

Environmental Factors

In addition to matters of the agricultural community, other factors may have an impact on agricultural productivity.

Ecological Concerns: People are understandably concerned about their health and the quality of their environment. Food quality is a high priority, as are air and water quality. Some chemical pesticides that enhance crop production have been banned, and others may be restricted or banned. Regardless of the effect on environmental quality and our ecological system, the result probably will be decreased crop production.

Offsite Damages: Some experts such as Crosson (1984) state that the offsite damages due to erosion are many times more costly than erosion's effect on productivity. Regardless, the offsite problems caused by rapid runoff plus sediment and chemicals in the runoff may strengthen efforts to control cropland runoff and reduce soil erosion. Some land currently used for cropland may have to be taken out of production or used less intensively.

The long-term benefits may be significant, but the methods used may also decrease current production.

The Net Effect, and Other Concerns

Obviously, no one can foretell the net effect of factors such as the foregoing examples on future cropland productivity. Most of these issues suggest that demands on our agricultural soils for crop production will increase, although some factors will help to alleviate such demands. One thing seems certain, both nationally and internationally: we will probably need to achieve more productivity on less land during the foreseeable future.

Regardless of the ways that these nontechnical factors affect our future situations, humanity should be seriously concerned about the effect of soil erosion on productivity for several reasons. First, many persons in our world are still short of food and other necessities made possible by agricultural production. Worldwide, a billion people suffer from hunger and malnutrition, and 400 million live on the edge of starvation (Mayer, 1976). Until that situation is remedied, sensitive persons will be concerned about anything that adversely affects food production.

Also, the continuing loss of any important resource is a concern to most responsible persons. Even if we believe that we can compensate for a resource or do without it, we cannot be certain. It is better to fail safe, than to fail sorry! Our productive soil is our most basic natural resource for good health and well-being, so it merits our best efforts to protect its productive potential. Collectively, we are stewards of our earth, entrusted with the task of managing its resources for the future of our family - the human race.

Finally, our astounding technological achievements have brought with them some possibilities that could affect productivity on massive areas of land in the future. These include the effects of acid rain, other types of chemical or biological pollution, major climatic changes, plagues such as southern corn blight, and even catastropic nuclear accidents. Far-fetched as these may be, they are not impossible problems, based on past history. To nationally and internationally maintain a considerably greater productive capacity than needed at any particular time could be a blessing of inestimatable value.

OUR TASK AHEAD

At this National Symposium on Erosion and Soil Productivity, we acquired new information about the interrelationship of soil erosion with cropland productivity, learned of the latest techniques being used by researchers of various disciplines, improved our abilities to assess the effect of soil erosion on productivity, and became better acquainted with persons and projects that are active in this field. We obtained new resources to use professionally, but we also were challenged by important questions that remain to be answered and by complex aspects of the problem that still need to be understood. We learned how crop yields are the net result of many factors, of which productive soil is one of the key ones; yet we know that in many parts of our nation and the world, soil is the weak link in the production chain due to past erosion. We identified some things that we can do professionally to help enhance cropland productivity, but recognized that other matters usually are beyond our control. Most important, we realized anew that our successes or failures in achieving wise management of our soil resources, in controlling soil erosion, and in maintaining soil productivity can and likely will make a great difference in the quality of life that we and our descendents will enjoy in the future.

This Symposium emphasized the technical aspects of quantifying the effects of soil erosion on productivity, with less consideration of the economic, political, and sociological aspects. However, concerns of at least a subtle nature have arisen about appraising the erosion versus productivity relationship from a dominantly economic perspective. Should economic considerations, based on present conditions and knowledge, be the primary criteria for decision making? Have large-area averages been used in analyses where more specific, high-hazard data are appropriate? Are we able to fully assess the economics of erosion control efforts, as compared to the future effects of "inadequate" control? How good are economic projections, and are present-day economic conclusions being properly weighed against the food and population situations that will exist 100, 500, 1000 years in the future? The consequences of accepting a false hypothesis (that present and future food production technology will assure us of an adequate supply indefinitely, regardless of our soil conservation policies) could be devastating compared to the consequences of rejecting a true hypothesis, as perused by Libby (1983). In addition to these "Type I" and "Type II" errors, he adds a Type III error --the probability of rejecting a false hypothesis when it is too late to make any difference, a fatal hazard so well illustrated by Mishan (1977) in his analogy of a man who blissfully gains confidence in his well-being during the first 99 stories of his 100-story fall.

As we look to the future -- to our future on our earth -- one of our greatest hurdles may be to overcome the shortsighted view we have traditionally taken toward agricultural productivity, land use, and the value of our soil resources. Planning horizons are often the Year 2000, sometimes 50 years in the future, and occasionally 100 years. Yet, soil has been the basis of life on earth for thousands of years and likely will be for thousands of years in the future.

Let's put ourselves in the place of citizens of our world several hundred years from now. How would we then counsel today's land users, agricultural scientists, political decision makers, and the generations that follow them? That counsel, or our best judgment of it, should be the goal for our future actions. This means that we need to use the best we know professionally toward ensuring a world of continued productivity, to work toward making such production economically feasible while maintaining environmental quality, and to endeavor to retain our natural resources including our soil in a condition that will sustain future humanity.

Briefly, our challenge is to use our talents to provide for a future of agricultural abundance such as most of us enjoy today. What better legacy could we hope to leave to future generations?

REFERENCES

1. Bennett, H. H. 1939. Soil Conservation. McGraw-Hill: New York. p.16-54.

2. Brown, L. R. 1981. Building a Sustainable Society. Norton, New York. Chapters 2 and 5.

3. Calhoun, C. R. 1979. Agriculture's future: Four challenges. In Soil Conservation Policies: An Assessment. Soil Conserv. Soc. Amer. 152-154.

4. Council for Agricultural Science and Technology (CAST). 1982. Soil erosion: Its agricultural, environmental, and socioeconomic implications. CAST Rept. No. 92, 29 p.

5. Crosson, Pierre. 1984. New perspectives on soil conservation policy. J. Soil and Water Conserv. 39(4)222-225.

6. Dudal, R. 1981. An evaluation of conservation needs. In Soil Conservation Problems and Prospects (R. P. C. Morgan, editor) p. 3-12.

7. Frye, W. W., L. W. Murdock and R. L. Blevins. 1983. Corn yield-fragipan depth relations on a Zanesville soil. Soil Sci. Soc. Am. J. 47:1043-1044.

8. Hagen, L. L. and P. T. Dyke. 1980. Merging resource data from disparate sources. Agric. Econ. Res. 32(4):45-49.

9. Hall, G. F., R. B. Daniels, and J. E. Foss. 1982. Rate of soil formation and renewal in the USA. In Determinants of Soil Loss Tolerance. ASA Spec. Publ. No. 45:23-39.

10. Heady, E. O. 1984. The setting for agricultural production and resources use in the future. In Future Agricultural Technology and Resource Conservation. Iowa State Univ. Press, Ames. p. 8-30.

11. Langdale, G. W., J. E. Box, Jr., R. A. Leonard, A. P. Barnett, and W. G. Fleming. 1979. Corn yield reduction on eroded southern piedmont soils. J. Soil and Water Conserv. 34:226-228.

12. Larson, W. E., F. J. Pierce, and R. H. Dowdy. 1983. The threat of soil erosion to long-term crop production. Science 219(4584): 458-465.

13. Libby, L. W. 1983. A perspective that strong public action is needed to deal with the problems of soil erosion. In Perspectives on the Vulnerability of U. S. Agriculture to Soil Erosion (L. A. Christensen, editor) NRE Staff Report No. AGES830315, USDA, ERS p. 43-53.

14. Lowdermilk, W. C. 1948. Conquest of the Land through 7000 Years. USDA SCS-MP-32. 33 pp.

15. Mayer, Jean. 1976. The dimensions of human hunger. Scientific American 235(3): 40-49.

16. Mishan, E. J. 1977. The Economic Growth Debate An Assessment. George Allen & Unwin Ltd., London, p. 82.

17. National Soil Erosion - Soil Productivity Planning Committee. 1981. Soil erosion effects on soil productivity: A research perspective. J. Soil and Water Conserv. 36(2): 82-90.

18. Perkins, H. F. and E. Kaihulla. 1981. Some characteristics of plinthite inhibiting plant growth. Soil Sci. Soc. Am. J. 73:671-673.

19. Resources for the Future. 1984. Twentieth annual highlights issue. Resources No. 75, 32 pp.

20. Ritchie, J. C. and R. F. Follett. 1983. Conservation tillage: Where do we go from here? J. Soil and Water Conserv. 38(3): 267-269.

21. Robinson, A. R. 1971. Sediment, our greatest pollutant? Agric. Engr. 53: 406-408.

22. Timmons, J. F. and C. F. Curtiss. 1979. Agriculture's natural resource base: Demand and supply interactions, problems, and remedies. In Soil Conservation Policies: An Assessment. Soil Conserv. Soc. Amer. p. 53-74.

23. U. S. Department of Agriculture. 1980. Soil and Water Resources Conservation Act Appraisal. Parts I, II, and III.

24. Williams, J. R., C. A. Jones, P. T. Dyke. 1984. A modeling approach to determining the relationship between erosion and soil productivity. TRANS. of the ASAE 27(1): 129-144.

Poster Session Abstracts

Soil Cover and Wind Erosion. Donald W. Fryrear, Agricultural Engineer, USDA-ARS, Cropping Systems Research Laboratory, Big Spring, TX.

Wind erosion on agricultural lands can be reduced if the soil surface is protected with crop residues. In evaluating the influence of residues on wind erosion, previous research has expressed residues of various crops as an equivalent of flat, small grain. This becomes difficult as the density of the residue changes with weathering, or as crops other than the major cultivated crops are grown. The influence of covering various percentages of the soil surface with simulated residues laying flat (wood dowels 3.1 to 25.4 mm in diameter), on the soil losses due to wind erosion were determined. Covering 20% of the soil surface reduced soil losses 58%, and a 50% cover reduced soil losses 90%. The relationship between percent soil loss and percent soil cover can be described with the expression % SL = 150 − 36 ln % SC with a correlation coefficient of −0.96 (soil cover limits 8 to 80%). The cover could be any nonerodible material such as large clods, gravel, cotton gin trash, or any diameter stick between 3.1 and 25.4 mm.

Percent soil cover can easily be measured in the field or can be estimated with a minimum of training and experience.

Use of Multiple Regression Analysis and Linear Equations to Predict Soil Productivity. Kenneth R. Olson, Assistant Professor of Pedology, Agronomy Dept., University of Illinois.

A systematic method was developed, supported by actual yield measurements to rank soils based on their productivity. Soil productivity functions in the form of linear equations with coefficients generated from multiple regression analyses were developed from experimental research plot areas. Hay yields under a high level of management were collected along with climate data. The soils at each of the eight plot areas were mapped, described, sampled, characterized, classified, and interpreted. Five parameters were identified which account for 56% of the yield variation. In descending order of significance, these factors were: (1) rainfall-soil storage, (2) effective drainage class, (3) organic carbon, (4) temperature, and (5) sum of bases. For most soils in the study, soil erosion would result in a significant reduction in water storage capacity and in a lower organic carbon content which reduces hay yields and soil productivity.

A Soil Erosion-Wheat Growth Model for California. M.P. Miller, Graduate
Research Assistant, and M.J. Singer, Associate Professor, Department of Land
Air and Water Resources, University of California, Davis, CA.

We are developing a wheat growth model which incorporates several soil
properties, including particle size distribution, percent organic matter, and
temperature. We are linking it to the Universal Soil Loss Equation to predict
long term changes in yield with changes in soil properties due to erosion.
The model differs from EPIC, by generalizing the erosion process and
increasing the detail in the crop growth model. It is simpler than EPIC
because it is designed for dryland crops and conditions where snow melt and
wind erosion are not critical. Output from the model will be daily growth and
seasonal crop yield plus soil loss under the prevailing climate and management. Surface soil properties influenced by erosion are changed seasonally,
prior to starting of a new crop growth period, and serve as inputs to the crop
growth model.

A preliminary study was started in the Dunnigan Hills, N.W. of Sacramento, CA,
to obtain baseline data for the soil erosion-wheat growth model. Five transects were made 50 m apart, running N-S over complex slopes. Depth of solum,
topsoil thickness, and depth to carbonates, were collected along with topsoil
samples every 20 meters. Moisture content and total weight of above ground
biomass increased from the knoll to the swales, while the proportion of grain
to total biomass increased from the swale to the knoll. Results suggest a
strong relationship between position on the landscape, and soil properties and
crop yield.

Influence of Soil Removal and Fertilizer Application on Spring Wheat
Production. D. L. Tanaka and J. K. Aase, Soil Scientists, USDA-ARS,
Sidney, MT.

Soil was mechanically removed to four depths (0, 6, 12, and 18 cm) on a
Williams loam soil (fine-loamy, mixed, Typic Argiborolls) 11 km northwest
of Sidney, Montana. Three levels of N (0, 35, and 70 kg/ha) and P (0, 20,
and 40 kg/ha) were used to evaluate soil loss effects on spring wheat
(Triticum aestivum L.) production. Grain yields averaged for 1982 and 1983
over fertilizer treatments resulted in yield losses of 10, 35, and 54% on
the 6-, 12-, and 18-cm soil removal plots, respectively, when compared with
yields on plots with no soil removal. While N alone increased yields, a
greater increase was obtained with P alone. Phosphorus increased yields 43
to 83% and 42 to 102% on the 12- and 18-cm removal plots, respectively,
when compared with the respective nonfertilized plots. None of the
fertilizer combinations on the 12- and 18-cm soil removal plots increased
grain yields to the equivalent of the yields on the nonfertilized,
zero-removal plots. The 35- and 20-kg/ha combination of N and P on the 6-cm
removal plots resulted in yields equivalent to the yields on the
nonfertilized, zero-removal plots.

Depth To Fragipan: A Method of Quantifying the Effects of Erosion on Soil Productivity. F. E. Rhoton, Soil Scientist; and L. D. Meyer, Agricultural Engineer, USDA Sedimentation Laboratory, Oxford, MS.

A detailed field, laboratory, and greenhouse study was initiated on a Grenada silt loam soil to (a) evaluate the suitability of using depth to fragipans as a reference from which relative depths of past erosion can be determined, (b) identify the more important site factors associated with designing research on fragipan soils, and (c) determine the effect of the measured erosion on soil productivity and soil properties.

During the process of locating 5 sites with depths to fragipan ranging from 18.9 to 59.1 cm and installing 60 experimental field plots, a number of factors were identified that should be considered in erosion/productivity research on fragipan soils. These included: conformation of soil morphological features at selected sites with established soil series criteria; selection of sites which have relatively constant depths; location of relatively uneroded ("virgin") pedons with which eroded sites can be compared; determination of depth to fragipan based on plant rooting characteristics; and measurement of fragipan water contents. In loess areas, the proximities of different experimental sites to the loess source should also be determined.

No trends were observed in the first-year soybean yield data that would indicate an obvious relationship among yields, depth to fragipan, and total soil water content. However, with additional years of study, this approach promises to be a relatively accurate method for measuring the effects of erosion on soil productivity.

Quantifying the Effects of Erosion on Productivity - An Economic perspective. Dennis L. Nef, Department of Agricultural Economics, California State University, Fresno, Fresno CA; and John A. Miranowski, Director USDA-ERS-NRED, Washington, D.C.

Quantification of the effects of soil erosion on cropland productivity has followed three analytical approaches. Researchers have (1) compared controlled and desurfaced plots; (2) examined erosion - soil characteristics - yield linkages; or (3) studied individual processes (hydrology, erosion sedimentation, nutrient cycling, crop growth, etc.) and specified these in simulation models. The results of these approaches can be used to calculate the value of diminished soil productivity. We suggest an alternative approach to valuing soil productivity losses based on concepts of production economics.

A farmer is assumed to manage land so as to maximize the present value of profits over a long run planning horizon. The farmer has an incentive to invest in soil conservation practices as long as the added long run gain in the income stream exceeds the added investment in soil conservation. At the margin, the present value of conservation investment equals the present value of productivity losses avoided. Using ASCS data for the Corn Belt, it is shown that an implicit price of soil approximating this value can be calculated. The results can be used in determining where soil conservation efforts would have the highest pay off. The implications for targeting of government soil conservation funds are explored in this context.

Modeling Corn Grain Yields and The Decline in Soil Productivity in Relation to Soil Erosion in New York State. D.J. Timlin, V.A. Snyder, R.J. Wagenet and R.B. Bryant, Cornell Univ., Ithaca, NY.

Shallow soils may be especially vulnerable to permanent reduction in productivity resulting from loss of available water holding capacity caused by soil erosion. A computer simulation model to evaluate the effect of soil erosion on corn grain yields in shallow soils of the Northeast is described. Easily obtainable soil and meteorological data are used as input.
The model is based on the relationship between relative yields and the relative transpiration ratio. A simple soil water budget estimates actual transpiration on a daily basis and calculates a daily moisture stress index which is a function of the relative transpiration ratio. The model includes a root growth function and water uptake is dependent upon the relative root density in each layer. Potential corn grain yield is considered to be a function of temperature for a given level of management. Grain yields are predicted from total seasonal stress and accumulated heat units. The model has been validated for moderate to deep soils.
The model is run using a range of meteorological data that represent varying climatic conditions. For a given distribution of rainfall and evapotranspiration, average corn grain yields and variance can be predicted for a range of rooting depths. The model predicts a sharp decrease in yields and increasing variability in yields as a result of erosion of soils with limited rooting depth.

Towards a General Method of Estimating Productivity-Soil Depth Response Relationships. David E. McElyea, Dept. Agr. Econ., Univ. of Ga.; Lee A. Christensen, USDA-ERS, Athens, GA; R. R. Bruce, USDA-ARS, Watkinsville, GA.

The recent renewal of concerns about the productivity effect of soil erosion has led to renewed efforts to estimate soil erosion-crop yield functions. Theoretical attributes and alternative functional forms are investigated. These functional forms include linear, polynomial, Cobb-Douglas, and Mitscherlich-Spillman. The Mitscherlich-Spillman is shown to better meet the theoretical requirements. Topsoil depth is shown to not necessarily be the best proxy for the soil qualities that promote plant growth. In cases where shallow topsoil overlays a less productive subsoil of different mechanical composition, a variable defined as the mechanical composition of the plant rooting zone is shown to be a superior predictor variable to topsoil depth. Soybean yield data for Georgia Cecil soils were fitted to a Mitscherlich-Spillman function which included both topsoil depth and the mechanical composition of the plant rooting zone. This produced results that are both theoretically satisfying and statistically significant. This method should result in improved estimation of the varied productivity-soil depth relationships found in the United States.

Performance of Eroded and Non-eroded Soils for Corn Production in Bedford County, Pennsylvania. John R. Hudak, Soil Scientist, USDA-SCS, Coudersport, PA; and Robert L. Cunningham, Agronomy Department, The Pennsylvania State University, University Park, PA.

A study was conducted during the 1979 and 1980 growing seasons on Hagerstown silt loam soil (Typic Hapludalf, fine, mixed, mesic) in the southwestern Morrison's Cove area of Bedford County, Pennsylvania, to determine the relationships between soil erosion characteristics and their influence on corn (Zea mays L.) yield. Yield data were gathered from 36 sites in a two hectare (five acre) field along with composite topsoil and subsoil samples from each site which were subsequently analyzed for total clay content, organic carbon content, and coarse fragment content. In addition, average topsoil depth was measured, soil fertility and plant tissue tests conducted, and slopes calculated from elevation data. Climatological data were collected for each growing season. Regression equations for each season were developed from the soils and slope information. The regression equation Yield = -8.636 + (0.004) Plant Population + (0.544) B-Horizon % Coarse Fragments ÷ (23.662) A-Horizon % Organic Carbon was generated for the 1979 growing season with an R squared value of 0.566. The regression equation Yield = -22.723 + (0.511) A-Horizon Thickness + (-0.657) B-Horizon % Clay + (163.608) A-Horizon % Organic Carbon + (-39.538) A-Horizon % Organic Carbon Squared was generated for the 1980 growing season with an R squared value of 0.705. Both equations had a significance probability of 0.0001.

Variations in Physical and Chemical Properties and Plant Extractable Water Among Adjacent Slightly and Moderately Eroded Soils. R.B. Daniels, D.K. Cassel, J.W. Gilliam and L.A. Nelson. North Carolina State University, Raleigh, NC.

Slightly, moderately, and severely eroded soils make up about 26, 36, 37 percent respectively of 10 Cecil fields studied. Each erosion class is related to Munsell hue of the plow layer, with the 10YR, 7.5YR and 5YR hues representing slight, moderate, and severe erosion classes, respectively. Each field is composed of interfluve, shoulder, linear, nose, head and foot landscape positions, erosion class with and among fields is closely related to landscape position.

Mean clay content of the Ap horizon increases progressively from about 10 to 14% in the 10YR to about 30-34% in the 5YR hues. Mean Ap horizon thickness usually decreases 4 to 6 cm as the clay content of the Ap horizon increases. However, the thickest Ap horizons are in the head and foot slope positions.

Plant extractable soil water content data by erosion class x landscape position is difficult to interpret, especially as it affects crop yield. Water extraction data by landscape position for the 1984 crop year are presented.

Water Use and Yields of Corn and Soybeans. T. R. McCarty, Asst. Prof., Agr. Engr. Dept.; J. M. Gregory, Assoc. Prof., Agr. Engr. Dept.; and C. J. Gantzer, Asst. Prof., Agron. Dept., University of Missouri-Columbia.

A field experiment was established in 1982 to study the effect of topsoil depth on crop yields for a Mexico silt loam (claypan) soil. Topsoil depths were established with scraper equipment. Topsoil depths are 0, 12, 24, and 36 cm (24 cm is the normal depth). The study was conducted with and without full fertility and irrigation treatments. Corn (nonlegume) and soybeans (legume) form separate experiments. The experimental design is a 4x2x2 factorial with 4 replications. The treatments are: topsoil depth (four depths), irrigation (irrigation and dry), and fertilizer (soil test and none).

Corn yields in 1983 and 1984 were significantly reduced on the yields of zero topsoil plots but were very similar across other treatments, eg. in 1984, 3600 vs 5900, 6000, 6100 kg/ha for the 0, 12, 24, and 36 cm high fertility dry land treatments. Total soil water use also followed a similar pattern. Soybean yields followed the corn pattern in 1984 but showed no effect of topsoil depth in 1983. Comparing high fertility, dryland treatments across topsoil depth for 1983 gives yields of 1700, 1700, 1700, and 1900 kg/ha. The same comparison for 1984 gives yields of 1600, 2300, 2800, and 2800 kg/ha.

Maintaining Soil Productivity of Idle Land During Rural-Urban Transition. Daniel S. Lynn, former graduate student, Landscape Architecture; Josef M. Broder, Associate Professor, Agricultural Economics, University of Georgia; and Bernard V. Tew, Assistant Professor, Agricultural Economics, Colorado State University.

The transition of agricultural land from rural to urban or suburban uses often exposes such land to poor soil management practices. Lands left idle in anticipation of future development or lands surrounding rural factories and businesses are subject to erosion and losses in soil fertility. This paper discussed alternative land management techniques which would convert these erosion prone buffers into economically viable small scale agricultural operations. Three small farming models were applied to the 24 acres surrounding the Herman Miller factory located on the rural/suburban fringe of Atlanta. Linear programming was used to assess the profitability of 1) producing strawberries, blueberries and grapes, 2) producing selected nursery stock -- junipers and azaleas and 3) maintaining the existing turf and shrub program. The study found 1) that small scale farming can increase the profitability of idle land and/or turf and shrub management practices, 2) that farming during transitional periods can maintain soil productivity, reduce erosion and generate income and 3) linear programming can be a valuable analytical tool for assessing alternative land management techniques.

Corn Yield Response to Erosion on Deep Loess Soils.   Ralph G. Spomer, Agricultural Engineer, and   E. Eugene Alberts, Soil Scientist,   USDA-ARS, Columbia, MO.

Corn yields from four erosion classes were determined annually for 17 years
(1968-1984) from several well managed and fertilized field-size watersheds
in southwestern Iowa.   The soils within the watersheds were developed from
deep and nonstratified loess parent material.   The erosion class of each
yield site was determined by Soil Conservation Service scientists and
classified as 1) slight - less than 25% of the topsoil eroded, 2) moderate -
25 to 75% of the topsoil eroded, 3) severe - greater than 75% of the topsoil eroded, and 4) depositional.   Analysis of variance results showed that
erosion class generally had a significant effect on yield.   Yields from the
depositional sites were generally significantly greater (p <0.05) than from
the other sites.   Differences in yield between the slightly and severely
eroded sites were generally small and nonsignificant.   These results show
that corn yields from well-managed deep loess soils are not affected by topsoil loss from natural erosion when studied on a field scale.   These soils
are unique, however, because of their favorable physical and chemical properties and the lack of a restrictive horizon within the root zone.

Quantification of Physical and Economic Impacts of Erosion on Soil Productivity.   Paul E. Rosenberry, Agricultural Economist, CARᴰ., Iowa State University; Wen-yuan Huang, Agricultural Economist, USDA, ERS, NRED, Iowa State University; Burton English, Associate Professor, CARD., Iowa State University;
Earl O. Heady, Distinguished Professor, CARD., Iowa State University.

A computer simulation model is described that quantifies the impact of farm
management decisions through time on soil depletion, productivity, and economic costs and returns.   The main purpose is to provide a method whereby
researchers and planners may recursively estimate annual soil loss and its
impact resulting from various crop production management decisions.

For a given soil and production system, the model estimates the quantity of
soil lost, adjusts the soil profile and properties, determines changes in
productivity and yields, and computes cost of soil depletion.

A typical data base file for selected soils and counties in Iowa is presented
to show that data are necessary to operate the model. The model was formu-
lated so that the required data would be readily available for most major
soils.

A General Crop Growth Model. J. R. Williams, Hydraulic Engineer, USDA-ARS, Temple, TX.

The EPIC crop growth model was developed for simulating the effects of erosion on crop yield. Thus, the model must be sensitive to changes in plant environment like climate, nutrient supply, and soil characteristics. The processes simulated include energy interception; energy conversion to biomass; division of biomass into roots, above ground biomass, and seed; root growth and sloughing; water use; and nutrient uptake. Potential plant growth is simulated daily and constrained by the minimum of four stress factors (water, nitrogen, phosphorus, and temperature). Root growth is also constrained by the minimum of four stress factors (soil strength, temperature, aluminum toxicity, and aeration). A single model is used in EPIC for simulating all the crops considered (corn, grain sorghum, wheat, barley, oats, sunflowers, soybeans, alfalfa, cotton, peanuts, and grasses).

Test results presented for several sites in the U.S. and other countries indicate that the model is capable of simulating crop yields realistically.

Relationship Between Erosion Control Benefits and Land Use Change in New York State. Ralph E. Heimlich and Nelson L. Bills, Agricultural Economist, USDA-ERS, Washington, D.C.

Potential on-site economic damages from soil erosion include reduced returns during the planning period and reduced agricultural land values at the end of the period. Yield depletion curves developed for 21 cropland soils in New York using Pierce's PI model were applied to 208 National Resource Inventory (NRI) sample points. Annualized maximum benefits from erosion control were estimated for corn grain, as a reference crop, using RKLS values from the NRI and estimated crop yields from SOILS5. Total benefits were estimated at $272,200 or $1.08 per acre. About a fifth of the cropland is likely to be abandoned due to negative net returns and remaining cropland is under urban pressure from the expanding Rochester metropolitan area. If expected future land values are divorced from agricultural productivity through urbanization or abandonment, total benefits are reduced 49 percent. Incentives to control erosion are severely reduced by incipient changes in land use.

Soil Depletion on Representative Farms. Dennis Miller, Agricultural Economist, Water Resources Planning Staff, USDA-SCS, Des Moines, Iowa.

One goal of the Soil Depletion on Representative Farms study was to estimate the effect continuing excessive erosion rates over the next 25 years will have on the project income of 14 representative farms in the Des Moines River Basin. Income is impacted by reduced productivity, increased fertilizer rates, and increased fuel consumption.

The representative farm is also used to calculate and display the historic and projected future income lost because of soil resource depletion. It was also used to calculate the cost of installing alternative resource management systems for erosion control, and then to estimate the amount of remaining depletion with each alternative.

Representative farms are used to help visualize the relationship and proportion of steep erosive soils with other soils on the landscape. An examination of actual farms permits a graphic display of the relative location of soil mapping units and their relationship to land use.

To accomplish this goal a representative farm was selected for each of 14 soil associations in the Des Moines River Basin. Each representative farm is depicted by the actual 160-acre tracts of land selected to have a typical mix of soil mapping units, land use, and current conservation practices.

Economic Analysis of Acreage Retirement Options to Protect Critically Erosive and Fragile Lands. Shwu-Eng Webb and Clay Ogg, Agricultural Economists,USDA-ERS, Washington D.C.

Three long-term acreage retirement options for retiring 17 million acres of cropland for 10 years are evaluated in this report. 1) In The Past Pattern Option, acreage retired follows closely the pattern of acreage set aside in past commodity programs. 2) The Targeting Option take as given the amount of land set aside by region and by crop in the Past Pattern Option and targets the critically erosive and fragile land within each region and crop group. 3) The Conservation Reserve Option retires all critically erosive and fragile land used in major crop production regardless of region and crop. The conservation reserve option is the most effective in protecting critically erosive and fragile land. About 60 percent of this land will be treated under the conservation reserve option as compared to about 33 percent in the targeting option and less than 5 percent in the past program pattern.

Cost Share Levels to Attain Soil Conservation Goals in the Panhandle Area of Florida. Gary D. Lynne, Associate Professor; and Leandro Rola, Research Assistant, Food and Resource Economics Department, University of Florida, Gainesville, FL.

A survey of 145 farmers in the Panhandle area of Florida revealed a strong and abiding conservation and stewardship ethic, along with a perception that erosion affects long term productivity. Favorable feelings toward conservation were strongest for current users of practices. Nonusers expressed a need to have larger cost shares, in the vicinity of 80-100 percent, as compared to 30-40 percent for current users. These differences were due to both attitudes and the economic condition of the farms.

Soil Erosion in Various Countries of the Caribbean Basin. M. A. Lugo-López, University of Puerto Rico, Mayaguez Campus, Mayaguez, PR; G. Acevedo, USDA Soil Conservation Service, Caribbean Office, San Juan, PR; F. Abruña, USDA-ARS-University of Puerto Rico, Mayaguez Campus, Río Piedras, PR; A. Wahab, USAID Haiti, Port-au-Prince, Haiti; R. Solórzano, Ministry of Agriculture, San José, Costa Rica; and G. Tirado, Secretariat of Agriculture, Santo Domingo, Dominican Republic.

Soil erosion is perhaps the most serious hazard to agriculture in the Caribbean. Indiscriminate hillside farming and inappropriate tillage systems throughout the watersheds have led to massive damage of the natural resource base in Puerto Rico, the Dominican Republic, Haiti, Jamaica, Costa Rica and others. The objective of this paper is to summarize the information obtained from on-site observations and direct participation of the authors in programs geared to assess the magnitude of the soil erosion problem and devise appropriate control measures. Actual soil losses of more than 180 t/ha/yr have been measured in steep slopes in Puerto Rico, in the Dominican Republic and in Jamaica. Observations throughout Haiti and Costa Rica indicate that rampant deforestation for fuel and lumber production, coupled with poor pasture management and clean cultivation of steep slopes are conducive to high losses and deterioration of the resource base. Soil conservation practices to be readily accepted by farmers in these areas must be simple, low cost and effective. The use of high-yielding crop cultivars, pest control, rational fertilization and liming must be considered as essential components of the soil conservation package of practices.

Profits, Soil Erosion and Risk.   William C. Nelson, Professor, Agricultural
Economics, North Dakota State University, Fargo, ND.

Recent changes in technology and economic conditions make it possible to
identify crop management systems which not only increase profit, but reduce
soil erosion and risk.   In Western North Dakota, the traditional and current
crop management system is chisel-plowed fallow followed by durum.   It
generates over 10 tons of soil loss per acre and less than $30 income.
Alternative crop management systems involving winter wheat, sunflower,
chemical fallow and no-till can increase profit by $10, reduce soil loss to
less than five tons and reduce income variability.

The Economic Impacts of Best Management Practices on the Camas Prairie,
Idaho.   R.O. Brooks, Extension Associate and E.L. Michalson, Professor,
Department of Agricultural Economics, University of Idaho, Moscow.

Conservation of our soil resource has been a major concern of policy-
makers, farmers and concerned citizens since the 1920's.   Programs designed
to encourage soil conservation have not met with unanimous support.
Currently, the Soil Conservation Service, in cooperation with local soil and
water conservation districts recommends a number of best management
practices (BMP's) for controlling soil erosion.

The Camas Prairie, located in northcentral Idaho, is a major dryland
wheat producing area with correspondingly high soil erosion rates.   Two
BMP's, crop residue management and terraces, are analyzed in this paper.
The objectives of the paper were to: 1) determine the impact the two BMP's
had on crop rotation patterns; 2) determine the level of use of each
practice given a soil loss constraint; and 3) evaluate the economic impacts
of the BMP's on net farm income in conjunction with the first two objectives.

The results of the linear programming showed net farm income was
decreased in all cases by crop residue management.   Terracing impacted net
income negatively until the yield benefits associated with this practice
reached five (5) percent.   As total allowable soil loss was lowered to four
(4) tons per acre from a high of twelve (12) tons per acre, crop rotation
patterns and the level of the BMP's changed.   The reduction in soil loss was
not without its costs, as net farm income was reduced twelve to fifteen
percent for the unconstrained model.